An Introduction to the
CHEMISTRY
of the
HYDRIDES

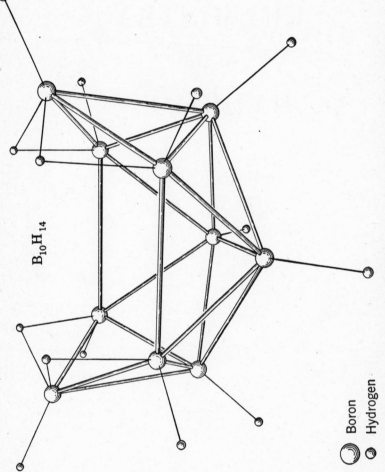

$B_{10}H_{14}$

Boron
Hydrogen

STRUCTURE OF THE DECABORANE MOLECULE AS DETERMINED
BY KASPER, LUCHT, AND HARKER.

An Introduction to the

CHEMISTRY

of the

HYDRIDES

DALLAS T. HURD

Research Associate
General Electric Research Laboratory
The Knolls, Schenectady, New York

NEW YORK · JOHN WILEY & SONS, INC.

LONDON · CHAPMAN & HALL, LIMITED

Library of Congress Catalog Card Number: 52–8069

PRINTED IN THE UNITED STATES OF AMERICA

Preface

During recent years chemists have become increasingly aware of the real need for a book which coordinates the widely diversified field of hydride chemistry. The fundamental importance of certain hydrides in life processes and in our economy is well recognized. Numerous books describing the properties and reactions of water, the hydrocarbons, ammonia, and the hydrogen halides are to be found on our library shelves. Nevertheless, the relationship of these compounds as hydrides to the salt-like hydrides of the alkali metals, to the obscure hydrides of gallium, bismuth, and tellurium, and to the metallic hydrides of the transitional elements generally has been overlooked. In truth, there are but few general classes of chemical compounds that exhibit as well as the hydrides the variations in physical and chemical properties that accompany the periodic variations in size, valence, and electronegativity of the different chemical elements.

It is particularly appropriate that a book on the chemistry and applications of the hydrides should be presented at this time. The field of hydride chemistry is undergoing a rapid expansion, both in the scope of academic research and in the extent of industrial application. Hydride compounds considered as laboratory curiosities only a few years ago are now being produced industrially on a large scale. Outstanding advances in the theoretical and descriptive aspects of hydride chemistry are being made in university laboratories. Exciting new avenues for research and investigation are being uncovered.

This book is not intended to be a "catch-all" reference book. My principal interest is in a critical and coordinated presentation of the theory, the properties, and the reactions of the hydrides that will be of value to the chemist. To industrial and academic chemists alike, I hope to convey the magnitude of a field unusually rich in possibilities for exploitation.

I have tried, insofar as possible, to maintain a balance in the treatment of the various phases of hydride chemistry. It obviously would be neither practical nor desirable to include in this book the complete chemistry of well-investigated hydrides like water or ammonia, yet a discussion of their places in the family of hydrides and their reactions as hydrides must not be excluded. The amount of space allotted to the discussion of unique hydride systems, such as the boron hydrides,

vii

is in my opinion primarily a function of their relative value rather than an expression of my own particular interest.

In conclusion, I wish to express my sincere gratitude and appreciation to Professor Eugene G. Rochow of Harvard University for reviewing the manuscript and for encouraging me in this project; to Dr. Thomas R. P. Gibb, Jr., formerly of Metal Hydrides, Inc., for general encouragement as well as for specific data on certain hydride systems; to Professor W. C. Fernelius of Pennsylvania State College for reviewing the chapter on nomenclature; to Dr. A. L. Marshall and Dr. A. E. Newkirk of the General Electric Research Laboratory for reviewing the manuscript, in particular the chapter on the boron hydrides, and for helpful suggestions; to Professor Egon Wiberg of the University of Munich, Germany, for much valuable information on hydride compounds; and to Professor A. W. Laubengayer of Cornell University, who first aroused my interest in the hydrides and who introduced me to the fascinating study of modern inorganic chemistry.

DALLAS T. HURD

The Knolls, Schenectady, N. Y.
June, 1952

Contents

Introduction to the Hydrides

Hydrogen not only is the lightest of the chemical elements, but, considering its chemical behavior, it certainly is one of the most unique elements. It is considerably distinguished from other chemical elements by its versatility as a chemical partner and by the remarkable variety of properties it assumes in its different chemical compounds. Furthermore, hydrogen will enter into chemical combination with almost all the known chemical elements; thus it is present as a constituent in a very large number of chemical compounds.

Certain of the compounds of hydrogen, in particular the binary compounds of hydrogen with other elements, are known as the *hydrides*, and, as such, are the subject of this book. The term *hydride* is used in a very general sense; strictly speaking, *hydride* should be applied only to those relatively few compounds in which hydrogen is present as a negative ion, that is, a *hydride ion*. Some authorities in the field of hydrogen chemistry feel that the term *hydride* should be applied to compounds, and only to such compounds, in which hydrogen is bonded chemically to a *metallic* element. This rule obviously excludes the hydrogen compounds of the non-metallic elements like nitrogen, oxygen, sulfur, and the halogens; it also raises questions concerning the definition of a metal. However, it is not likely that one can get an adequate view or comprehension of hydride chemistry as a whole without considering, at least briefly, the hydrogen compounds of the non-metallic elements as well as those of the metallic elements. Therefore, it is most convenient for the purpose of discussion to use the term *hydride* as a general name for any binary compound comprising one other element and hydrogen. We also shall employ the term *hydride*, again for convenience, in naming complex derivatives of certain of the binary hydrides. These compounds may be called *complex* or *secondary* hydrides to distinguish them from the *simple* or *binary* hydrides. In discussing the hydrides, we shall denote as the *parent element* that element with which hydrogen is combined.

The Classes of Hydrides. The binary compounds of hydrogen may be classified or divided into three principal categories according to broad differences in their structures, physical properties, and chemical behavior.

I. *The ionic hydrides* are salt-like compounds in which the hydrogen is present as the negatively charged *hydride ion,* H^-. This ion comprises a hydrogen nucleus, or proton, associated with a pair of electrons, and it is formally analogous to a halide ion. Hydrogen, by virtue of its single valence electron and its valence shell which can become saturated by the addition of one extra electron, may be considered formally either as the lightest member of the alkali metal group or as the lightest member of the halogen group. In combination with strongly positive elements, such as the alkali metals or alkaline earth metals, hydrogen appears to be strongly negative in character and acts as a pseudo-halide ion. Thus, the ionic halides of the strongly positive alkali and alkaline earth metals are typical ionic crystals which are quite similar to the ionic halides in their structures and physical properties. These compounds have high melting points, high heats of formation, a high degree of thermal stability, and they are able to conduct electricity if they are melted.

In combination with strongly negative elements, such as the halogens, hydrogen will be relatively positive in nature. However, the electrical properties of the hydrogen atom resemble those of the halogens more than they do those of the alkali metals; salt-like compounds containing hydrogen as the positive ionic component are not known, although in a few reactions hydrogen may behave as though it were a positive ion.

II. *The covalent hydrides* are volatile gases, liquids, and (in a few cases) solids in which the chemical bonding is primarily of the non-polar, electron-pair-sharing type. This class of compounds comprises a major proportion of the known hydrides. There are considerable variations in the chemical properties of the covalent hydrides, but these compounds have much in common in their physical properties. They are similar in many ways to the organometallic compounds for, in many instances, hydrogen appears to behave as the most simple, or prototype, organic radical.

III. *The transitional metal hydrides* are the hydrides of the transitional elements; that is, those elements lying in the center of the long-form Periodic Table and in which incomplete electron shells underlying the valence shells become progressively occupied and expanded from element to element across the Periodic Table (Figure 1). These compounds are considered as a group largely out of convenience since there are wide variations in the nature and properties of the transitional metal hydrides. A few of the transitional metal hydrides appear to

GROUP	I	II		III	IV	V	VI	VII	0
Period I	H								He
Period II	Li	Be		B	C	N	O	F	Ne
Period III	Na	Mg		Al	Si	P	S	Cl	A

SUBGROUP	IA	IIA	IIIA	IVA	VA	VIA	VIIA	VIII			IB	IIB	IIIB	IVB	VB	VIB	VIIB	0
Period IV	K	Ca	Sc	Ti	V	Cr	Mn	Fe	Co	Ni	Cu	Zn	Ga	Ge	As	Se	Br	Kr
Period V	Rb	Sr	Y	Zr	Nb	Mo	Tc	Ru	Rh	Pd	Ag	Cd	In	Sn	Sb	Te	I	Xe
Period VI	Cs	Ba	57–71	Hf	Ta	W	Re	Os	Ir	Pt	Au	Hg	Tl	Pb	Bi	Po	At	Rn
Period VII	Fr	Ra	89–96															

IONIC HYDRIDES

TRANSITIONAL METAL HYDRIDES

BORDERLINE HYDRIDES

COVALENT HYDRIDES

Elements 57–71 (Rare Earth Metals): La, Ce, Pr, Nd, Pm, Sm, Eu, Gd, Tb, Dy, Ho, Er, Tm, Yb, Lu
Elements 89–96 (Actinide Elements): Ac, Th, Pa, U, Np, Pu, Am, Cm, Cf, Bk,

FIGURE 1. Long-Form Periodic Table of the Elements Showing Distribution of Hydride Types.

comprise little more than molecular hydrogen physically adsorbed in rifts or defects in the structure of the metal.   Others of the transitional metal hydrides appear to be formally analogous to alloys; that is to say, the hydrogen behaves as though it, too, were a metal.   It assumes definite positions in the metal lattice structure, and the properties of the "compound" remain metallic.

Certain of the transitional metal hydrides resemble the ionic hydrides to a considerable degree.   These compounds have high heats of formation and unique crystal structures which differ considerably from those of elements from which they are derived.   In the formation of these hydrides, the metallic character of the element is lost and the hydrides appear definitely to be chemical compounds.   However, their chemical compositions are variable, depending upon the method by which they are synthesized, and they seldom approach a stoichiometric content of hydrogen.   Not all the transitional elements are known to form hydrides.

In addition to the three principal classes of hydrides, there is a group of hydrides which we may designate as the *borderline hydrides*. These compounds are known only as transient or, at best, relatively unstable compounds which appear to have properties intermediate between those of the covalent hydrides and those of the transitional hydrides.

It is of interest to observe the relationships between the various classes of hydrides as outlined above.   Figure 1 shows the long-period arrangement of the chemical elements blocked out according to the type of hydride that each element forms.   It should be emphasized that there are no sharp dividing lines between the different classes of hydrides except at the ending of each period with an inert gas.

element plays an important role in determining the type of hydride which that element will form.   It will become apparent also that there is a gradual transition in hydride type across the periodic arrangement of the elements, although in some places this transition may become somewhat obscure and confused.

In combination with the strongly positive metals of the first and second groups, hydrogen is, relatively speaking, strongly negative; the hydride compounds are predominantly ionic, exhibiting definite crystalline structures, high heats of formation, and relatively high decomposition temperatures.   In the second and third periods, there are no transitional elements.   In these periods, the hydrides of beryllium and magnesium form a "bridge" between the ionic hydrides and the covalent hydrides, and these compounds exhibit properties intermediate between those of the two groups.

In the higher periods, there is a transition in hydride type from the ionic hydrides through the first groups of the transitional metal hydrides, including the rare earth hydrides, in which the hydride compounds are also relatively stable solids with definite crystal structures and large positive heats of formation. However, these compounds differ from the ionic hydrides of the alkali metals and alkaline earth metals in several respects. During the formation of a hydride in this group, an expansion of the crystal structure, or lattice, of the metal occurs rather than the lattice contraction which accompanies hydride formation with the metals of Groups I and II, and the compounds do not have exact formulas; that is, they are of variable and indefinite composition.

Toward the end of the transitional series the hydrides become much less well defined, less like chemical compounds in the conventional sense, and behave more like alloys or interstitial solutions of hydrogen in the metal lattices. In the extreme cases, hydrogen adsorption may be limited to physical adsorption on the surface, or in rifts or defects in the metal structure.

The gap between the last of the transitional metal hydrides and the first of the covalent hydrides is bridged by the relatively unstable or "borderline" hydrides in Groups IB and IIB. Since these elements have completed electron shells underlying their valence electron shells, they are in some ways more closely related to the alkali metals than they are to the transitional elements. However, in the formation of chemical bonds by these elements, electrons may be removed from the completed lower shells into the valence shell, and thus the chemical properties of these elements in their compounds may resemble those of the adjacent transitional elements. The group of "borderline" hydrides belonging to this classification actually should be divided into two subgroups. (1) Copper and zinc form hydrides that appear to be intermediate in properties between those of the covalent hydrides and the hydrides of the alkali metal or alkaline earth metals. (2) The other elements, silver, gold, cadmium, and mercury act more like the transitional elements in the matter of hydride formation. Indium and thallium probably should be included in this classification also.

The remaining elements in Groups III and IIIB through VII and VIIB form volatile covalent hydrides which resemble one another considerably in their gross physical properties. Even the most highly polar of the covalent hydrides, hydrogen fluoride, behaves like a predominantly covalent compound in its normal state. Thus, the covalent hydrides stand together as a well-defined group on the basis of their physical properties. The chemical properties of the various covalent hydrides depend on the atomic size and weight of the parent element and on the group that the parent element occupies in the Periodic Table.

After the covalent hydrides, the sequence of hydride compounds in a given period is interrupted by the occurrence of a rare gas. With the next period, the sequence just described begins again with an alkali metal hydride.

It may be pointed out that, in addition to the normal hydrides, hydrides of a special sort have been observed for most of the chemical elements. These are transient molecules, ususally of the type MH (where M denotes the parent element atom), which are observed by their spectra under the high-temperature conditions of an electric discharge. Such hydrides may be, or may have been, of importance in cosmological processes such as those occurring during the formation of planetary systems. They are of considerable importance in the investigation of the physics of molecular structure, such as, for example, determinations of interatomic bond distances.

GENERAL REFERENCES

Emeléus and Anderson, *Modern Aspects of Inorganic Chemistry*, Routledge, London, 1938.
Sidgwick, *Chemical Elements and Their Compounds*, Oxford, London, 1950.
Ephraim, *Inorganic Chemistry*, Nordeman, New York, 1939.

Chemical Bonding and the Structure of Hydrides

To understand and interpret the behavior of hydrogen in its reactions with the various chemical elements, and the compounds that hydrogen forms with these elements, we should have an adequate working knowledge of the principles of chemical bonding and valence. It would be much beyond the scope of this book to present a detailed explanation of these principles. The reader interested in refreshing his knowledge of chemical bonding and valence should consult one or more of the many treatises on this subject.* However, it is considered appropriate to include with this discussion of hydrogen and its chemical bonding a brief resume of the principal types of chemical bonding and the influence of factors, such as electron affinity and atomic size, on chemical behavior.

The Mechanism of Chemical Bonding. It is convenient to describe chemical bonding in terms of *atomic* and *molecular orbitals*. Each chemical element atom has a certain number of orbitals, or *energy levels*, which can be occupied by electrons or electron pairs. These orbitals are grouped into general energy levels which usually are called *electron shells*. If we begin with an atomic nucleus that has been stripped of electrons and then add electrons to it in stepwise fashion, we observe that the process of occupying the vacant orbitals, first by single electrons and eventually by electron pairs, releases energy until a sufficient number of electrons has been added to just balance the positive charge on the atomic nucleus. In this electron

---

* Several references may be suggested. Since the viewpoints presented will differ slightly, it may be desirable to consult several of these to obtain a broader concept of chemical bonding: Pauling, *Nature of the Chemical Bond*, Cornell University Press, Ithaca, N.Y., 1940. Sidgwick, *Electronic Theory of Valence*, Oxford, London, 1946. Rice, *Electronic Structure and Chemical Bonding*, McGraw-Hill, New York, 1940. Lewis, *Valence and the Structure of Atoms and Molecules*, American Chemical Society Monograph, 1923. A short but excellent description of basic principles may be found in Luder and Zuffanti, *The Electronic Theory of Acids and Bases*, Wiley, New York, 1946.

addition process, the levels of lower energy are filled first, then levels of higher energy, until the valence shell is reached. The electronic configuration in the highest general energy level normally occupied, that is, the *valence shell* of the atom, will depend on the different energy sublevels within the valence shell; with most uncombined atoms there will be both unpaired electrons and vacant or partially occupied orbitals within the valence shell.

Once the positive nuclear charge of the atom is balanced, the insertion of additional electrons into vacant orbitals will be hindered by the repulsion of the electronic charge. For most elements, this process requires more energy than will be liberated by the process of orbital occupancy and electron pairing. However, if the electronic charge can be balanced in some other way, considerable amounts of energy may be released by the addition of extra electrons to fill vacant orbitals. That is, if a means is available whereby the atom can acquire additional electrons, either to pair with single electrons in valence shell orbitals or to occupy vacant orbitals, and still maintain a favorable electrical balance, the atom will do so since this process releases energy. It is possible for electrons to occupy orbitals on more than one atom, and unfilled orbitals on one atom may be filled by electrons from another atom. This is the basis for the formation of chemical bonds between atoms.*

* A rule that often is used for predicting the valences, and to some extent the chemical behavior, of relatively simple elements like the alkali metals, the halogens, and most of the elements in the first two rows of the Periodic Table, is the rule of "eight or two." Simply stated, this rule predicts that an atom will tend to gain or lose electrons in the formation of its chemical compounds so that it can assume as closely as possible a stable electronic configuration like that of the closest inert gas. For the elements in the first row of the Periodic Table, the stable configuration of the outermost electron shell may correspond to that of helium (two electrons) or to that of neon (eight electrons). Thus, in the formation of lithium fluoride, for example, the lithium atom can lose its one valence electron to expose an underlying structure of two electrons in a closed shell, and the lithium ion has the same electronic configuration as the inert gas helium. The fluorine atom can acquire the electron lost by the lithium atom and add it to its incomplete shell of seven electrons. The fluoride ion thus formed has a completed "octet" of electrons, and its electronic configuration resembles that of the inert gas neon. By this reasoning, we might expect that the hydrogen atom could lose its one electron to become the equivalent of a positive alkali metal ion, or gain one electron to resemble the helium atom and become the equivalent of a negative halide ion.

We know, however, that the rule of "eight or two" is a considerable oversimplification applicable only in rather special cases, and that there are many exceptions to this rule. For example, sulfur forms a very stable compound, *sulfur hexafluoride*, SF_6, in which there are apparently twelve electrons in the valence shell of the sulfur atom. The rule breaks down also when one tries to apply it to atoms which can show a variety of valence structures, such as those of the transitional elements.

The number of general energy levels will depend, of course, on the particular atom. In hydrogen and helium, the normal electronic configuration involves only one such level and, at most, two electrons; in the second-period elements, proceeding from lithium to neon, occupancy of the four orbitals in the second general energy level, or electron shell, occurs until a maximum of eight electrons (four electron pairs) has been reached; in the third-period elements, from sodium to argon, the third electron shell is progressively occupied although not completely filled. In the higher periods, the system of orbital occupancy is more complicated. The energy relationships in the complex electronic structures of the heavier elements are such that some overlapping of electron shells can occur. Certain orbitals in the valence shell may be occupied before all the underlying shells are completely occupied.

It will be apparent that the light elements, with relatively few valence electrons and valence orbitals, will tend to be rather restricted in their chemical behavior as compared with the heavier elements, which have many outlying orbitals in which there are only slight differences in energy, and many electrons potentially available for the formation of chemical bonds. The overlapping energy-wise of electron shells is reflected in the chemical properties of the heavier elements, and in many of these elements we can observe several different states of valence and kinds of chemical behavior. The heavier elements do, in fact, fall into several different groups, for example, the *transitional metals* and the *rare earths*, depending upon their electronic configurations and chemical properties.

We designate the *relative* tendency of an atom within a molecule to attract and hold extra electrons from other atoms as its *electronegativity*. This value is related to the *electron affinity* of the atom, that is, the amount of energy released in the addition of an electron to a normally vacant valence shell orbital, but it also depends on other factors, such as the size of the atom and the extent to which the cloud of electrons surrounding the nucleus can be distorted by other atoms. The electronegativity value has a very important bearing on the chemical behavior of the element and its chemical compounds; repeated references will be made to electronegativity throughout this book.

The Principal Types of Chemical Bonds. There are several ways in which an atom can acquire additional electrons in the formation of chemical bonds: by outright transfer of electrons from another atom or atoms; by the reciprocal sharing of one of more electrons with another atom or atoms; and by the acceptance in a share in an electron or an electron pair donated by another atom or atoms.*

* On theoretical grounds it may be shown that two atoms may be bonded by one electron occupying normally vacant orbitals in each of the atoms, that is, a *one-*

An *ionic bond* involves (in theory, at least) the complete transfer of electrons from one atom to another. This is a process that can occur only between atoms of widely different electronegativity, and in which one or, at the most, two electrons are involved in the electron transfer between atoms. For example, in *sodium hydride* the energy released by the pairing of the odd electron in the valence shell of the hydrogen atom to form a *hydride ion* is more than sufficient to compensate for the removal of the lone valence electron of the sodium atom to form a positive sodium ion. Consequently, the combination of sodium and hydrogen to form sodium hydride releases energy. This does not imply that the sodium atom has no tendency to retain its valence electron (and certainly not that the sodium atom has a tendency to lose this electron), only that such tendency is relatively weak as compared to the strong tendency of the hydrogen atom to acquire an additional electron. (We shall examine this tendency in more detail further on.) Although the hydrogen atom acquires a charge of -1 in the process of electron transfer, the hydride ion is surrounded by positively charged sodium ions, and vice versa, and the system as a whole, that is, the crystal of sodium hydride, is in electrical balance. Under these conditions, the hydride ions and the sodium ions will behave as stable entities.

Because of the strong electrostatic forces holding the aggregate of positive and negative ions together, considerable amounts of energy are required to separate the component ions of an ionic crystal. Consequently, ionic compounds generally are solids that exhibit high melting points and are soluble only in highly polar solvents.

A *covalent bond* is formed by the *reciprocal sharing* of electrons between atoms. This is the basic type of bonding responsible for the existence of a majority of the known chemical compounds, as well as for the dimeric form of most of the elemental gases. It is entirely possible for an electron pair to occupy orbitals in both of two atoms or, for that matter, to occupy orbitals in more than two atoms if the compound is complex.* True covalence, or the *completely reciprocal*

---

electron bond. It is necessary, however, that the two atoms have closely similar electronegativities for such bonding to be possible, and the one-electron bond is normally expected to occur only between like atoms. Only a few examples are known in which the presence of a one-electron bond is obvious. One of these is the *hydrogen molecule ion*, H_2^+, and it is certain that the one-electron bond is much weaker than a normal electron pair bond.

* The occupancy of orbitals in more than one atom by an electron pair can be described quantum-mechanically either in terms of *molecular orbitals* or as a combination of the separate *atomic orbitals*.

sharing of electrons, can occur only between two atoms of identical electronegativity, as in the dimeric elemental gases. For example, two hydrogen atoms combine to share and pair their odd valence electrons in the formation of the hydrogen molecule, the usual form of this element:

$$H \cdot \quad \cdot H \leftrightarrow H : H$$

(In writing such electronic formulas, it is customary to indicate only the valence shell electrons and to consider the atomic symbol as indicating the nucleus together with any underlying electron shells.) It will be seen that this mutual electron sharing does not unbalance the system electrically.

It also is possible for atoms to form covalent bonds which involve the sharing of two electron pairs, as in the carbon-carbon double bond, or three electron pairs, as in the nitrogen molecule $:N:::N:$. No compounds are known in which more than three pairs of electrons are shared between two atoms.

It should be apparent that if the electronegativities of the two atoms sharing a pair of electrons are not equal, the more electronegative atom will have a somewhat larger share in the electron pair and the electron density in the chemical bond will not be evenly distributed between the two atoms; that is, the more electronegative atom will be somewhat negatively charged, and the less electronegative atom will be somewhat positively charged, owing to the unbalance in electron distribution between the two atoms. Since this is the situation in most chemical compounds, most chemical bonds are somewhat polar.

Although the intramolecular forces holding the component atoms of a covalent molecule together may be very strong, there usually exist only slight attractive forces between neutral molecules, and the energy required to separate such molecules from each other is small. Consequently, most covalent compounds are gases, volatile liquids, or relatively low melting solids, depending largely upon the molecular weights of the particular compounds. Covalent compounds usually are soluble only in nonpolar solvents. It should be pointed out, however, that although the intermolecular forces between covalent molecules are generally small, the covalent intramolecular bonds may be very strong; giant covalent molecules such as the diamond and silicon carbide are very hard and refractory.

A *coordinate covalent bond* may be formed when one atom is able to *donate* a *share* in a pair of electrons (usually a pair of electrons not being used in the formation of a covalent bond with some other atom) to an atom which has available an unfilled orbital which can accommodate the donated pair.   Since the electron sharing may be rather one-sided, this type of covalent bond formation often results in a considerable degree of polarity between the two atoms.   The amount of polarity depends, however, on the relative electronegativities of the combining elements.   Once formed, the coordinate covalent bond is no different in principle from the covalent bond—the two atoms are chemically bonded through the mutual sharing of a pair of electrons. The difference between the coordinate covalent bond and the covalent bond is, therefore, largely a matter of definition.

Coordinate covalent compounds may exhibit the type of physical properties generally characteristic of covalent compounds, or they may resemble ionic compounds to a considerable degree.   This depends largely on the polarity of the coordinate covalent bond.

An important difference between covalent bonds and ionic bonds is that covalent bonds are *spatially directed*.   That is, the valence bonds by which one atom may be covalently linked to several other atoms will be directed in space according to the particular orbitals used by the central atom in forming the bonds.*   Thus, for example, the four hydrogen atoms in the *methane* molecule, CH_4, are located at the corners of a regular tetrahedron; the three hydrogen atoms in the *phosphine* molecule, PH_3, are located so that the three bond angles H—P—H are all close to 90°; the two hydrogen atoms in the *hydrogen selenide* molecule, H_2Se, are located 90° apart; and the two hydrogen atoms in the *water* molecule, H_2O, would be 90° apart were it not for the mutual repulsion of these two atoms attached to the rather small oxygen atom.   Ionic bonds, on the other hand, are not located in any particular direction with respect to the central atoms except as dictated by the arrangement of ions within the crystal structure of an ionic compound.

Factors Determining Bond Type.   It has been implied in the foregoing discussion of bond types that most covalent bonds are somewhat polar.   Actually, we observe that the limiting types of purely covalent bonding and purely ionic bonding are very rare, particularly the latter type.   Most chemical bonds represent a compromise between electron sharing and electron transfer.   This compromise can be nicely described by saying that a particular chemical bond has so much ionic character and so much covalent character (1).   Even sodium chloride, which usually is thought of as being a typical ionic compound, has been estimated to have some 30% of covalent character (1).   Therefore, we often describe such a compound as being *pre-*

---

* The rules for predicting the spatial configuration of covalent molecules are discussed by Pauling in *The Nature of the Chemical Bond* (1).

dominantly ionic, and a compound such as ammonia as being *predominantly covalent.*

It may be desirable to look more closely into the factors which determine to what extent a particular chemical bond will be covalent or ionic, that is, whether the bonding electrons will be more or less equally shared between two atoms, or will be largely transferred to one atom. Pertinent factors to be considered are the sizes of the combining atoms, the number of electrons involved in the bonding, and the electron affinites of the combining atoms. These factors, however, are not independent.

If we consider an isolated system comprising two ionized atoms, one positive and one negative, as a hypothetical limiting case, we observe that as the ions approach each other the attraction of the positive ion causes some distortion in the distribution of electron density about the negative ion. That is, the attraction of the positive ion pulls some of the electrons surrounding the negative ion toward it. This distortion of the electron density decreases the polarity of the electrostatic bond between the two atoms. It will be seen that the amount of this distortion will depend on:

(*a*) The size of the positive ion; the smaller the positive ion, the greater its charge density and its effectiveness in distorting the negative ion.

(*b*) The size of the negative ion; the larger the negative ion, the more tenuous and easily distorted is the electron cloud surrounding the nucleus.

(*c*) The charges on the ions; more highly charged positive ions are smaller and have higher charge densities, and on more highly charged negative ions, the electron cloud is much more tenuous (owing to mutual repulsion of the electrons) and easily distorted by a positive ion.*

If the electron density of the negative ion is sufficiently distorted so that an electron pair, or electron pairs, from it can occupy orbitals of the positive ion, the bond is partly covalent.

Actually, it would be more realistic to consider a purely covalent combination of two atoms as a limiting case from which to extrapolate toward polarity or ionicity in the chemical bond, since this situation is much nearer to reality than the assumption of a purely ionic combination. Therefore, all other factors being equal, we should expect a single and predominantly covalent bond between two different atoms

* These concepts were first proposed by Fajans, *Z. Electrochem.*, **34,** 507 (1928).

to become more polar if a larger atom were substituted for the relatively electropositive component or a smaller atom were substituted for the relatively electronegative component. If we start with a purely covalent bond between two similar atoms, a larger atom substituted for one of these atoms will become the more positive component.

Although the discussion in the preceding few paragraphs has made no specific mention of electron affinity, Fajans' rules are, in actuality, quite dependent on electron affinity since the electron affinity of an atom, as well as the electron affinity of the atom with which it is combined, plays an important role in determining the *effective size* of the atom.

The *electronegativity values* of chemical elements, as calculated by Pauling (1) and others (2) from experimental data, represent an integration of the effects of various factors such as electron affinity, ionization potential, and atomic size on the chemical behavior of atoms.

Table I shows some estimated values of electronegativity, covalent radius, and ionic radius for a number of the different elements. All the covalent radii values are for single covalent bonds. The ionic radii are for ions with completed octets, that is, Na^+, F^-, etc. In considering this table, it should be noticed that within a given group of related elements (vertical columns) the heavier elements are increasingly less electronegative than the lighter elements, owing to their greater atomic dimensions. Within a given row of elements, for example, the series from Li to F, or from Na to Cl, the electronegativity values increase steadily as the removal of electrons becomes more difficult and the addition of electrons becomes more easy energy-wise. Within the same sequences it also will be observed that there is a steady decrease in the covalent radius, that is, the effective size of the atom in its covalent compounds.

Pauling has given rules for estimating the amount of ionic character in a covalent bond from the difference between the electronegativity values of the combining elements (1). To this extent, the electronegativity values are fairly linear functions and, thus, they comprise a very useful set of data. However, in considering the electronegativity and the behavior of atoms in complex compounds where one atom may be attached to more than one other atom, it should be remembered that each of the attached atoms will have some effect on the chemical bond between the central atom and the other attached atoms. Thus, for example, the bond between hydrogen and silicon in *trichlorosilane*, $HSiCl_3$, will not be the same as the bond between hydrogen and silicon in *trimethylsilane*, $HSi(CH_3)_3$; and the hydrogen to silicon bonds in *monosilane*, SiH_4, will be still different.

TABLE I

						2.1 H .30 (2.08)
1.0 Li (0.60)	1.5 Be 1.07	2.0 B 0.89	2.5 C 0.77	3.0 N 0.70	3.5 O 0.66	4.0 F 0.64 (1.36)
0.9 Na (0.95)	1.2 Mg 1.40	1.5 Al 1.26	1.8 Si 1.17	2.1 P 1.10	2.5 S 1.04	3.0 Cl 0.99 (1.81)
0.8 K (1.33)	1.0 Ca (1.18)	1.3 Sc	1.7 Ge 1.22	2.0 As 1.21	2.4 Se 1.17	2.8 Br 1.14 (1.95)
0.8 Rb (1.48)	1.0 Sr (1.32)		1.7 Sn 1.40	1.8 Sb 1.41	2.1 Te 1.37	2.4 I 1.33 (2.16)
0.7 Cs (1.26)	0.9 Ba (1.53)		Pb 1.46	Bi 1.46		

Figures above symbols indicate electronegativity.
Figures not in parentheses below symbols indicate covalent single-bond radii.
Figures in parentheses below symbols indicate univalent ionic radii.

The Covalent and Ionic Bonding of Hydrogen. Elemental hydrogen normally exists as a dimeric molecular species, H_2, in which two hydrogen atoms are bonded covalently by the reciprocal sharing of an electron pair; this electron pair occupies the orbitals of both hydrogen atoms. Hydrogen can exist as an atomic species, H, and small amounts of atomic hydrogen can be detected in molecular hydrogen at elevated temperatures by special methods. Only at very high temperatures, however, such as are present in an electric arc or electrical discharge, can appreciable amounts of atomic hydrogen be present. This is not surprising, considering the large amount of energy, 103.4 Kcal per mole H_2, necessary for the dissociation of molecular hydrogen into atoms; this bond energy is roughly the same as the bond energy in the hydrogen chloride molecule. If sufficient energy is supplied to the hydrogen *atom*, it can be ionized to a positive hydrogen ion, or *proton*, and an electron, but the energy required for this process is very large indeed, 312 Kcal per mole H, or 13.53 electron volts (ev). This value is, in fact, larger than the energy required to ionize a chlorine atom to a free electron and a positive chlorine ion, 12.96 ev, and is far larger than the ionization potentials of the alkali metals.

It will be apparent that the rather large amount of energy necessary to separate the hydrogen nucleus from its associated electrons makes it impossible for hydrogen to be present in a chemical compound as a positive hydrogen ion, or proton, and it is very doubtful that hydrogen ever takes part in chemical reactions with other atoms as an independent proton.* Furthermore, the very small size of the hydrogen atom also precludes such a behavior. Even in its compounds with highly electronegative elements, such as the halogens, the small hydrogen atom is able to cause a large distortion of the electron density distribution of the electronegative atom. The chemical bonds between hydrogen and electronegative elements, therefore, are largely covalent. The limiting case, hydrogen fluoride, is estimated to be approximately 50% ionic and 50% covalent (although its physical properties are those of a predominantly covalent compound); all the other hydrogen halides, and water, are essentially covalent (1).

It will be seen from the foregoing discussion that the hydrogen atom has a strong tendency to be associated with a *pair* of electrons. This conclusion is adequately supported by experimental evidence. In fact, the electron affinity of the hydrogen atom appears to be similar to the electron affinities of elements like bromine and iodine (2). Like the halogens, hydrogen is observed to form negative ions by electron transfer from highly electropositive atoms such as those of the alkali metals and alkaline earth metals. The ionic hydrides of Li, Na, K, Rb, Cs, Ca, Sr, and Ba appear to be quite similar in many respects to the corresponding halides of these elements. It should be carefully noted, however, that even in these compounds, just as in the ionic halides, a considerable amount of covalent character may be present in the chemical bonding between atoms in the solid phase.

* There are, of course, many examples in which hydrogen atoms do move from one atom to another during the course of a reaction. We know, however, that hydrogen atoms can form stable bridges between two atoms in which the electron pair associated with the hydrogen atom can occupy orbitals on both neighboring atoms as well as that of the hydrogen atom. Thus any migrations of hydrogen atoms, such as occur in the course of the ionization of an acid in water, are explainable without assuming the transitory existence of free protons.

However, the observed discharge of hydrogen at the anode in the electrolysis of a molten alkali hydride is convincing evidence for the existence of the hydride ion *per se*.

The theoretical radius of a free hydride anion is estimated to be ca. 2.08 A. U. (1). The few measurements that have been made of the effective radius of hydrogen in ionic hydrides give values somewhat smaller than this. In lithium hydride, for example, the measured radius of the hydrogen atom, or hydride ion, is 0.58 A. U. (3). This value is quite a bit lower than 2.08 A. U., but it is significantly larger than the normal covalent radius of hydrogen—0.30 A. U. The hydride ion owes its large size to the mutual repulsion of the two electrons occupying an orbital about a nucleus which comprises but a single positive charge, and such an ion must be highly compressible. By virtue of its "tenuosity," the hydride ion must tend toward a certain degree of covalency even in its most ionic compounds.

If we consider the series of compounds that hydrogen forms with the second-period elements from lithium to fluorine, we note that the type of bonding rapidly changes from ionic to become predominantly covalent, and the effective radius of the hydrogen atom drops to values close to the normal covalent radius of 0.30 A. U. The actual value of the covalent hydrogen radius does vary slightly, depending upon the electronegativity of the chemical partner, from 0.28 A. U. in hydrogen fluoride to 0.32 A. U. in methane. In diborane, the covalent radius of hydrogen is about 0.39 to 0.40 A. U. Figures are not available for beryllium hydride although the radius of hydrogen in this compound presumably is between the 0.40 A. U. value for diborane and the 0.58 A. U. value for lithium hydride. It has been reported that the radius of hydrogen in calcium hydride, an ionic hydride, is 1.45 A. U. (4). We should expect this value to be somewhat similar to the 0.58 A. U. value for lithium hydride, however, since calcium presumably is about as electropositive as lithium.

If we consider the hydrides as a group, including the ionic hydrides and the covalent hydrides, but exclusive of the transitional hydrides, we observe that the stability of a hydride compound toward thermal dissociation into molecular hydrogen and the free parent element depends in a general way on the electronegativity of the element with which hydrogen is combined. For example, the thermal stability of the hydrides of the second-period elements decreases steadily as we progress from fluorine (E. N. = 4.0) toward less electronegative elements and appears to reach a minimum with beryllium at an electronegativity value of 1.5; with lithium (E. N. = 1.0) the hydride compound is relatively stable. Similar effects can be noticed in considering the hydrides of elements in other rows of the Periodic Table; in the third period, for example, the stability minimum is reached with aluminum (E. N. = 1.5). It may be possible to put a satisfactory interpretation on this behavior, but it should be apparent that the dissociation of a hydride molecule will depend on the lattice energy or the bond energy of the parent element thus liberated as well as on the bond energy of the hydrogen molecule and the bond energy of the hydride molecule. We notice also a somewhat different effect in considering the thermal stability of the hydrides. The hydrides of the heavier elements tend to be less stable than those of the lighter elements. For example, hydrogen telluride (E. N. of Te = 2.1) is much less stable than diborane (E. N. of B = 2.0), and other similar examples may be pointed out. Such comparisons may not be exactly fair since the effective electronegativity of the parent element and the strength of a given hydrogen-element bond will depend on the presence of the other attached hydrogen atoms. However, it is generally observed that the covalent bonds of the heavier elements tend to be relatively weak. The orbitals involved in covalent bond formation are far removed from the nuclei and, with many of the heavier elements, lower valence states in which the elements act as positive ions are preferred energy states.

The stability of the transitional metal hydrides decreases rapidly with increasing group number. The most stable of these compounds are the hydrides of Group IIIA elements, that is, the *rare earth metal hydrides*. The hydrides of Group IVA elements also are relatively stable, but in the succeeding groups it is doubtful in many cases that hydride compounds as such really exist. It also is apparent that among the transitional metal hydrides, the hydrides of the heavier elements are somewhat less stable than those of the lighter elements.

The General Reactions of Hydrogen in the Hydrides. A characteristic of chemical bonds in general is that *substitutions* can be made. That is, one atom may displace another from a chemical bond to a third atom. It probably is safe to say that a majority of chemical reactions involve such displacement processes. In essence, it is possible for a strong electron donor atom to displace a weak electron donor atom, and it is possible for a strong electron acceptor atom to displace a weak electron acceptor atom. There are, of course, many factors involved which determine the occurrence and course of such reactions. Some of these are: the relative electronegativities of the different atoms involved, particularly as these may be modified by the presence of other attached groups, and the bond energies of the chemical bonds involved; the relative sizes of the atoms, and whether there are vacant orbitals on one atom which may be points of attack for an electron donor atom, or unshared electrons on one atom that may be a point of attack for an electron acceptor atom; the activation energies necessary to effect reaction; and spatial factors which may allow or prevent the close approach of one atom to another necessary for a chemical reaction process.

We shall not attempt to discuss these points in detail here as many of them are elaborated in the descriptive material presented later in this book. It should be pointed out, however, that the hydrides as a group are rather unique in that they are highly reactive chemically in a variety of situations. In considering the chemistry of the hydrides, we should keep these points in mind:

(a) Hydrogen is a very strong electron acceptor and, if the energy balance of the reaction is favorable, it will tend to acquire as large a share in a pair of electrons as possible.

(b) The covalent radius of hydrogen is smaller than that of any other element by a factor of at least two; consequently, the hydrogen atom will tend to be mobile in chemical reactions where larger atoms or groups would be hindered by spatial factors. In many reactions, such as the ionization of acids, the phenomenon of *proton transfer* is observed. (As explained previously, such reactions probably do not involve the existence of a free proton as such, although the net effect in each case is that of a transfer of a proton from one atom to another.)

(c) The hydride ion, or relatively negative hydrogen, can donate a share in its electrons to strong electron acceptor atoms.

The Metallic Bonding of Hydrogen. The type of bonding in *metals* and *metallic compounds* is believed to be closely related to covalent bonding. Metals are *electron-deficient*. That is, since there are more valence shell orbitals than there are valence electrons to fill them, and since the bonding between the atoms in a metal must involve some sort of electron sharing between atoms, there are not enough electrons to furnish electron pairs for all the bonds that each atom must make with half a dozen or more neighboring atoms in a metallic crystal. The present theory of metals indicates that at least some of the valence electrons in a metallic crystal are relatively mobile and can move through the lattice structure of the crystal in rather broad molecular orbitals. Since the *average* electron density between any two adjacent atoms must be such that actual bonding by electron sharing occurs between the two atoms, we can, if we wish, conceive of the valence electron pairs as resonating between various bonding positions in the metallic structure. The net effect, however derived, is that each metal atom is bonded to each of its neighbors by a *fractional covalent bond*. In considering the different elements in the Periodic Table, it will be obvious that metallic properties increase with the surplus of valence shell orbitals over the number of valence electrons.

In the formation of *alloys*, two or more atomic species may donate electrons to the general bonding-electron structure. It is not necessary that both these species be metallic; a considerable number of metallic compounds are known between the heavier transitional metals and non-metallic elements of relatively small atomic size, such as hydrogen, boron, carbon, and nitrogen. In these compounds, the physical properties are modified from those of the original metals, but the metallic character is usually retained to a considerable degree. It is believed that the small non-metallic component atoms in a compound of this type are able to fit into the interstices between the large metal atoms in the metallic crystal and form fractional bonds by electron sharing with the surrounding metal atoms. The usual result of such *interstitial compound* formation is a great strengthening of the internal bonds within the metallic crystal; ductility decreases, hardness increases, and the electrical resistivity increases somewhat owing to a tighter bonding of the valence electrons by the more electronegative non-metallic component atoms. It should be mentioned, however, that the formation of this type of compound is exhibited only by the transitional metals. These metals not only are of intermediate electronegativity, but they also have relatively large numbers of electrons occupying rather closely related energy levels and, hence, available for bonding. The non-transitional metals have relatively few valence electrons available for bonding of this type since the different energy levels, even within the valence shells, are rather widely separated energy-wise.

It is known from the work of Rundle (5) that in some of the compounds that hydrogen forms with the transitional metals, for example, *uranium hydride*, the hydrogen atoms occupy positions between the metal atoms, that is, separating the metal atoms rather than occupying interstitial positions, and they bond these metal atoms together by the formation of "half bonds," or "hydrogen-bridge bonds." In a bond of this type, a pair of electrons occupies a vacant orbital on each of the atoms adjacent to the hydrogen atom as well as the valence orbital of the hydrogen atom. This type of bonding also is believed to be responsible for the structure of such odd molecules as diborane and aluminum hydride, and it is quite possibly present in a number of the compounds of hydrogen with the more electropositive transitional metals, such as the rare earth metal hydrides. For such hydrogen-bridge bonding to occur, it is necessary that the electronegativity of the metal be similar to that of hydrogen. The electron pair involved in the hydrogen-bridge bond possibly may be able to bond more than just three atoms together by an extension to occupy orbitals in more than three atoms, and resonance among different bonding positions is conceivable. It will be seen that the extension of this concept reduces to the previously drawn concept of the resonant electron bonding in a purely metallic structure where "fractional bonds" also are present between atoms.

Secondary Types of Bonding. Atoms and molecules can be held together by forces other than those of true chemical bonds. Because strong attractive forces exist between opposite electrical charges, we observe that many polar molecules tend to be *associated* by electrostatic forces, that is, the positive end of one molecule will be attracted by the negative end of another molecule, and so forth. This type of intermolecular attraction is known as *dipole-dipole interaction*. Similarly, a polar molecule may be strongly attracted to an ion. For example, the water molecule, which is quite polar, can associate with a small highly charged ion, such as the lithium ion, by *ion-dipole interaction*. This phenomenon is responsible for some examples of *salt hydration*, particularly with the salts of the alkali and alkaline earth metals, but it should be distinguished from the formation of *aquo-complexes* which water molecules form with certain metallic ions, such as the *cupric ion*. The aquo-complexes involve coordination of water molecules to the ions by electron sharing. There probably is, however, no sharp dividing line between the examples of hydration by ion-dipole interaction and hydration by coordination.

The phenomenon of *hydrogen bonding*, which is responsible for the association of ammonia, water, and hydrogen fluoride, as well as many of the derivatives of these molecules, is now believed to result from dipole-dipole interaction. Hydrogen bonding occurs to an appreciable extent only between *small* and *highly electronegative* atoms. It will be seen that these conditions, together with the very small size of the hydrogen atom, are most favorable for a high degree of polarity in the hydrogen-element bonds. The energy of the hydrogen bond is about 5 Kcal/mole. This type of hydrogen bonding between highly electronegative elements should not be confused with the hydrogen-bridge bonding present in certain electron-deficient hydrides. Hydrogen bonding does form, however, an effective electrostatic link, through hydrogen, between two negative atoms.

There also exist rather weak general forces between molecules or atoms, known as the *van der Waals* forces. The nature of these forces is such that their magnitude increases with the sizes of the atoms or molecules concerned. The effects of the van der Waals forces will be observed principally in the physical properties of relatively neutral covalent molecules; the electrical forces operating between highly polar molecules usually are sufficiently strong to mask the effects of the van der Waals forces.

REFERENCES

1. Pauling, *The Nature of the Chemical Bond*, 2nd Ed., Cornell University Press, Ithaca, N.Y., 1940.
2. Rice, *Electronic Structure and Chemical Bonding*, McGraw-Hill, New York, 1940.
3. Bijovet and Karssen, *Rec. trav. chim.*, **42,** 859 (1923).
4. Proskurnin and Kazarnovskii, *Z. anorg. Chem.*, **170,** 310 (1928).
5. Rundle, *J. Am. Chem. Soc.*, **69,** 1719 (1947).

The Ionic Hydrides—General Considerations

It was mentioned in Chapters 1 and 2 that hydrogen in chemical combination with an electropositive element behaves in many ways as though it were a member of the halogen family of elements; that is, the hydride ion, H^-, behaves chemically and physically as if it were a halide ion.

In the alkali metals *lithium, sodium, potassium, rubidium, cesium,* and the alkaline earth metals *calcium, strontium, barium,* the valence electrons are rather loosely bound. It is relatively easy, therefore, for a reagent, such as hydrogen, which has a considerably greater affinity for electrons to effect the removal of these electrons from the metal atoms. Since the positive metal ions thus produced have only a small affinity for electrons, the negative ions formed by the transfer of electrons to the attacking groups will be relatively stable. The aggregation of positive and negative ions resulting from the electron transfer process will be highly polar and will be bonded together by the strong electrostatic forces that exist between dissimilar electric charges. Such a compound will exhibit the properties of crystallinity, high melting point, the conduction of electricity in the molten state, etc., that are associated with ionic compounds, or salts, in general.*

It should be emphasized that the ability of the hydride ion to exist as an entity in the ionic hydrides depends upon the absence of any stronger electron acceptor. Like all the salts of strongly electropositive metals with very weak acids, the salt-like hydrides are very susceptible to hydrolysis in aqueous solution since positive hydrogen ions formed by the ionization of water molecules are strong electron acceptors.

The formal analogy between the hydrolysis of sodium hydride, for example, and the hydrolysis of sodium acetate, to pick a common example of a salt of an electropositive metal and a weak acid, is illustrated in the following equations:

---

* From the viewpoint of salt formation, the hydrides of the metals of Groups I and II may be considered salts of a hypothetical and exceedingly weak acid, hydrogen hydride, H^+H^-.

$$Na^+H^- + H^+OH^- \rightarrow Na^+OH^- + H\text{---}H$$ (unionized or molecular hydrogen)

$$Na^+CH_3COO^- + H^+OH^- \leftrightarrows Na^+OH^- + CH_3COOH$$ (unionized) acetic acid

Note that in the case of sodium acetate the reaction products remain in the solution and the reaction is reversible.   In the hydrolysis of sodium hydride, the unionized hydrogen escapes as a gas and the hydrolysis reaction goes to completion.   Furthermore, molecular hydrogen is such a weak "acid"* that the hydrolysis reaction would be practically irreversible even if the hydrogen could be kept in solution. Because of the accompanying gas evolution, and because the reactions are quite exothermic, the reactions of the ionic hydrides with water usually are quite vigorous.   It should be pointed out that in other reactions where electron accepting groups are present, such as in alcoholysis, the ionic hydrides also will be subject to decomposition. The ionic hydrides are very strong reducing agents and have been found useful in a number of chemical syntheses because of their chemical reactivity (see below).

The ionic hydrides of the metals in Groups I and II resemble the corresponding halides of these elements physically as well as formally. They are, when pure, white or colorless crystalline solids.   Were it not for the vigorous hydrolysis reaction, most of these compounds probably would be soluble in water.   Most of them have been shown to be insoluble in liquid ammonia.   With the exception of lithium hydride, they are insoluble in the usual organic solvents.   Lithium hydride has a limited solubility in certain ethers such as diethyl ether and dioxane; it resembles the lithium halides in this respect.

All the alkali metal hydrides have face-centered cubic crystal structures analogous to the structure of sodium chloride.   The alkaline earth metal hydrides have structures which are similar, one to another, but which are not like those of the corresponding halides.   In the formation of an ionic hydride from an alkali or alkaline earth metal, a considerable contraction of the spacing between metal atoms occurs because of the strong attraction between the metal ions and the hydride ions.   A result of this contraction is that the ionic hydrides are more dense than the metals from which they are derived.   In the alkali

* Many substances which are not real *acids* or *bases* in the conventional sense of the terms can be considered such as a convenient way of describing their relative affinities for acquiring or releasing electrons, that is, for taking part in chemical reactions.   (See section on acids and bases in Chapter 13.)

metal hydrides this difference in density amounts to 45% to 75%, depending upon the particular metal and hydride under consideration. The difference in density between the alkaline earth metals and their hydrides is less, amounting to 20% to 25%.

It was pointed out in Chapter 2 that the ionic radius of a hydride ion is quite large; the value estimated by Pauling is 2.08 A. U. It is probable that such a tenuous ion is compressible. At any rate, Zintl and Harder have estimated the effective radii of hydride ions in the alkali metal hydrides as ranging from 1.26 A. U. in lithium hydride to 1.54 A. U. in cesium hydride.* These values are still very large in comparison with the covalent radius of hydrogen which is only 0.30 A. U. (and are somewhat at variance with the value of .58 A. U. for hydrogen in lithium hydride as reported by Bijovet and Karssen (Chapter 2).

Aside from crystallographic investigation through the use of X-rays, there is evidence of another sort for the existence of discrete hydride anions in the ionic hydrides. It has been shown that in the electrolysis of a fused alkali metal hydride, hydrogen gas is evolved at the anode (positive electrode) while an equivalent amount of the metal component is deposited at the cathode. The conclusions to be drawn from such an experiment are clear. The hydride ion has a unit negative charge and is capable of moving within the liquid salt; its behavior is analogous to that of a chloride ion in, for example, the electrolysis of molten sodium chloride.

Although the ionic hydrides appear to resemble each other quite closely in many of their properties, especially when considered as a group in comparison with the other hydrides, there are differences between the compounds, particularly in their chemical properties. It was pointed out in Chapter 2 that the terms *ionic* and *covalent* are relative and that the chemical bonds in most chemical compounds are a compromise between complete electron transfer and complete electron sharing made necessary by the different electronegativities, or electron affinities, of the combining elements. In the majority of the alkali metal hydrides the electron affinities of the metals are so small in comparison with the electron affinity of hydrogen that the chemical bonds should be predominantly ionic. It appears, however, that lithium hydride has some covalent character. Since lithium is the smallest and least electropositive of the alkali metals we should expect it to be the most likely member of this group to show evidences of covalency in its compounds. Lithium hydride is unique within the group of ionic hydrides in that it exhibits some degree of solubility

* Zintl and Harder, Z. *physik, Chem.*, **B14,** 265 (1931).

in polar organic solvents, such as diethyl ether.* Furthermore, lithium hydride lends itself more readily to certain reactions, such as methatheses, than the other ionic hydrides, most of which appear to be inert under similar conditions. However, this may not be entirely a matter of solubility.

The effect of electronegativity also may be seen in the hydrolysis reactions of the ionic hydrides. For example, the reaction of sodium hydride with water is much more violent than the reaction of lithium hydride with water, whereas the reaction of calcium hydride is less violent. The hydrides of the heavier alkali metals are still more reactive than sodium hydride; cesium hydride has been reported as being spontaneously inflammable in air. This inflammation, however, may be started by heat liberated in an exceedingly rapid reaction with atmospheric moisture.

The heats of formation of the ionic hydrides are high as compared with the values for most hydride compounds. This is true also of the thermal stabilities of the ionic hydrides. However, in addition to electronegativity differences, other factors such as the sizes of the ions and the crystal structures have a considerable effect on the heats of formation and free energies of ionic crystals. It is difficult, therefore, to make any generalization concerning the variations in heat of formation and thermal stability within the group of ionic hydrides.

Only one general method is practical for preparing the ionic hydrides. It is the direct reaction of the metal with elemental hydrogen at an elevated temperature and at a hydrogen pressure greater than the decomposition pressure of the hydride at the reaction temperature.

* This tendency for covalency is demonstrated in other lithium compounds, lithium chloride, for example, is soluble in organic solvents such as alcohol and ether.

CHAPTER
4

The Hydrides of the Alkali Metals

LITHIUM

LiH—*lithium hydride*
White or gray crystalline solid
Melting point: ca. 680° (dissociation pressure = 27 mm)
Density: 0.76 to 0.8 g/cc
Heat of formation: ca. 22 Kcal/mole (1)
Dissociation pressures: 0.07 mm at 500°, 760 mm at ca. 850°*

Structure. Lithium hydride has a structure of the sodium chloride type, comprising positive lithium ions and negative hydrogen, or hydride (H⁻), ions in a face-centered cubic lattice. The length of a unit cell is 4.1 A. U. (2).

Preparation. Lithium hydride is prepared by the direct reaction at elevated temperatures of lithium metal with gaseous hydrogen. In the usual preparation hydrogen gas is passed over molten lithium, which absorbs it rapidly to form the higher-melting hydride. The compound has also been made by hydrogenating a suspension of finely divided lithium metal in an inert medium such as molten paraffin. Upon completion of the absorption reaction, the paraffin is allowed to solidify and the resulting suspension of lithium hydride is thus kept protected in an easily handled form. Since lithium hydride is unique in that its dissociation pressure is low at its melting point, the article of commerce usually is produced in the form of large crystalline lumps which can easily be ground to any desired particle size.

Properties. Lithium hydride in the molten state is a good conductor of electricity, the charge carriers being Li^+ and H^-, and the compound may be electrolyzed into its component elements. A deposition of lithium occurs at the cathode and an evolution of hydrogen takes place at the anode. Molten lithium hydride also is an ionizing solvent to some extent, and compounds such as *lithium carbide*, Li_2C_2, and *calcium carbide*, CaC_2, can be electrolyzed into their respective components in a magma of molten lithium hydride (3).

* All temperature data in this book are expressed in degrees Centigrade.

27

In the massive form lithium hydride reacts fairly briskly, but without ignition, upon being dropped into a large excess of water. The reaction produces lithium hydroxide and hydrogen according to the equation:

$$LiH + H_2O \rightarrow LiOH + H_2$$

However, the addition of a small amount of water to a sizable amount of finely divided lithium hydride results in the generation of sufficient heat to ignite the mass of hydride, and a violently exothermic reaction occurs.

Lithium hydride reacts with alcohols to form lithium alcoholates and hydrogen, but the reaction is much slower than the reaction with water.

The material is stable in dry air or oxygen at room temperature, but will be decomposed slowly by atmospheric moisture if exposed to room air. Very finely powdered lithium hydride has been observed to ignite spontaneously upon exposure to air on very humid days.

Lithium hydride appears to be very slightly soluble in polar organic solvents, such as ether, whereas the other alkali metal hydrides, such as sodium hydride, appear to be insoluble.

Like most of the inorganic hydrides, lithium hydride will react violently with oxygen and the halogens at elevated temperatures.

When heated with nitrogen, lithium hydride forms the compounds *lithium amide*, $LiNH_2$, *lithium imide*, Li_2NH, and *lithium nitride*, Li_3N, depending upon the reaction conditions. In liquid or gaseous ammonia, lithium hydride forms lithium amide. With sulfur dioxide, lithium hydride forms lithium thiosulfate. At temperatures above 50° this reaction forms *lithium sulfide*, Li_2S.

Lithium hydride is a powerful reducing agent and, like sodium hydride, it may be used for organic reduction reactions. For example, benzoyl chloride has been reduced with lithium hydride to form phenylbenzyl ether in a 65% yield with the simultaneous formation of lithium phenolate (4). Lithium hydride presumably could be useful for many organic condensation and reduction reactions in which sodium hydride is effective, but it is more expensive than sodium hydride.

Metathetical Reactions. As a result of the work of Schlesinger and his coworkers at the University of Chicago, lithium hydride has become not only a springboard for the preparation of many new hydrides, but a powerful reagent for the production in quantity of many hydrides hitherto obtainable only by difficult syntheses and in small yields (5, 6, 7). The advantage possessed by lithium hydride in this respect that differentiates it from the other ionic hydrides appears to be its very slight solubility in ether.

The general reaction between lithium hydride and an inorganic halide is metathetical, although in some instances the reaction mechanism is known to be more complex than that indicated by the simple equation:

$$LiH + MX \rightarrow MH + LiX$$

As an example of this general reaction, we may cite the reaction in dry ether between finely divided lithium hydride and silicon tetrachloride to produce monosilane (7):

$$4LiH + SiCl_4 \rightarrow SiH_4 + 4LiCl$$

Reactions similar to those effected in ether solution will occur if the vapors of an inorganic halide, such as boron fluoride, are passed over heated lithium hydride (8).

However, for the preparation of many of the covalent hydrides lithium hydride by itself may react inconveniently slowly in ether solution. A derivative of lithium hydride known as *lithium aluminum hydride*, $LiAlH_4$, has been found to be a much more powerful chemical tool for synthesis reactions. Discovered by Finholt and Schlesinger at Chicago, this complex compound is quite soluble in ether; and it has been used successfully for the preparation of a large number of covalent hydrides and hydride derivatives. Its reactions with inorganic halides are metathetical like those of lithium hydride (5). Lithium aluminum hydride is formed by the reaction of lithium hydride with aluminum chloride in ether solution. It and other complex hydride salts of lithium are discussed in more detail in Chapter 14.

Precautions in Handling Lithium Hydride. Lithium hydride in massive form is not particularly dangerous and it can be handled safely with reasonable precautions if it is protected from moisture. The finely powdered material, on the other hand, is quite hazardous since it is highly inflammable and is very sensitive to moisture. Once started, a lithium hydride fire is very difficult to extinguish since all the usual fire-extinguishing agents, water, carbon dioxide, and carbon tetrachloride, will be reduced by the burning hydride with the liberation of considerable amounts of heat. The best procedure for extinguishing small lithium hydride fires in the laboratory is to blanket the burning material with an inert gas such as argon or nitrogen, or otherwise exclude air.

In addition to the explosion hazard, lithium hydride dust in the air, even in small amounts, is quite irritating to the membranes of the nose and throat. A respirator should always be worn if the material is handled outside a fume hood. Gloves should be worn in any case since the material is also irritating to the skin. If lithium hydride powder is spilled or dusted on the skin, it should be flooded off with large volumes of running water.

On the usual laboratory scale, small amounts of lithium hydride can be easily disposed of in a fume hood by dropping very small portions into a large volume of water.

Uses.   In addition to its possible uses in organic reduction reactions, and its application in the preparation of other hydrides and hydride derivatives, lithium hydride is a convenient source of hydrogen. Lithium hydride treated with water will generate as much as 45 cu ft of hydrogen per pound of hydride at pressures as high as 2100 psi and at a rate as high as 8 cu ft per minute per pound.   One cubic foot of lithium hydride, weighing about 50 lb, will generate 2250 cu ft of hydrogen (S. T. P.).   Lithium hydride also may be useful as a drying agent, or desiccant.

REFERENCES—LITHIUM HYDRIDE

1. Hurd and Moore, *J. Am. Chem. Soc.*, **57**, 332 (1925).
2. Bijvoet and Karssen, *Proc. Acad. Sci. Amsterdam*, **25**, 27 (1922).
3. Guntz and Benoit, *Compt. Rend.*, **176**, 970 (1923).
4. Hodaghian and Levaillant, *Compt. Rend.*, **194**, 2059 (1932).
5. Finholt, Bond, and Schlesinger, *J. Am. Chem. Soc.*, **69**, 1199 (1947).
6. *Chem. and Eng. News*, **29**, 1202 (1951).
7. Finholt, Bond, Wilzbach, and Schlesinger, *J. Am. Chem. Soc.*, **69**, 2692 (1947).
8. Hurd, *J. Am. Chem. Soc.*, **71**, 20 (1949).

SODIUM

NaH—*sodium hydride*
Gray-white crystalline powder
Melting point: decomposes
Density: 1.396 g/cc
 (Article of commerce = 0.93 to 0.95 g/cc in bulk)
Heat of formation: 13.8 Kcal/mole
Dissociation pressure: $\log p_{mm} = -5700/T + 2.5 \log T + 3.956$ (1)
 ca. 1 atm at 425°

Structure.   The structure of sodium hydride is similar to that of sodium chloride, comprising a face-centered cubic lattice of positive sodium ions and negative hydride ions.   The lattice constant is 4.880 A. U.   The spacing Na—H is 1.89 A. U. (2).

Preparation.   Sodium hydride is prepared by the direct reaction of metallic sodium with elemental hydrogen at elevated temperatures. The ambient pressure of hydrogen naturally must be higher than the dissociation pressure of the hydride since the reaction is reversible.

A contraction in structural volume of nearly 27% occurs in this reaction. As a result, sodium hydride has a higher density than elemental sodium.

The absorption of hydrogen by sodium begins at about 200° and is quite rapid at temperatures of 300° to 400°. However, sodium hydride is a solid at the usual reaction temperatures and forms a film over the metallic sodium. Thus the absorption reaction is incomplete unless special means are employed to disperse the liquid sodium. This has been done by preparing a fine dispersion of sodium metal in a suitable hydrocarbon liquid, such as kerosene, and hydrogenating it under a high pressure of hydrogen (3). Also, surface active agents have been found which will disperse liquid sodium over a supporting layer of inert material, or preformed sodium hydride, and a rapid and complete hydrogenation reaction can be effected. These surface active agents include the sodium salts of acid derivatives of hydrocarbons such as anthracene, phenanthrene, and fluorene. Only traces of these very active materials are necessary to facilitate the hydrogenation reaction. Fatty acid soaps have also been employed. By using these techniques, sodium hydride can easily be made at temperatures of 250° to 300° under a hydrogen pressure of one atmosphere (4).

Properties. Sodium hydride cannot be melted at atmospheric pressure since it decomposes into hydrogen and elemental sodium. It can, however, be dissolved in a fused non-oxidizing salt, such as a eutectic mixture of lithium chloride and potassium chloride (352°), or in molten sodium hydroxide. In such solvents, sodium hydride is ionized. If a molten salt solution of sodium hydride is electrolyzed, hydrogen is evolved only at the anode since it is present in the compound as negative hydrogen, or hydride, ions.

Sodium hydride appears to be stable in dry air or dry oxygen at temperatures up to about 230° before an ignition of the compound will occur. In moist air, however, sodium hydride is rapidly decomposed and, if the material is finely powdered, a spontaneous ignition may occur as a result of the heat evolved in the hydrolysis reaction.

The reaction of sodium hydride with water is considerably more violent than the reaction of sodium with water. The hydrolysis reaction forms sodium hydroxide and elemental hydrogen:

$$NaH + H_2O \rightarrow NaOH + H_2$$

The hydrogen usually is ignited by the heat of the reaction. Sodium hydride appears to be insoluble in liquid ammonia, but at elevated temperatures sodium hydride and ammonia react to form sodamide:

$$NaH + NH_3 \rightarrow NaNH_2 + H_2$$

Sodium hydride is a powerful reducing agent, particularly at elevated temperatures. It will react with a wide variety of oxidizing reagents, as well as with the halogens and many of the covalent halides. At 400°, sodium hydride will reduce titanium tetrachloride to titanium metal (5):

$$TiCl_4 + 4NaH \rightarrow Ti + 4NaCl + 2H_2$$

If the vapors of a boron halide, such as boron trifluoride or boron trichloride, are passed over sodium hydride at 200° a reduction and hydrogenation reaction occurs with the formation of diborane and a sodium halide (6):

$$2BF_3 + 6NaH \rightarrow B_2H_6 + 6NaF$$

Sodium hydride slurries in dry ether may be used for certain metathetical hydride-forming reactions similar to those described for lithium hydride. However, sodium hydride is, in general, much less desirable than lithium hydride since the reactions give poorer yields and are more difficult to run. This may be due in part to the insolubility of sodium hydride in organic solvents.

Sodium hydride will reduce sulfuric acid to hydrogen sulfide and free sulfur. If heated with sulfur, it forms sodium sulfide and free hydrogen.

If sodium hydride is dissolved in a solvent in which it can ionize, such as sodium hydroxide, it is capable of reducing many metallic oxides, such as iron oxide, to the corresponding metals. This is the basis for the commercial use of sodium hydride for descaling metals. (See *Uses.*)

Sodium hydride has been found to be a very useful reagent for many reactions in synthetic organic chemistry although it appears to be insoluble in all organic solvents except those with which it reacts, such as the alcohols and acids. With alcohols, sodium hydride forms alcoholates:

$$NaH + ROH \rightarrow NaOR + H_2$$

This reaction is particularly desirable for the preparation of sodium alcoholates since it is possible in this way to prepare these compounds free of excess alcohol. This is difficult to accomplish with metallic sodium. Furthermore, with certain unsaturated alcohols, such as furfuryl alcohol, sodium causes a reduction reaction and a loss of unsaturation which does not occur with sodium hydride.

Sodium hydride is particularly suitable for organic reduction and condensation reactions. In this respect it acts similarly to metallic sodium and sodium alkoxides. However, under relatively mild conditions sodium hydride will not reduce carbonyl compounds; in this respect it has an advantage over sodium since higher temperatures may be used in the reactions. For example, benzaldehyde can be condensed with acetic esters:

$$C_6H_5CHO + CH_3COOCH_3 + NaH \rightarrow$$
$$C_6H_5CH=CHCOOCH_3 + NaOH + H_2$$
(methyl cinnamate)

In many of the acetoacetic ester syntheses it is generally necessary to use, as a condensation agent, the sodium alcoholate corresponding to the particular ester of acetoacetic acid being used. However, sodium hydride may be used universally in place of any particular alcoholate with good results. An additional advantage of sodium hydride for acetoacetic ester syntheses is that it reacts with, and removes, the alcohol formed during the reaction, and thus drives the reaction to completion. This removal of alcohol eliminates the distillation procedure usually necessary to complete the reaction.

Other types of condensation reactions, such as the condensation of esters with ketones to form beta-diketones, may be accomplished through the use of sodium hydride (7). Thus the sodium derivative of pentadecane-2,4-dione (mono-enol form) may be prepared from methyl laurate and acetone:

$$CH_3(CH_2)_{10}COOCH_3 + CH_3COCH_3 + 2NaH \rightarrow$$
$$CH_3(CH_2)_{10}COCH=CCH_3 + NaOCH_3 + 2H_2$$
$$|$$
$$ONa$$

At temperatures in the neighborhood of 150° and above, sodium hydride becomes an efficient agent for reducing certain esters and other carbonyl derivatives to alcohols. It is reported to give better yields in such reactions than metallic sodium (8). For example, at 145° benzophenone can be reduced to diphenylcarbinol with a yield of 83% (9):

$$\phi_2CO + NaH \rightarrow \phi_2CHONa \xrightarrow{H_2O} \phi_2CHOH$$

Sodium hydride will act as a catalyst in the catalytic hydrogenation of aromatic hydrocarbons. There is evidence, however, to show that this activity is exhibited only in those cases in which sodium can form intermediate compounds with the organic materials. Thus the hydrogenation reaction usually does not proceed to completion, and partially hydrogenated compounds are obtained. For example, at hydrogen pressures of 500 to 1000 psi and temperatures of 250° to 300°, in the presence of sodium hydride, napthalene is rapidly converted to tetralin. No decahydronaphthalene is formed. Similarly, partially hydrogenated derivatives of phenanthrene, anthracene, fluorene, etc., may be formed by treating these materials with hydrogen in the presence of sodium hydride (10, 11).

Sodium hydride will also act as a polymerization catalyst for butadiene and related olefins, polymerizing these materials rapidly to rubber-like substances (12).

Derivatives. Since sodium hydride contains only one hydrogen atom, there can be no hydride derivatives of sodium hydride *per se.* Sodium does form substitution compounds with a number of the covalent hydrides (for example the *sodium alkyls, sodium germanyl*). The *complex ionic hydrides* of sodium, such as *sodium borohydride,* $NaBH_4$, are described in Chapter 14.

Uses. In addition to its value in organic chemistry, which has already been described, sodium hydride is of potential interest in the metallurgical industries as a descaling agent (13). The general technique involves a dipping of the metal part or material to be descaled into a bath of molten sodium hydroxide containing 1.5 to 2.0% of sodium hydride. This dissolved sodium hydride usually is prepared right in the bath in a special compartment in which hydrogen is kept bubbling, and to which blocks of sodium are added from time to time to maintain the desired concentration of hydride in the bath. The reducing action of the hydride rapidly converts the oxide scale to free metal at the operating temperature of 375°. The action is complete in a time ranging from a few seconds to several minutes, depending on the nature and thickness of the oxide film. The piece then is withdrawn and is sprayed with water or plunged into water. The sudden release of hydrogen gas from the resulting decomposition of the sodium hydride on the hot surface of the metal literally blows all the loose scale material from the surface. A short acid dip then leaves the metal clean and bright. It is claimed that the sodium hydride descaling process is more rapid and more thorough than the conventional acid picking processes, and more economical since it requires fewer operations. The hydride treatment does not cause pitting or hydrogen embrittlement of steel.

Sodium hydride has been proposed as a portable source of hydrogen since the hydrolysis of one pound of the hydride will liberate approximately 15 cubic feet of hydrogen gas. Sodium hydride, however, is somewhat less convenient for hydrogen generation than other hydrides, such as calcium hydride, lithium hydride, or sodium borohydride, since its reaction with water yields relatively smaller amounts of hydrogen and is considerably more violent. Because of its reaction with traces of moisture, sodium hydride has been employed as a laboratory drying agent for organic reagents, such as ethers. It is not as suitable as calcium hydride, however, because of the dangers in handling the material. Sodium hydride also finds some applications as the sensitive element in photocells.

Handling and Disposal. Sodium hydride is a highly reactive and dangerous substance, and a considerable amount of caution should be observed in handling this material or disposing of unwanted or residual amounts. Finely powdered sodium hydride will absorb moisture from the atmosphere rapidly enough to raise its temperature to the ignition point. Therefore, material transfer should be done quickly and with a minimum of exposure. For laboratory manipulations, a dry box filled with nitrogen or other inert atmosphere is recommended. (See Appendix C.) If sodium hydride does ignite, the blaze is not violent, and the burning material can be extinguished by excluding air, either by covering the containing vessel with a lid or by dumping a large excess of sand onto the hydride. One should not use a carbon tetrachloride fire extinguisher.

Non-porous gloves and an aspirator should be worn by the operator if sodium hydride is handled in more than gram quantities. The caustic dust from sodium hydride can cause severe irritation to the tissues of the nose and throat, and can produce itching and irritation of the skin. If sodium hydride powder is spilled on the skin it should be blown off; then the remaining dust can be flooded off with a large excess of water.

The recommended method for disposing of residual amounts of sodium hydride is to burn the material in a flat open metal dish in a fume hood or outdoors. Wetting the solid with kerosene will aid in burning the material completely. The caustic residue can then be flushed away with a large excess of water.

REFERENCES—SODIUM HYDRIDE

1. Keyes, *J. Am. Chem. Soc.*, **34**, 779 (1912).
2. Zintl and Harder, *Z. physik. Chem.*, **B14**, 265 (1931).
3. Muckenfuss, U.S. Patent 1,958,012; 2,021,567.
4. Hansley, U.S. Patent 2,372,670; 2,372,671.
5. Billy, *Ann. chim.* (9), **16**, 5 (1921).
6. Hurd, *J. Am. Chem. Soc.*, **71**, 20 (1949).
7. Hansley, U.S. Patent 2,158,071; 2,211,419.
8. Darzens, *Compt. rend.*, **224**, 570 (1947).
9. Swamer and Hauser, *J. Am. Chem. Soc.*, **68**, 2647 (1946).
10. Egloff, U.S. Patent 1,950,721; 1,954,477; 1,954,478; 1,962,182.
11. Hugel et al., *Bull. Soc. chim.*, **49**, 1042 (1931); **51**, 639 (1932).

12. Schirmacher and Van Zutphen, U.S. Patent 1,838,234.
13. Gilbert, *Metal Finishing*, **43**, 492, 533 (1945).

See also: Hansley and Carlisle, *Chem. Eng. News*, **23**, 1332 (1945).

POTASSIUM

KH—*potassium hydride*
White crystalline solid
Melting point: decomposes
Density: 1.43 g/cc
Heat of formation: 14,450 cal/mole (1)
Dissociation pressure: log p_{mm} = $-5850/T$ + 11.2 (2)

Structure. The structure of potassium hydride is similar to that of sodium hydride, and the compound has a sodium chloride type of lattice. The lattice constant is 5.700 A. U. compared to a value of 4.880 A. U. for sodium hydride (3). This increase reflects the larger size of the potassium ion and the increase in the effective radius of the hydride ion in its combination with a more electropositive element.

Preparation. Potassium hydride is prepared by the direct reaction of hydrogen and elemental potassium. The absorption of hydrogen by potassium begins at about 200°, and the metal will absorb about 125 times its volume of hydrogen at temperatures in the range 300° to 400°. Potassium hydride has also been prepared by passing an electric arc between electrodes of potassium metal in a stream of hydrogen (4).

Properties. The properties of potassium hydride are quite similar to those of sodium hydride except that potassium hydride is somewhat more reactive. It ignites in air at a lower temperature than sodium hydride and is more reactive toward hydrolysis. It is a powerful reducing agent.

With dry hydrogen chloride, potassium hydride reacts to form potassium chloride and free hydrogen. With sulfur dioxide it forms potassium thiosulfate and hydrogen, even at relatively low temperatures. With moist carbon dioxide, the compound reacts to form potassium formate. If this reaction is carried out at 100°, the carbon dioxide is partially reduced, and the reaction products include free carbon, potassium carbonate, and free hydrogen. Potassium hydride reacts with acetylene at 100° to form potassium acetylide and free hydrogen, but does not react with methane or ethylene under the same conditions (5).

Uses. Potassium hydride could be used for many of the present applications of sodium hydride but, of course, it would be more expensive. The compound does find a limited use as a sensitive coating for some types of photocells. It has been suggested that potassium may be used to separate hydrogen from deuterium since there is a considerable difference in the decomposition pressures of KH and KD at elevated temperatures (1).

REFERENCES—POTASSIUM HYDRIDE

1. Sollers and Crenshaw, *J. Am. Chem. Soc.*, **59**, 2015 (1937).
2. Herold, *Compt. rend.*, **224**, 1826 (1947).
3. Zintl and Harder, *Z. physik. Chem.*, **B14**, 265 (1931).
4. Siegmann, U.S. Patent 2,313,028.
5. Mellor, *Comprehensive Treatise on Theoretical and Inorganic Chemistry*, Vol. II, Longmans, London (1922).

RUBIDIUM

RbH—*rubidium hydride*
White crystalline solid
Density: 2.59 g/cc
Heat of formation: 12 Kcal/mole
Dissociation pressure: $\log p_{mm} = -4533.5/T + 9.20$ (1)

Structure. Rubidium hydride has a face-centered cubic lattice (sodium chloride type) similar to that of the other alkali metal hydrides. The lattice constant is 6.037 A. U., and the bond distance Rb—H is 2.368 A. U. (2).

Preparation. Rubidium hydride may be prepared by the direct reaction of metallic rubidium with hydrogen at elevated temperatures although the reaction does not proceed as readily as with lithium, sodium, or potassium. Ephraim observed that molten rubidium did not absorb hydrogen in any significant amounts at 300°, but at a temperature of 620° to 680° the conversion reaction was 90% complete in 48 hours (3). A preferred method for preparing rubidium hydride is the reaction between hydrogen and rubidium vapor at temperatures above 700°.

Properties. Rubidium hydride has not been studied at all extensively. Most of its chemical reactions are similar to those of the other alkali metal hydrides although more vigorous in many respects because of the greater electropositivity of the rubidium. It is not definitely known at what temperature rubidium hydride will ignite in air or oxygen. Under ordinary conditions the compound probably will ignite on contact with air because of the exothermic reaction of the hydride with traces of moisture. Rubidium hydride is insoluble in organic solvents. It will, however, dissolve and ionize in fused salts.

It is soluble in molten rubidium metal. The compound begins to dissociate appreciably at temperatures above 200°, and at 320° its dissociation pressure is 33.8 mm.

Rubidium hydride is undoubtedly a more powerful reducing agent than the hydrides of lithium, sodium, and potassium. It will react spontaneously and with ignition with fluorine and chlorine, and will react with bromine at room temperature. (Sodium hydride does not react with bromine in the cold.) Its reaction with water to form hydrogen and rubidium hydroxide is violent.

Uses.   Rubidium hydride has been investigated as a light-sensitive element for photocells (4). Otherwise, it has no applications. Presumably it could be used for catalyzing certain reactions of organic compounds similar to those effected by sodium hydride were it not for the prohibitive cost of rubidium metal.

REFERENCES—RUBIDIUM HYDRIDE

1. Hackspill and Borocco, *Bull soc. chim.*, **6**, 91 (1939).
2. Stevenson, *J. Chem. Phys.*, **8**, 898 (1940).
3. Ephraim and Michel, *Helv. Chim. Acta*, **4**, 762 (1921).
4. Seiler, *Astrophys. J.*, **52**, 129 (1920).

CESIUM

CsH—*cesium hydride*
White crystalline solid
Density: 3.42 g/cc
Heat of formation: 19.9 Kcal/mole
Dissociation pressure: $\log p_{mm} = -3475.5/T + 7.50$ (1)

Structure.   The structure of cesium hydride is similar to that of the other alkali metal hydrides, comprising a face-centered cubic lattice of the sodium chloride type. The lattice constant is 6.376 A. U., the bond distance Cs—H is 2.49 A. U., and the effective radius of the hydride ion is 1.54 A. U. (2,3).

Preparation.   Cesium hydride is prepared by the direct reaction of cesium metal, liquid, or vapor with hydrogen although the reaction proceeds less readily than with the other alkali metals. At a temperature of 580° to 620° in hydrogen, cesium is converted to the extent of about 48% in 26 hours (4). A large lattice contraction, about 45%, occurs in the formation of cesium hydride. This may explain the relative difficulty encountered in preparing the compound.

Properties.   Cesium hydride is the most reactive of the alkali metal hydrides and the most powerful reducing agent. (The hydride

of element 87 would, presumably, be more reactive, but this compound
is not known.) With due allowance for the greater electropositivity
of cesium, many of the reactions of cesium hydride are similar to those
of the other alkali metal hydrides. Cesium hydride ignites spontaneously with air or oxygen, and its reaction with water is quite
violent. It readily, and in most cases vigorously, combines at room
temperature with all the halogens. Cesium hydride reacts with carbon disulfide at room temperature although the hydrides of sodium
and potassium will not react under the same condition. When
heated with nitrogen, cesium hydride reacts to form cesium amide:

$$4CsH + N_2 \rightarrow 2CsNH_2 + 2Cs$$

whereas lithium hydride reacts with nitrogen to form lithium nitride·
Cesium hydride similarly will react with phosphorus to form the phosphorus analog of cesium amide, $CsPH_2$. The hydrolysis of this compound liberates phosphine. Ammonia and cesium hydride react at
elevated temperatures to form cesium amide, but at the temperature
of liquid ammonia the reaction apparently is exceedingly slow.

Cesium hydride is insoluble in organic solvents, but it will dissolve
and ionize in fused salts. It also is soluble in molten cesium. The
dissociation pressure of cesium hydride at 320° is 36 mm. This is
very close to the value of 33.8 mm for rubidium hydride at the same
temperature. At 210°, the dissociation pressure is somewhat less
than 2 mm. A partial dissociation of cesium hydride occurs if the
compound is exposed to ultraviolet light of 2500 to 3000 A. U.

Uses. Cesium hydride may find some use as the sensitive element
in photocells, particularly since it is quite sensitive to red and infrared
light (5).

REFERENCES—CESIUM HYDRIDE

1. Hackspill and Borocco, *Bull. soc. chem.*, **6,** 91 (1939).
2. Stevenson, *J. Chem. Phys.*, **8,** 898 (1940).
3. Zintl and Harder, *Z. physik. Chem.*, **B14,** 265 (1931).
4. Ephraim and Michel, *Helv. Chim. Acta*, **4,** 762 (1921).
5. Seiler, *Astrophys. J.*, **52,** 129 (1920).

CHAPTER

5

The Hydrides of the Alkaline Earth Metals

CALCIUM

CaH_2—*calcium hydride*
White crystalline solid
Melting point: over 1000°
Density: 1.9 g/cc
Heat of formation: 46.6 Kcal/mole
Dissociation pressure: $\log p_{cm} = 7782/T + 8.070$ (1)

Structure. The structure of calcium hydride is orthorhombic; the lattice dimensions are: a, 5.936 A. U.; b, 6.838 A. U.; c, 3.600 A. U. The unit cell comprises four calcium ions and eight hydride ions. The calcium ions are arranged in a slightly deformed hexagonal structure (2). The effective radius of the hydride ion is 1.45 A. U.

Preparation. All the methods used for the preparation of calcium hydride involve the reaction of hydrogen with metallic calcium or calcium metal formed *in situ* by the reduction of a calcium compound.

Calcium metal does not react with hydrogen at room temperature, but at temperatures of several hundred degrees the absorption reaction is rapid. At very high temperatures (800° to 900°) the reaction usually does not proceed beyond a conversion of about 90%, but at temperatures in the range of 250° to 300° it is possible to get practically complete conversion of calcium to calcium hydride.

For the commercial preparation of calcium hydride, lumps of metallic calcium are heated in hydrogen at about 400° until the metal has been completely converted. If the temperature is maintained below about 600°, impure hydrogen may be used for this synthesis since the calcium does not react with carbon monoxide or dioxide under these conditions. The formation reaction is quite exothermic. Commercial calcium hydride usually is dark gray in color because of the presence of small amounts of metallic calcium.

The finely divided and highly reactive metallic calcium formed by evaporating a solution of calcium in liquid ammonia will absorb and react with hydrogen to form calcium hydride at a temperature as low as 0°C.

40

In the process of hydride formation, a structural volume contraction of about 4.2% occurs. Consequently, calcium hydride is more dense than metallic calcium, but the volume contraction is much less than that which occurs in the formation of the alkali metal hydrides.

A second commercial synthesis of calcium hydride involves the reduction of calcium oxide with metallic magnesium in the presence of hydrogen at a high temperature (3):

$$CaO + Mg + H_2 \rightarrow CaH_2 + MgO$$

Other syntheses employ ammonia or zinc vapor together with hydrogen to reduce and convert calcium chloride to calcium hydride at temperatures of 1000° or over (4). The calcium salt of an acid phenol (for example, cresols, napthols, picric acid) will react at room temperature with hydrogen under very high pressures, ca. 200 atm, to form calcium hydride. The acid phenol is liberated in this process and may be recycled (5). Calcium hydride also has been prepared by reducing calcium oxide or lime in an electric arc or furnace in the presence of hydrogen.

Properties. Calcium hydride is a brittle solid which is insoluble in all the conventional inorganic and organic solvents. It can be dissolved in a fused eutectic mixture of lithium and potassium chlorides, and, if such a solution is electrolyzed, hydrogen is liberated at the anode. As in the alkali metal hydrides, hydrogen is present in calcium hydride as a negative hydride ion (6).

The decomposition of calcium hydride has been studied in detail by W. C. Johnson and his coworkers (1). These investigations have shown that, at a given temperature, the dissociation pressure of various calcium-calcium hydride compositions remains essentially constant over the range of about 20 to 90% CaH_2; that is, there is no change in dissociation pressure with changing composition over this range. At concentrations above 90% the dissociation pressure rises sharply with increasing percentages of CaH_2. Below the 20% concentration limit, the dissociation pressure falls sharply with decreasing CaH_2 content. The authors consider that this behavior is due to the existence of eutectic phases in the system Ca—CaH_2. Upon the removal of hydrogen from pure calcium hydride, a hydride-rich phase is formed.

At a CaH_2 concentration of about 90% this hydride-rich phase is the only phase present. As the hydride-rich phase loses hydrogen it is converted to a hydride-poor phase, and the system remains a two-phase system until at a concentration level of about 20% only the hydride-poor phase remains. At lower concentrations, the hydride phase and metallic calcium are present in the system. This seems to be a reasonable explanation for the large range of composition over which the dissociation pressure of the system calcium-calcium hydride is independent of the percentage of hydrogen in the system.

Johnson and his coauthors also consider that the melting point of pure calcium hydride must lie at a temperature above 1000°.

The dissociation pressure of calcium hydride is about 0.1 mm at 600°. It reaches 1 atm at about 1000°.

Calcium hydride is a strong reducing agent, but it is not as powerful in this respect as the hydrides of the alkali metals. Calcium hydride is hydrolyzed readily by water, but the reaction is relatively mild and does not generate sufficient heat to ignite the hydrogen liberated:

$$CaH_2 + 2H_2O \rightarrow Ca(OH)_2 + 2H_2$$

If a lump of calcium hydride is placed in a beaker of water it fizzes quietly much as a piece of Dry-Ice of the same size would do. With alcohols, calcium hydride reacts smoothly to form calcium alcoholates and hydrogen.

Calcium hydride does not react with dry oxygen or nitrogen at temperatures up to about 400° to 500°. If ignited, however, it will burn in air or oxygen to form calcium oxide and water. At temperatures above 500°, calcium hydride will react with nitrogen to form calcium nitride, Ca_3N_2.

Calcium hydride will not react with chlorine at room temperature. In fact, most of its reactions as a reducing agent require elevated temperatures. These include reactions with hydrogen sulfide to form calcium sulfide; carbon dioxide to form calcium formate; carbon monoxide to form formaldehyde and some methane; nitrogen oxides to form ammonia and calcium oxide; phosphorus to form calcium phosphide; ammonia to form calcium amide, etc.

Calcium hydride is capable of reducing many inorganic oxides to free metals. This is the basis of one of the many commercial uses of calcium hydride. A partial list of metallic oxides that have been reduced with calcium hydride includes titanium dioxide, vanadium sesquioxide, oxides of columbium and tantalum, iron oxide, silicon dioxide, boric oxide, copper oxide, manganese dioxide, tin dioxide, lead dioxide, and tungsten trioxide. The general technique is to heat an intimate mixture of a finely divided metal oxide and an excess of powdered calcium hydride at temperatures between 600° and 1000°:

$$2CaH_2 + MO_2 \rightarrow 2CaO + 2H_2 + M$$

Hydrogen usually is passed through the mixture to exclude air during the reaction. Under the conditions of this reaction, calcium hydride is a rapid and effective reducing agent. A particular advantage of using calcium hydride is that the calcium oxide formed in the reaction, as well as any unreacted calcium hydride, can be washed from the reaction products with water, leaving the metal powder in a very pure condition with no metallic contaminants.

Calcium hydride similarly can be used to reduce metallic halides to metals. The alkali metals, sodium and potassium, may be prepared by heating halides of these metals, for example, NaCl, with calcium hydride. The reaction is done at a temperature sufficiently high to distill out the alkali metal as it is formed from the reaction mixture.

Calcium hydride will react with carbon tetrachloride at 400° to form hydrogen chloride, calcium chloride, and carbon. It also will reduce many other covalent halides, such as silicon tetrachloride and boron trichloride, at relatively elevated temperatures. If the vapor of a boron halide is passed over calcium hydride heated to a moderate temperature, in the range of 200° to 250°, a reduction reaction occurs with the formation of the boron hydride, diborane:

$$3CaH_2 + 2BCl_3 \rightarrow 3CaCl_2 + B_2H_6$$

To prevent a pyrolysis of the diborane in the heated reaction zone, the boron halide vapor is accompanied by a carrier gas such as hydrogen or nitrogen (7).

Presumably, other covalent hydrides, such as the silanes and germanes, could be prepared in similar reactions. Unlike lithium hydride, however, calcium hydride cannot be used for metathetical hydride-forming reactions in ether media.

Calcium hydride will react with sulfur at elevated temperature to form calcium sulfide. On the basis of this reaction calcium hydride has been used as a reagent for the determination of sulfur in oils and rubbers (8). Calcium hydride also is able to reduce inorganic sulfates to sulfides. The use of calcium hydride as an analytical reagent for the determination of sulfur in insoluble sulfates involves heating the compound to be analyzed with a considerable excess of calcium hydride, then determining the soluble sulfide thus formed (9). The reaction of calcium hydride with sulfuric acid is slow at room temperature; the acid is reduced to a variety of products including SO_2, S, and H_2S.

In its reactions with organic compounds, calcium hydride is quite effective as a condensing agent, but it is not generally applicable as a reducing agent under the conditions in which sodium hydride is

effective.   As a condensing agent it is capable of effecting many of
the same reactions for which sodium hydride has been used (see page
33).   For example, *acetone* may be condensed at its boiling point to
mesitylene oxide through the use of calcium hydride (10).   *Quinoline*
is condensed to *biquinoyl* at 220° (10).   At the somewhat higher
temperature of 450° calcium hydride has been used for the reduction of
diphenyl oxide to *diphenyl* (11).

Pease and Stewart (12) have described the hydrogenation of ethylene
at 200° with calcium hydride as a hydrogenation catalyst.   The
hydride appeared to be considerably more active as a catalyst than
metallic calcium.   It definitely was shown, however, that a direct
reaction of calcium hydride, itself, with ethylene was not one of the
stages in the reaction.

Derivatives.   No partially substituted derivatives of calcium
hydride are known nor is it likely, considering the ionic character of
CaH_2, that such compounds will be prepared.   It should be possible
to prepare complex anionic hydride derivative of calcium, such
as *calcium borohydride*, $Ca(BH_4)_2$.   (See Chapter 14, "Complex
Hydrides.")

Uses.   Calcium hydride is a versatile material and the compound
has a number of important applications.

AS A PORTABLE SOURCE OF HYDROGEN.   The reaction of one pound
of calcium hydride with water generates approximately 16 cubic feet
of hydrogen (S. T. P.) at pressures as high as 1800 pounds per square
inch and at rates as high as 1.5 cubic feet per minute per pound.   It is
marketed for this purpose under various trade names such as Hydro-
lith and Hydrogenite, and was used to a considerable extent in World
War II as a source of hydrogen gas for filling signal and meteorological
balloons.

AS A DRYING AGENT.   Calcium hydride is a very powerful desiccant,
or drying agent, and is particularly valuable in laboratory work for
drying ether and various solvents.   It has been used industrially for
drying transformer oil as well as for removing traces of moisture from
hydrogen gas.   The reaction of calcium hydride with traces of water
is so complete that this compound has found some application as a
reagent for determining traces of water in organic solvents such as
benzene and carbon tetrachloride.   The small amounts of hydrogen
liberated can be measured quite accurately by manometric or volu-
metric methods.   It is possible by this technique to determine amounts
of water as small as 0.1% to an accuracy of 0.001% (13).   It also is
possible to determine the water content of hydrated salts with calcium
hydride.

As a Reducing Agent for the Preparation of Metals. This application has been mentioned in the discussion of the properties of calcium hydride. The well known Hydrimet process of P. P. Alexander is used for preparing metals such as titanium, zirconium, columbium, and tantalum, and the hydrides of these metals.

The uses of calcium hydride as an analytical reagent, and as a reagent for organic reductions and condensation reactions, have been described above.

REFERENCES—CALCIUM HYDRIDE

1. Johnson, Stubbs, Sidwell, and Pechukas, *J. Am. Chem. Soc.*, **61**, 318 (1939).
2. Zintl and Harder, *Z. Elecktrochem.*, **41**, 33 (1935).
3. Alexander, U.S. Patent 2,082,134.
4. Gardner, Brit. Patent 496,294.
5. Pechet, U.S. Patent 2,392,545.
6. Bardwell, *J. Am. Chem. Soc.*, **44**, 2499 (1923).
7. Hurd, *J. Am. Chem. Soc.*, **71**, 20 (1949).
8. Caldwell and Krauskopf, *J. Am. Chem. Soc.*, **52**, 3655 (1930).
9. Caldwell and Krauskopf, *J. Am. Chem. Soc.*, **51**, 2936 (1929).
10. Reich and Serpek, *Helv. Chim Acta*, **3**, 138 (1920).
11. Fuchs, *Ber.*, **61B**, 2599 (1928).
12. Pease and Stewart, *J. Am. Chem. Soc.*, **47**, 2763 (1925).
13. Rosenbaum and Walton, *J. Am. Chem. Soc.*, **52**, 3568 (1930).

STRONTIUM

SrH_2—*strontium hydride*
White crystalline solid
Density: 3.72 g/cc
Heat of formation: 42.2 Kcal/mole (1)

Structure. The structure of strontium hydride is orthorhombic, similar to that of calcium hydride. The unit cell dimensions are: a, 6.364 A. U.; b, 7.343 A. U.; c, 3.875 A. U. (2).

Preparation. The methods by which strontium hydride have been prepared are similar to those employed for the preparation of calcium hydride, that is, the direct reaction of strontium metal with hydrogen or the reduction of strontium oxide or halides in the presence of hydrogen. The reaction of strontium with hydrogen is vigorous at temperatures of a few hundred degrees, and the reaction rapidly goes to completion (3). Strontium hydride has also been synthesized by distilling a cadmium-strontium alloy in hydrogen, or by distilling an amalgam of strontium in mercury in the presence of hydrogen.

Properties. The properties of strontium hydride have not been studied at all thoroughly, but they appear to be quite similar to those of calcium hydride.   Strontium hydride probably is somewhat more reactive as a reducing agent than calcium hydride.

Strontium hydride can be sublimed and thus recrystallized by heating the compound to very high temperatures (1000°) in hydrogen. This sublimation undoubtedly is due to a partial dissociation of the hydride and the volatilization of strontium metal at the elevated temperature rather than an actual volatilization of the hydride as such.   A recombination of strontium and hydrogen occurs in the cooler zones where the metal vapor condenses.   There are no authoritative data available on the dissociation pressures of strontium hydride at various temperatures, but these pressures probably are in the same order of magnitude as the dissociation pressures of calcium hydride, possibly somewhat higher.   As in the case of calcium hydride, the dissociation pressure is dependent upon the presence of free metal in the hydride (3).

Strontium hydride can be dissolved in fused non-oxidizing salts, such as those of the alkali halides, but it is insoluble in any of the common organic solvents.   A solution of strontium hydride in a fused salt may be electrolyzed to form strontium metal at the cathode and liberate hydrogen at the anode.

Strontium hydride is not attacked by chlorine at room temperature, but if the hydride is heated slightly a reaction will occur with the formation of strontium chloride and hydrogen chloride.   Similarly, strontium hydride does not react with liquid bromine, even at 60°. At a red heat, a reaction occurs with both bromine and iodine to form the corresponding halides of strontium and hydrogen.

Under thoroughly dry conditions, strontium hydride will not ignite in air except at a temperature of 500° to 600°.   Once ignited, it burns slowly owing to the formation of a protective film of strontium oxide on the surface of the hydride.   Strontium hydride will react with sulfur at a red heat to form strontium sulfide, and with nitrogen at about the same temperature to form strontium nitride.

Mixtures of strontium hydride with solid oxidizing reagents, such as chlorates, perchlorates, and chromates, will react with explosive violence if these mixtures are heated slightly to initiate the reactions.

Strontium hydride reacts vigorously with water to liberate hydrogen and form strontium hydroxide.   With alcohols, the reaction is more moderate and strontium alcoholates are formed.

Strontium hydride can be used to effect many of the organic condensation and reduction reactions for which calcium hydride is effective.

Derivatives. No derivatives of strontium hydride are known. Presumably complex anionic hydride derivatives, such as strontium borohydride, should be possible.

Uses. The applications of strontium hydride as a reagent for organic condensation and reduction reactions are covered in a number of patents on the uses of the alkaline earth metal hydrides.

REFERENCES—STRONTIUM HYDRIDE

1. Guntz and Benoit, *Ann. chim.*, **20**, 5 (1923).
2. Zintl and Harder, *Z. Elektrochem.*, **41**, 34 (1935).
3. Ephraim and Michel, *Helv. Chim. Acta*, **4**, 900 (1921).

BARIUM

BaH_2—*barium hydride*
White crystalline solid
Density: 4.21 g/cc
Heat of formation: 40.96 Kcal/mole
Dissociation pressure: ca. 0.24 mm at 600° (1)

Structure. The structure of barium hydride is analogous to the structures of calcium and strontium hydrides. It is orthorhombic with unit cell dimensions of: a, 6.788 A. U.; b, 7.829 A. U.; c, 4.167 A. U. (2).

Preparation. The methods used for preparing barium hydride are the same as those described for the preparation of calcium and strontium hydrides: the direct reaction of hydrogen with barium metal, the reduction of barium oxide or halide in the presence of hydrogen, or the distillation of a barium-cadmium alloy in hydrogen.

The absorption of hydrogen by barium metal becomes noticeable at 120°. At 180° the absorption is vigorous, and the reaction to form barium hydride goes rapidly to completion. The formation reaction is highly exothermic, and the reacting metal usually is heated to incandescence if the reaction is not controlled (3, 4). A structural volume contraction of 13.3% occurs when barium metal is converted to barium hydride.

Properties. The chemical and physical properties of barium hydride are closely similar to those of the other alkaline earth metal hydrides. It is, however, somewhat more reactive chemically than the hydrides of calcium and strontium, and it is a more powerful reducing agent.

The dissociation pressure of barium hydride, like that of calcium hydride, is dependent upon the composition; that is, upon the presence of free barium. At a given temperature the dissociation pressure of barium hydride probably is higher than the value for calcium hydride. Schumb and his coworkers (1) have measured the dissociation pressure of barium hydride at relatively low temperatures. They have reported pressures of: 10 microns at 350°; 30 microns at 500°; 160 microns at 550°; 0.24 mm at 600°. They were unable to extend their measurements above 600° because the volatility of barium metal became appreciable in this temperature range. Because of the volatility of barium, barium hydride may be crystallized by subliming the compound in hydrogen at rather high temperatures (600° to 1000°) (2). There are no authoritative data on the dissociation pressures of barium hydride at these temperatures, however.

Barium hydride is insoluble in common solvents, except those with which it reacts. It may be dissolved in fused salts, however, and it may be electrolyzed into its component elements in such solvents.

The reaction of barium hydride with water is quite vigorous. If the hydride is finely powdered, it may ignite spontaneously if it is exposed to moist air. In very dry air it will ignite and burn at a red heat. The combustion reaction is slow, however, owing to the formation of a protective film of barium oxide.

The reactions of barium hydride with the halogens, nitrogen, sulfur, and oxidizing agents are analogous to the corresponding reactions of calcium hydride and strontium hydride except in that they are initiated at somewhat lower temperatures. At elevated temperatures barium hydride is capable of reducing a large number of metal oxides to free metals.

The organic reactions of barium hydride also parallel those of calcium hydride. The compound is an efficient agent for effecting condensation reactions and reductions. With alcohols, it reacts to form barium alcoholates.

Derivatives. No derivatives of barium hydride are known. It should be possible to prepare complex hydride derivatives of barium hydride, however, such as a borohydride.

Uses. The applications of barium hydride, particularly as a reducing agent and as a condensation and reducing agent for organic reactions, are covered in a number of patents on the uses of the alkaline earth metal hydrides.

REFERENCES—BARIUM HYDRIDE

1. Schumb, Sewell, and Eisenstein, *J. Am. Chem. Soc.*, **69**, 2029 (1947).
2. Zintl and Harder, *Z. Elektrochem.*, **41**, 33 (1935).
3. Dafert and Miklauz, *Monatsh.*, **34**, 1685 (1913).
4. Ephraim and Michel, *Helv. Chim. Acta*, **4**, 900 (1921).

CHAPTER

6

The Hydrides of Beryllium and Magnesium

The hydrides of beryllium and magnesium may be considered to be bridges in the second and third periods of the Periodic Table between the ionic hydrides of lithium and sodium and the covalent hydrides of the remaining elements in these periods. Their properties are intermediate between those of the two groups, and they illustrate the effect of factors such as electronegativity, atomic size, and electronic configuration in determining the chemical and physical behavior of hydride compounds. From the relatively little we know of them, it appears that the hydrides of beryllium and magnesium have more covalent character than lithium hydride although, in general, they appear to resemble this compound more than they do the hydrides of boron and aluminum.

Both beryllium hydride and magnesium hydride are solids. It has been suggested, however, that these compounds, rather than being ionic crystals like lithium hydride, comprise highly polymerized hydride molecules held together by hydrogen bridge bonding similar to that responsible for the unique chemical bonding in the boron hydrides and the polymeric nature of aluminum hydride. This explanation seems reasonable since beryllium and magnesium are fairly strong electron acceptors.

Beryllium hydride and magnesium hydride are less stable toward thermal decomposition than lithium hydride. Magnesium hydride, however, is considerably more stable than aluminum hydride.

The chemical properties of both beryllium hydride and magnesium hydride resemble those of lithium hydride to a considerable degree although they are considerably more reactive than lithium hydride. The compounds are strong reducing agents and react vigorously with water. Of the two compounds, beryllium hydride appears to be more covalent than magnesium hydride. This difference would be expected in view of the smaller size and greater electronegativity of beryllium.

BERYLLIUM

BeH_2—beryllium hydride
Non-volatile white solid

In 1947, Finholt, Bond, and Schlesinger (1) indicated the synthesis of beryllium hydride by the reduction of beryllium compounds with lithium aluminum hydride. A later publication (2) reports in considerable detail the synthesis of beryllium hydride by the reaction in ether solution of dimethylberyllium with lithium aluminum hydride:

$$(CH_3)_2Be + LiAlH_4 \rightarrow BeH_2 + LiAlH_2(CH_3)_2$$

As obtained from this reaction, the beryllium hydride was contaminated with small amounts of residual ether, ca. 0.15 mole of ether per mole of BeH_2, which were impossible to remove without some decomposition of the hydride.

Beryllium hydride was observed to be a white solid, insoluble in ether, toluene, and isopentane. The material appeared to be relatively stable at ca. 80°, but decomposed rapidly at 125°. It did not react appreciably with dry air or oxygen at room temperature; however, its reaction with water, even at −196°, was quite violent. Beryllium hydride undoubtedly is a very strong reducing agent, and will be highly reactive chemically toward other reagents such as alcohols, acids, and the halogens.

The molecule BeH has been observed and studied in the spectra of electric discharges, and BeH_2 has been observed as a transitory molecule in solar spectra.

Derivatives. In 1940 Burg and Schlesinger (3) reported the preparation of *beryllium borohydride*, $Be(BH_4)_2$, by the reaction of dimethylberyllium with diborane. This compound also may be made by the direct reaction of beryllium hydride with diborane in an ether medium (2). (See Complex Hydrides, Chapter 14.)

Schlesinger and his coworkers also have found evidence for the existence of a *methyl beryllium hydride*, $(CH_3)BeH$ (2). This compound has not been investigated in detail as yet.

REFERENCES—BERYLLIUM HYDRIDE

1. Finholt, Bond, and Schlesinger, *J. Am. Chem. Soc.*, **69**, 1199 (1947).
2. Barbaras, Dillard, Finholt, Wartik, Wilzbach, and Schlesinger, *J. Am. Chem. Soc.*, **73**, 4585 (1951).
3. Burg and Schlesinger, *J. Am. Chem. Soc.*, **62**, 3425 (1940).

MAGNESIUM

MgH_2—*magnesium hydride*
White, non-volatile polymeric solid

Structure. Although the structure of magnesium hydride has not been determined, the compound is believed to be polymerized by hydrogen "bridge" bonds between magnesium atoms. This type of bonding is similar to that responsible for the polymeric nature of beryllium hydride as well as aluminum hydride, diborane, and the covalent borohydrides.

Preparation. Wiberg and Bauer* have prepared magnesium hydride by the pyrolysis of a magnesium dialkyl or a Grignard reagent:

$$Mg(C_2H_5)_2 \xrightarrow[\text{vacuum}]{175 \text{ to } 200°} MgH_2 + 2C_2H_4$$

$$2Mg(C_2H_5)I \xrightarrow{200°} MgH_2 + MgI_2 + 2C_2H_4$$

Magnesium hydride may also be prepared by the reaction of a magnesium dialkyl with a reactive hydride, such as diborane or lithium aluminum hydride:†

$$3MgR_2 + B_2H_6 \rightarrow 3MgH_2 + 2BR_3$$

$$MgR_2 + LiAlH_4 \rightarrow MgH_2 + LiAlH_2R_2$$

If excess diborane is present in the above synthesis it will react with the magnesium hydride to form magnesium borohydride, $Mg(BH_4)_2$.

Properties. Magnesium hydride is a white, non-volatile solid material that does not ignite spontaneously on exposure to air. It is surprisingly stable against thermal decomposition; on heating, this compound does not begin to decompose until a temperature of 280° to 300° has been reached. Magnesium hydride is not soluble in ether; thus it is either very highly polymerized or partially ionic, possibly both. It does react vigorously with water to evolve hydrogen and form magnesium hydroxide. Similarly, it will form magnesium alcoholates by reaction with alcohols:

$$MgH_2 + 2CH_3OH \rightarrow 2H_2 + Mg(OCH_3)_2$$

---

* Wiberg and Bauer, *Z. Naturforsch.*, **5b** (7), 396 (1950).
† See reference 2 under Beryllium Hydride.

Like the hydrides of related elements—beryllium, aluminum, lithium, etc.—magnesium hydride is a very strong reducing agent.

Derivatives. Wiberg and Bauer have prepared *magnesium borohydride*, $Mg(BH_4)_2$, and *magnesium aluminum hydride*, $Mg(AlH_4)_2$. (See *Complex Hydrides*.) Both these compounds, as well as magnesium hydride itself, may possibly be useful as specialized reducing agents for particular syntheses.

The Covalent Hydrides—General Considerations

The *covalent hydrides* are the hydrides of the elements in Groups III and IIIB through VII and VIIB of the Periodic Table (as shown in Figure 1, page 3, Chapter 1). These compounds are distinguished physically from the other types of hydrides in that they are *volatile* substances; for the most part, they are gases or liquids under normal conditions.

In the covalent hydrides, the chemical bonds between hydrogen and the various elements are primarily of the *electron-sharing* type. In this type of chemical bond, the valence electrons are shared more or less equally between the elements held in chemical combination by the bond, and large differences in electric charge are not present as they are in the ionic hydrides. Since the covalent bond is not highly polar, the covalent hydride molecules are, in general, not very polar. Therefore, individual covalent hydride molecules will not be strongly attracted to each other, and in condensed phases the molecules will be held together by relatively weak forces. It is the absence of strong intermolecular forces that is responsible for the properties of volatility and low melting point that are characteristic of the covalent hydrides.

Although the covalent hydrides are non-polar compounds as compared to the ionic hydrides, it must be remembered that polarity and non-polarity are relative quantities. As explained in Chapter 2, some degree of polarity must be inherent in most covalent bonds since the electronegativities of two combining elements rarely are equal. There are, then, certain differences among the covalent hydrides, particularly in their chemical properties, which can be explained on the basis of bond polarities. The essential feature of the covalent hydrides is, however, that covalent or electron-sharing bonding plays a predominant role in all these compounds. This is true even in the hydrogen halides, where the greatest electronegativity differences exist. (Hydrogen fluoride is the only exception; it is estimated to be slightly more ionic than it is covalent, although its physical properties are those of a covalent compound.) A degree of

53

ionic character such as that exhibited by hydrogen in the ionic hydrides is never approached by hydrogen in its combinations with electronegative elements.

Physical Properties. With a few important exceptions, we can make some valid generalizations about the physical properties of the covalent hydrides. The exceptions which we shall make are those compounds, such as ammonia, water, and hydrogen fluoride, in which strong hydrogen bonding occurs between molecules (see Chapter 2) and the polynuclear hydrides of boron and aluminum.

The *volatilities* of the covalent hydrides are functions primarily of the respective molecular weights of the compounds. As we observed previously, this is because in most of the covalent hydrides there is relatively little polar character and the individual molecules in a liquid phase are held together mainly by the van der Waals forces; it is easy to separate and volatilize the molecules of the condensed phase by supplying small amounts of energy in the form of heat. In the gas phase there is little attraction between molecules. All this means that the covalent hydrides boil at relatively low temperatures, and the lighter a molecule is the lower its boiling point should be.

In a given series of hydrides of elements lying in the same row of the Periodic Table, for instance, GeH_4, AsH_3, SeH_2, and HBr, the effect of molecular weight on the boiling point may be masked by other factors, such as partial polarity and molecular size, and the differences in molecular weight actually are slight. However, in a series of hydrides of related elements lying in the same *group* of the Periodic Table, CH_4, SiH_4, GeH_4, SnH_4, and PbH_4, for example, the boiling points increase markedly with molecular weight since the differences in molecular weight are large. Figure 2 shows the boiling points of the covalent hydrides in Groups IV through VII. It will be observed that, with the exception of ammonia, water, and hydrogen fluoride, the boiling points lie on fairly regular curves.

Ammonia, water, and hydrogen fluoride are abnormal since the molecules of these compounds are associated in condensed phases by the relatively strong forces of hydrogen bonding. It has been calculated that the normal boiling point of ammonia in the absence of hydrogen bonding would be $-130°$, that of water would be $-112°$, and that of hydrogen fluoride would be $-136°$ (1). Hydrogen bonding in these compounds similarly causes abnormalities in the heats of vaporization. The calculated value of the heat of vaporization of water in the absence of hydrogen bonding is 3.23 Kcal per mole; the actual value is 9.72 Kcal per mole. For ammonia the calculated value is 2.85 Kcal per mole; the actual value at the boiling point

$(-33.4°)$ is 5.56 Kcal per mole. Similarly, for hydrogen fluoride the calculated value of the heat of vaporization is 2.75 Kcal per mole whereas the actual value is about 7.2 Kcal per mole. The values for the heats of vaporization of the other covalent hydrides, again with the omission of the Group III hydrides, are normal and, as would be expected, show a regular increase with molecular weight within any given group of related compounds.

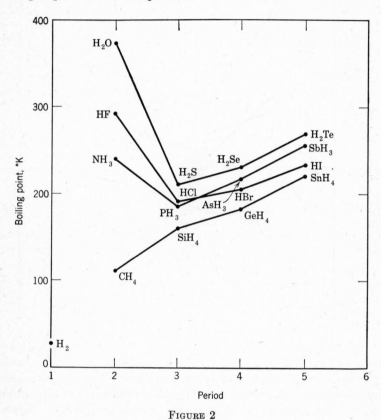

FIGURE 2

The *melting points* of the covalent hydrides are low for the same reasons that the boiling points are low, that is, the lack of strong intermolecular forces in the condensed phase. There is, however, less regularity in the melting points of the covalent hydrides since other factors in addition to molecular weight, such as molecular size, molecular configuration, and crystal structure, are of importance in determining the melting point of a solid phase.

Melting points of the covalent hydrides are plotted in Figure 3.

Again it will be noted that the values for NH_3, H_2O, and HF are abnormal because of hydrogen bonding. Values have been calculated for the "normal" melting points of these compounds, assuming the absence of hydrogen bonding. These values are $-167°$ for NH_3, $-120°$ for H_2O, and $-141°$ for HF.

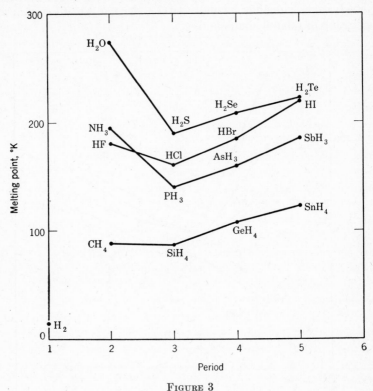

FIGURE 3

The hydrides of boron, aluminum, and gallium have been excluded from these generalities about volatility and melting point. Aluminum hydride is known only in solution or as a polymeric solid. Because mononuclear hydrides of boron and gallium cannot be isolated as such there are no experimental values to compare with those of the simple covalent hydrides.

It will be apparent that the above generalizations about melting point and volatility have been applied only to mononuclear hydrides. Many of the covalent hydrides do exist in polynuclear forms, for example, C_2H_6, Si_2H_6, Si_3H_8, N_2H_4.

Chemical Properties. In general, the chemical reactivity of the covalent hydrides toward attack by strongly electronegative groups such as oxygen and the halogens, or by hydrolysis, decreases with increasing electronegativity of the parent element. For example, arsine (E. N. of As = 2.0) is more readily oxidized than ammonia (E. N. of N = 3.0). Silane (E. N. of Si = 1.8) is halogenated more easily than methane (E. N. of C = 2.5) and is hydrolyzed less readily than aluminum hydride (E. N. of Al = 1.5). However, in many cases the chemical properties of the parent elements are of more importance in determining reactivity than the polarity of the attached hydrogen. We should be cautious, therefore, in extending generalizations about the effect of relative electronegativity on chemical reactivity to cases in which only slight differences in electronegativity are involved. For example, it would be difficult to compare the chemical reactivities of diborane and disilane solely on the basis of the electronegativities of boron and silicon alone.

Outside the obvious exceptions, all the covalent hydrides can be oxygenated or halogenated to form, in most cases, the corresponding derivatives of both the hydrogen, that is, water or hydrogen halide, and the parent element, that is, oxide or halide. In some reactions, such as the oxidation of ammonia or hydrogen chloride, the parent element is simply liberated.

In *hydrolysis reactions*, several reaction mechanisms are possible, depending on the nature of the hydride compounds. The hydrides of strongly electronegative elements, in which hydrogen is relatively positive, may be dissociated by the action of hydroxyl ion as an electron donor on the positive hydrogen to form water. These compounds generally are not decomposed by acidic solutions although some of them may undergo a reversible ionization, depending on the acidity of the solution and the electronegativity of the parent element, for example, HCl and H_2S. (See Chapter 13.)

The hydride compounds of the less electronegative elements, in which the hydrogen is the relatively negative component, are quite susceptible to hydrolysis in acids by attack of positive hydrogen ions on the negative hydrogen in the hydride to form water. Such compounds may be relatively stable in basic solutions where the concentration of positive hydrogen ions is very low; for example, the *borohydride ion*, BH_4^-, is stable in basic solutions but is decomposed by acids.

Still a third mode of hydrolysis reaction involves the attack of positive hydrogen ion or hydroxyl ion on the parent element itself. The nature and course of this type of reaction depends not only on the electronegativity of the parent element, but also on its ability to coordinate with the attacking groups during the course of the reaction.

It should be pointed out that these remarks on hydrolysis reactions may be extended to similar reactions, such as ammonolysis.

A great many of the covalent hydrides can be made to add to unsaturated hydrocarbons, thus providing one method of preparing organic derivatives of covalent hydrides. For example, monosilane will add to the carbon-carbon double bond in ethylene at 100°:

$$SiH_4 + H_2C{=}CH_2 \rightarrow C_2H_5SiH_3$$

$$C_2H_5SiH_3 + H_2C{=}CH_2 \rightarrow (C_2H_5)_2SiH_2, \text{ etc.}$$

Similarly, diborane will add readily to olefins to form boron trialkyls, ammonia can be added to form amines, hydrogen halides to form alkyl halides, and water can be added to form alcohols, and so forth. The reactivity of a covalent hydride toward this addition reaction appears to depend, in part at least, on the difference in electronegativity between hydrogen and the parent element of the hydride. The addition proceeds more readily in those cases where this difference is large. Undoubtedly, the behavior of the parent element as an electron acceptor or as an electron donor also influences the addition reaction. For example, the electronegativity of boron is not far different from that of hydrogen; yet, because of the strong electron acceptor tendencies of boron, diborane is unique in the rapidity with which it will add to olefin double bonds, even at low temperatures. The nature of the olefin also is an important factor since the higher alkyl olefins undergo addition more rapidly and at lower temperatures than ethylene.

The partial substitution of other groups for hydrogen in a covalent hydride molecule can markedly affect the stability and chemical reactivity of the remaining hydrogen atoms. If the substituting groups are highly electronegative, the *effective* electronegativity of the parent element is increased and the chemical bonds with the remaining hydrogen atoms are made more polar. For example, *monosilane*, SiH_4, is readily hydrolyzed by water in the presence of traces of acid or base to form *disiloxane*, $(SiH_3)_2O$. In acid-catalyzed hydrolysis, the mechanism presumably involves an attack by a positive hydrogen ion, or hydronium ion, H_3O^+, on one of the relatively negative hydrogen atoms in the silane molecule; it is the negative character of the silane hydrogen atoms which makes this reaction possible. Hydrogen gas is formed, while the positive *silyl* radical attaches a hydroxyl ion to form a short-lived *silanol*, which soon condenses to form *disiloxane*:

$$H_3Si{-}H + H_3O^+ \rightarrow \quad H_2 + \quad H_3Si^+ + H_2O$$

$$H_3Si^+ + \quad OH^- \rightarrow H_3SiOH \rightarrow (SiH_3)_2O + H_2O$$

In base-catalyzed hydrolysis, the initial reaction appears to be an attack by hydroxyl ion on the relatively positive silicon atom in the silane molecule. A negative hydrogen thus is displaced to combine with a positive hydrogen ion to form gaseous hydrogen, and the end product again is disiloxane.

Since in disiloxane, the molecule is influenced by the electronegativity of oxygen, the remaining hydrogen atoms attached to silicon become less negative, that is, more positive. Thus it is observed that disiloxane is less susceptible than monosilane to hydrolysis by acids, although it still is readily hydrolyzed by bases since with bases direct attack on the silicon atom by hydroxyl ion is involved. If the hydrogen becomes sufficiently positive it can be attacked by hydroxyl ion, but is stable toward attack by hydronium ion. The hydrolysis of *trichlorosilane* or *silicochloroform*, $SiHCl_3$, can be effected even in the presence of comparatively large concentrations of acid to form $(HSiO_{3/2})_x$ without disruption of the single silicon-hydrogen bond. With so much negative substitution on the silicon atom, the hydrogen becomes quite positive. This means, however, that the hydrogen is quite acidic, and the compound is easily decomposed by bases.

These general considerations of hydrolysis can be applied to others of the covalent hydrides, such as diborane and germane. The effect of substituting groups on the nature of the hydrogen in the hydrides of the more electronegative elements is of great importance since our common acids and bases result from such effects. (See Chapter 13, "Acids and Bases.") The effect of substituting groups will also play a role in determining the behavior of the covalent hydrides toward many other reactions, such as addition to olefins, oxidation (including the phenomenon of spontaneous inflammability), and halogenation.

Some of the covalent hydrides are *spontaneously inflammable* and burn on exposure to air or oxygen. This phenomenon is not well understood, and in many cases it may be caused by traces of impurities or catalytic traces of water in the air. It can be related to electronic unsaturation of the parent atom, as in diborane, aluminum hydride, or silane, where the parent atom is relatively positive. Most of the covalent hydrides are spontaneously reactive with strong halogens like fluorine and chlorine. Again, the reactivity of the compound will be determined by the nature of the attacking group as well as that of the compound.

Thermal Stability. Many of the covalent hydrides are not very stable against thermal decomposition into their component elements. Indeed, some of these compounds, such as the hydrides of lead and bismuth, are unstable at room temperature. This instability is indicated by the relatively low heats of formation, or even negative heats of formation, of many of these compounds. As a general rule the thermal stability of a covalent hydride depends upon (a) the electronegativity of the parent element, and (b) the atomic weight of the parent element. Therefore, in considering the members of a particular *row*, or period, of hydride forming elements in the Periodic Table, there will be a general *increase* in stability from left to right since the electronegativity increases steadily in this direction. For example, there is a general increase in the thermal stability of the hydrides of the elements in the series comprising Al, Si, P, S, and Cl. There is a general *decrease* in the stability of the hydrides of elements in a particular *group* of the Periodic Table with *increasing* atomic weight. For example, there is a marked decrease in the stability of the hydrides in the series of elements C, Si, Ge, Sn, and Pb. In regard to hydride stability, the effect of atomic size of the parent element probably is more important a factor than electronegativity. If we compare the hydrides of elements having about the same electronegativity we observe that the hydrides of the heavier elements are much less stable; for example, methane is more stable than hydrogen sulfide, phosphine is more stable than tellurium hydride, and silane is more stable than stibine.

Preparation—General Methods. Many of the volatile covalent hydrides have been prepared by the *direct reaction* of hydrogen with the parent elements. However, the conditions necessary to effect this reaction and the ease with which the reaction proceeds depend upon the electronegativity of the element. The direct reaction does not give good yields of hydride except with highly electronegative elements such as nitrogen, oxygen, and the halogens.

The reaction of hydrogen with fluorine is spontaneous upon bringing the two elements into contact, even at temperatures well below the boiling point of liquid nitrogen ($-196°$).

The reaction of hydrogen with oxygen to form water, and with chlorine or bromine to form hydrogen chloride or bromide, does not proceed spontaneously under normal conditions, but may be initiated in a mixture of the gases by elevated temperatures, such as from a spark or a flame, or by certain metallic catalysts such as platinum. The reaction of a hydrogen-chlorine mixture may be initiated photochemically by illumination with a high-intensity light source. The reactions in all these cases are highly exothermic and usually are explosive.

The union of hydrogen with sulfur, selenium, or iodine may be effected by heating the vapors of these elements with gaseous hydrogen. However, with the lesser electronegativity of these elements, the hydrides are less stable against thermal dissociation, and the formation reactions are equilibrium reactions which go only part way to completion at elevated temperatures:

$$H_2 + S \rightleftharpoons H_2S$$

In the combination of nitrogen and hydrogen to form ammonia, the use of a catalyst, high gas pressures, and rapid quenching of the reaction product are necessary to obtain a good yield of ammonia from the equilibrium reaction.

With the remaining elements in the covalent hydride group, the hydrides are generally so unstable thermally that the amount of compound in equilibrium with the free element and hydrogen is very small at the elevated temperatures necessary to initiate reaction, and in many cases the amounts of hydride formed are negligible. However, if a stream of hydrogen is passed rapidly over a finely divided sample of the element at a high temperature and rapidly quenched thereafter, it is possible to obtain traces of hydrides with elemental silicon, boron, arsenic, phosphorus, etc.

Methods of activation other than high temperatures are more productive with the less electronegative elements. For example, arsine and stibine have been prepared in relatively good yields by passing an electric discharge of the glow type between electrodes of arsenic or antimony in an atmosphere of hydrogen. Traces of volatile hydrides from aluminum and zinc have been observed when a rapid stream of hydrogen has been passed through an electric arc struck between electrodes of these metals. Transient hydrides of the type MH have been observed spectroscopically for many elements under the conditions of glow discharge between metallic electrodes in hydrogen.

Most of the chemical elements form hydrogen containing compounds of some sort when they are subjected to the action of atomic hydrogen at moderate or low temperatures.

Hydrolysis reactions comprise a very general method for preparing covalent hydrides. In this method, a binary compound of the hydride-forming element and of a strongly electropositive element is subjected to decomposition by hydrolysis in water or in acidic solutions. For illustration, we may consider the formation of monosilane by the hydrolysis of magnesium silicide in dilute acid:

$$Mg_2Si + 4HCl(aq) \rightarrow SiH_4 + 2MgCl_2$$

or the hydrolysis of calcium phosphide by water to yield phosphine:

$$Ca_3P_2 + 6H_2O \rightarrow 2PH_3 + 3Ca(OH)_2$$

Similarly, the acid hydrolysis of calcium fluoride forms hydrogen fluoride. Nearly all the covalent hydrides have been prepared by such hydrolysis reactions.

Certain binary compounds will react readily with water to form the hydrides of their negative or "non-metallic" components, for example, *calcium carbide*, whereas other compounds may require acids for their hydrolysis, for example *ferrous sulfide*. A few compounds, such as certain metal nitrides, may be reactive toward alkaline hydrolysis. Some reactions analogous to hydrolysis can be effected in liquid ammonia or similar non-aqueous media to form volatile hydrides. However, a great many of the binary compounds of the type we are discussing are inert and will not yield hydrides upon decomposition.

The compounds most readily forming covalent hydrides upon hydrolysis are, in general, those in which the "metallic" components are strongly electropositive metals. For example, the alkali metal carbides, silicides, nitrides, etc., react vigorously with water to form the corresponding hydrides. This reactivity to water is shown to a lesser degree by the compounds of magnesium and the alkaline earth metals. With less electropositive elements as the "metallic" constituents, the presence of acids usually is necessary for hydrolysis; many compounds of this type will not yield hydrides on hydrolysis.

The greater the electronegativity of the "non-metal" component, the greater is the number of its binary compounds that will form its hydride upon hydrolysis. With weakly electronegative elements like boron and silicon only those compounds with strongly electropositive metals are hydrolyzable to form hydrides. With more electronegative elements such as carbon and phosphorus, compounds with less electropositive metals are found to be reactive. Strongly electronegative elements like oxygen, fluorine, and nitrogen are readily obtained as hydrides from their compounds with very weakly electropositive elements. Thus, for example, although very few metal borides may be hydrolyzed to form boranes, virtually all fluorides will yield hydrogen fluoride upon hydrolysis. It appears, therefore, as a general observation that a certain minimum difference must exist between the electronegativities of the components in a binary compound in order that the hydride of the "non-metallic" component be produced upon hydrolysis of the compound. This implies a certain degree of ionicity or partial polarity in the binary compound. It has been postulated that the mechanism whereby covalent hydrides are formed in hydrolysis reactions is the reaction:

$$M^+X^- + H^+Y^- \rightarrow XH + M^+Y^-$$

where MX represents a binary compound between a relatively positive element M and a relatively negative element X, and in which the bond between M and X is at least partially ionic in character. Y may represent any convenient anion such as OH^-, Cl^-, or SO_4^-.

The binary compounds that form volatile hydrides are of definite composition and have formulas corresponding to normal chemical valencies of their component elements. Although apparent contradictions to this statement may be found, particularly among the carbides, it may be shown that even in these cases the compounds have formulas consistent with the normal free valencies of the complex ions present; that is, the valence of the "non-metal" is that which would be expected if the "non-metal" atoms were present as complex negative ions. With a carbide, for example, the type of hydride produced depends upon the disposition of carbon in the crystal lattice of the compound. Beryllium carbide, which yields methane upon hydrolysis, is known to have a structure comprising individual carbon atoms isolated by surrounding metal atoms. Acetylides of the type MC_2, for example, CaC_2, can be shown to have carbons present in the crystal lattice in pairs, that is, as $C_2^=$ ions. It also is of interest to note that whereas magnesium silicide yields principally monosilane, lithium silicide, Li_6Si_2, yields disilane upon hydrolysis. Similar behavior is observed with the compounds of other hydride-forming elements, for example, boron and germanium (2).

With a few elements, such as tin and lead, hydrides may be formed by subjecting a mechanical mixture of the element with an active metal like magnesium to the action of dilute acid.

A serious difficulty with hydrolysis reactions, particularly for the preparation of very reactive compounds like the hydrides of boron and silicon, is that the hydride products may not be stable under the conditions of the hydrolysis. For example, the hydrolysis of magnesium boride does not yield any diborane since this compound is decomposed by water as rapidly as it is formed; only the less reactive higher boranes are obtained, and the overall yield of hydrides is small.

Electrolytic reactions have been employed to prepare hydrides of the heavier and more metallic elements in the covalent hydride group. The technique varies somewhat, but in essence it involves the electrolysis of an acidic solution with a cathode of the desired metal. In the process of discharging positive hydrogen ions at the cathode, some reaction between the cathode metal and hydrogen may occur to form a volatile hydride.   The yields generally are not very large, but are sufficient to make the method of some utility.   A variation of the electrolytic method is to electrolyze a solution, usually acidic, of a salt of the desired element between inert electrodes or electrodes of the same element.   Both the element and hydrogen are discharged at the cathode and unite there to form a hydride.   Hydrides of arsenic, antimony, and bismuth have been prepared in this fashion.

Perhaps the most useful synthetic tool for preparing covalent hydrides is the method involving *metathetical reactions with ionic hydrides*.   This very general method may be used for preparing any of the covalent hydrides.   However, since the ionic hydrides are relatively expensive materials, this method is useful principally in the preparation of hydrides difficult to obtain in good yields by other methods.   This is true in particular of the hydrides of the less electronegative elements in the covalent hydride group.

The basic reaction, which is one of metathesis, is illustrated by the preparation of aluminum hydride from aluminum chloride and lithium hydride:

$$3LiH + AlCl_3 \rightarrow AlH_3 + 3LiCl$$

This sort of reaction usually is carried out at room temperature in a medium of diethyl ether.   If the covalent hydrides being formed are sufficiently stable, the metathetical reduction reaction also can be effected by passing the vapor of a halide to be reduced over powdered lithium hydride heated to ca. 180° to 200°:

$$2BF_3 + 6LiH \rightarrow B_2H_6 + 6LiF$$

Any of the alkali metal or alkaline earth metal hydrides appear to be satisfactory for the vapor phase reduction at elevated temperatures, but, of the ionic hydrides, only lithium hydride is barely sufficiently soluble to be used in ether solution.

The scope of the reduction method for hydride preparation has been greatly extended by the discovery of *complex anionic hydrides*, in particular, *lithium aluminum hydride*, $LiAlH_4$ (3).   This compound not only is a very powerful reducing agent; it is much more soluble in ether than lithium hydride (see Chapter 14, "Complex Hydrides").   Lithium aluminum hydride also is very convenient in that stepwise reductions of halides, etc., can be effected to yield intermediate hydride derivatives:

$$4SiCl_4 + LiAlH_4 \rightarrow 4SiHCl_3 + LiCl + AlCl_3$$

$$SiHCl_3 \xrightarrow{LiAlH_4} SiH_2Cl_2$$

and so forth to SiH_4. Similarly, organic derivatives can be prepared by the reduction of appropriate halide compounds:

$$4(CH_3)_3SiCl + LiAlH_4 \rightarrow 4(CH_3)_3SiH + LiCl + AlCl_3$$

The synthesis reactions that have been illustrated are specific (and terminal) examples of a general type of metathetical reaction:

$$MH + NX \rightarrow NH + MX$$

that may occur when element M is more electropositive than element N, and X represents a group more electronegative than hydrogen. Since the hydride compounds most difficult to prepare by other methods are the hydrides of relatively electropositive elements like boron, silicon, aluminum, magnesium, and zinc, we find that the hydride or hydride derivatives of a more electropositive element like lithium is a convenient synthesis reagent. However, aluminum hydride or magnesium hydride can, in turn, be used as a reagent for the preparation of other hydrides, for instance, arsine from arsenic trichloride.

A variation of the metathetical synthesis is the vapor phase reaction in which the vapor of a volatile halide, such as boron trichloride, is mixed with hydrogen and passed at 300° to 400° through a bed of a finely divided reactive metal such as aluminum or zinc; or the gaseous reaction mixture is bubbled through molten sodium at 150° to 200°.

$$2Al + 3H_2 + 2BCl_3 \rightarrow B_2H_6 + 2AlCl_3$$

In reducing silicon halides by this reaction, a stepwise replacement results, and a mixture of halogen-substituted silanes, as well as some monosilane, is formed. It has been postulated (although it is by no means certain) that, with aluminum or zinc, transient hydrides are formed by the action of hydrogen on the hot metal, and that these hydrides are responsible for the reduction reactions.

REFERENCES

1. Taft and Sisler, *J. Chem. Educ.* **24,** 175 (1947).
2. Hurd, *J. Am. Chem. Soc.,* **69,** 1647 (1947).
3. Finholt, Bond, and Schesinger, *J. Am. Chem. Soc.,* **69,** 1199 (1947).

CHAPTER

8

The Hydrides of the Group III Elements

GENERAL CONSIDERATIONS

The hydrides of the elements in Group III (and IIIB), *boron, aluminum, gallium*, stand at the beginning of the large family of covalent volatile hydrides. Although each of these elements is more electropositive than hydrogen, the actual differences in electronegativity are small. Furthermore, in chemical combinations the atoms of the Group III elements tend to be rather small and highly charged. The Group III hydrides, therefore, are predominantly covalent compounds. *Indium* and *thallium*, the heavier elements in Group IIIB, do not form stable, well-defined hydrides; for this reason they are included with the borderline hydrides described in Chapter 16.

The hydrides of boron, aluminum, and gallium are unique in several respects. Most important, and most difficult to explain, are the variations from normal behavior they exhibit in their chemical bonding and valence relationships. No stable mononuclear hydrides are observed; the simplest hydrides are dimers—*diborane*, B_2H_6, and *digallane*, Ga_2H_6. Aluminum hydride forms highly polymeric systems, and low-molecular-weight forms are observed only as etherate compounds. In each of the dimeric hydrides, the formal valence of the parent element appears to have a value of *4*, whereas the usual theories of valence by electron pair bonding would predict a normal valence of *3* and the existence of the compounds BH_3, AlH_3, and GaH_3. Of these, only *borine*, BH_3, is known by indirect evidence to exist in small amounts in equilibrium with the dimeric *diborane*, B_2H_6. Furthermore, a whole series of polynuclear boron hydrides exist in which unusual valence relationships are evident.

The Group III elements are known to be very strong electron acceptors. If the three valence electrons of a free aluminum atom, for example, are paired with three electrons from three chlorine atoms in the formation of a molecule of $AlCl_3$, three normal covalent bonds should result between the aluminum and the three chlorine atoms. The molecule is electrically neutral. However, the aluminum atom has both the ability and the tendency to acquire a share, at least, in

66

still a fourth pair of valence electrons since, by doing so, it can complete an octet of valence electrons. This course of action will take place if a donor atom of suitable size makes available an extra pair of electrons for sharing with the aluminum atom, and a coordination complex will be formed. In the case of aluminum chloride, the extra pair of electrons can be acquired by the aluminum atom from a chlorine atom on a neighboring molecule of aluminum chloride. Since the aluminum atom is large enough to accommodate four chlorine atoms about it, the result of the electron sharing is the dimerization of aluminum chloride. This sharing may be depicted as:

In the case of boron trichloride, the boron atom is too small to accommodate four chlorine atoms, and the dimerization does not occur.

We might be tempted to reason by analogy and postulate that the dimerization or polymerization of the prototype Group III hydrides proceeds along similar lines of donor-acceptor bonding. A major difficulty, however, is that a covalent hydrogen atom has only one pair of electrons, which, presumably, is used to form a normal covalent bond to the parent atom and is not readily available for donation to another atom. In other words, if we assume that all the bonds in a compound like diborane should be electron pair bonds, there are not enough electrons available to satisfy the requirements of all the obvious chemical bonds in the compound; the molecule is *electron-deficient*.

Much effort has been spent in trying to solve the riddle of the missing electrons in the chemical bonding of electron-deficient compounds. Most of this effort has been directed toward the boron hydrides, and to diborane in particular. It will be appreciated, however, that the same problems and the same possible answers are pertinent also to the electron-deficient hydrides of aluminum and gallium.

Structure Theories. We know several things about the diborane molecule that are clues to its structure. It is fairly certain, both from physical measurements and from the chemical behavior of diborane, that two of the hydrogen atoms are unique. Structure investigations have indicated that two of the six hydrogen atoms are located very close to or within the boron-boron bond in the diborane molecule, and that the rotation of the BH_3 units about the boron-boron bond is restricted. If the hydrogen atoms in diborane are successively substituted by alkyl groups in the formation of alkyldiboranes (see below), the molecule divides into monomeric *borine* derivatives as soon as more than two alkyl groups are present on one of the boron atoms. From this behavior it appears that at least two hydrogen atoms may be necessary to maintain the dimeric structure of the diborane molecule. On the other hand, there are a few compounds, such as *dimethoxyborine*, $(CH_3O)_2BH$ (see below), in which the presence of one hydrogen on each boron atom does not lead to the formation of dimeric molecules because of the steric hindrance of large attached groups.

In view of what now is known about the diborane molecule, many of the early theories made to explain the bond between the boron atoms are untenable. These theories include the "one-electron bond" theory advanced by Sidgwick and by Pauling (1), which, though plausible on theoretical grounds, either fails to differentiate between the hydrogen atoms or fails to provide double-bond character for the link between the boron atoms; the "no-electron bond" theory of Lewis, which fails for the same reasons; and various theories which regard diborane as an ionic compound (2, 3).

In 1921, Dilthey proposed a hydrogen-bridge structure for diborane without making any assumptions as to the electronic configuration:

$$
\begin{array}{ccccc}
H & & H & & H \\
\diagdown & \diagup & \cdots & \diagup & \\
& B & & B & \\
\diagup & & \diagdown & & \diagdown \\
H & & H & & H
\end{array}
$$

This concept has been elaborated by many investigators, including Wiberg, Longuet-Higgins, Pitzer, and Rundle. The ideas which have developed from this elaboration offer a reasonable explanation on theoretical grounds, not only for the bonding in diborane, but also for the bonding in many other electron-deficient compounds.

In 1943, Longuet-Higgins and Bell published a paper in which they discussed the possibility that the two boron atoms in the diborane molecule were bonded together by hydrogen bridges similar to those suggested by Dilthey's model (4). They considered that these hydrogen bonds were possible because each of the two hydrogen atoms could "resonate"* between two equivalent bond possibilities:

$$
\begin{array}{ccccccc}
H & H & & H & H & & H & H \\
\diagdown & \diagup & & \diagup & \diagdown & & \diagdown & \diagup \\
B & B & \rightleftharpoons & B & & B & \\
\diagup & \diagdown & & \diagup & & \diagdown \\
H & H & & H & H & & H & H
\end{array}
$$

* It should be appreciated that the concept of resonance does not imply the independent existence of the two resonating forms.

Longuet-Higgins and Bell argued that this sort of hydrogen bridging could occur in those cases where the atoms of the parent element had *no* unshared electron pairs. It may be recalled that unshared electron pairs on different atoms cause a mutual repulsion between these atoms; only atoms having no unshared electron pairs can approach each other closely enough for the formation of this type of hydrogen pair bridging. The authors postulated that any covalent hydride molecules—XH, XH_2, or XH_3—could form condensed systems if the above requirement regarding the absence of unshared electron pairs was met. A number of examples of electron-deficient compounds appeared to substantiate these qualitative observations.

(It should be pointed out that the type of hydrogen bridging discussed here is different from the hydrogen bonding between the hydrides of highly electronegative elements, for example, NH_3, H_2O, and HF. This latter type of hydrogen bonding is believed to result from the electrical attraction of highly polar molecules, that is, *dipole interaction*.)

In a later paper, Longuet-Higgins considered that his ideas on hydrogen bonding between electron-deficient atoms were in essential agreement with those of K. S. Pitzer, and he gave additional examples of electron-deficient compounds in added proof of these ideas:

Beryllium borohydride

Beryllium hydride

And there is also *aluminum hydride*, $(AlH_3)_x$, which, since the aluminum atom can accommodate six surrounding groups, may comprise a structure in which each aluminum atom is bound to three other aluminum atoms through two-atom hydrogen bridges (4).

In a paper published in 1945, Pitzer proposes a theory explaining the structure of the boranes on the basis of what he calls the "*protonated double bond*" (5). Pitzer says that in compounds of the type R_nMH, in which the number of electron pairs being shared with the attached groups by the atom M is less than the number of available orbitals of the atom M, we can find the establishment of a new type of chemical bonding in the formation of compounds of the type R_nHMMHR_n. The R groups may be hydrogen atoms also, or may be other groups. The actual bond between the two M atoms involves an electron pair occupying the hydrogen atom orbital and one vacant orbital on each M atom; it is best described by the theory of molecular orbitals (see Chapter 2).

The physical picture of this bond can be derived from resonance structures similar to those proposed by Longuet-Higgins and Bell and illustrated above. Pitzer also points out the importance of resonant ionic forms, particularly the contribution that such ionic forms will make to the structure if atoms of different elements are combined by this type of bond (for example, Be and B in *beryllium borohydride*). However, in contrast to the hydrogen-bridge structure originally proposed by Longuet-Higgins and Bell, or the physically similar structure proposed by Rundle (see below), Pitzer considers that the bond, such as that between the two boron atoms in the diborane molecule, is essentially a double electron-pair bond and that the hydrogen atoms are present within the bond as *protons;* hence the name *"protonated double bond."*

Similar structures can be written for protonated double bonds between other electron-deficient atoms. Pitzer considers that the distribution of electron density within this bond would be similar to that derived from a consideration of the various possible resonance forms.

It will be apparent that a protonated double bond between two boron atoms would behave as a double bond and that free rotation about this bond would be restricted. Because of the repulsion of the protons, the bond distance should be larger than the normal calculated boron-boron bond distance (which it is). Also, the protons would easily be lost to negative groups.

An important part of Pitzer's protonated double-bond theory is that conjugation can occur between the protonated double bond in the diborane unit and vacant orbitals on adjacent boron atoms; that is, a resonance of the double bond between different possible positions should occur. Normal single covalent bonds between borons also are possible. Such single boron-boron bonds, which can be formed with relative ease by the loss of protons or hydrogen atoms from a protonated double bond, can add additional units in the formation of new protonated double bonds. On the basis of such considerations, Pitzer has been able to make a number of predictions and explanations regarding the structure of the boranes, particularly as to the absence of stable borine or triborane molecules.

Rundle has applied his general interpretation of the bonding mechanism in electron-deficient molecules (see Chapter 2) to the structure of the boranes (6). He suggests that the hydrogen atom can form a bond between two boron atoms in which an electron pair, the orbital of the hydrogen atom, and orbitals of each boron atom are involved. The boron-boron bond in the diborane molecule thus comprises two hydrogen atoms, each forming a half bond to each boron atom. This type of bonding is consistent with the theory of molecular orbitals. Prerequisites for the formation of such *half bonds* are that the different atoms involved in the bonding must have similar electronegativities, that is, the electronegativity differences must be small, and that the combining atoms must have vacant orbitals available. It will be apparent that this bonding mechanism is similar to that proposed by Longuet-Higgins and Bell, but without the concept of resonance, and similar to that of Pitzer, but without any assumptions regarding the existence of the hydrogen atoms as protons within the bond structure.

Rundle's bonding mechanism explains why the link between the boron atoms in the diborane molecule will be, in effect, a "double bond," and why free rotation of the BH_3 units about the bond will be restricted. Since each boron atom has four orbitals being used in chemical bonding, it will try to orient the four bonds to the corners of a tetrahedron; thus the two "bridge" hydrogens will lie above and below the plane of the two boron atoms and the four normal hydrogen atoms. It has been shown by physical measurements that the diborane atom does have this configuration. The single-atom hydrogen bridges that occur in a few positions in the decaborane structure also are explainable in terms of hydrogen "half bonds."

Rundle considers that if it were not for steric hindrance, molecules such as dimethoxyborine and the trialkylborines should form dimeric molecules. The boron atom is very small, however, and steric factors are important. The aluminum atom is larger than the boron atom and is less easily crowded. An aluminum trialkyl, such as trimethylaluminum, can, and does, dimerize through hydrogen bridges, or half bonds, between the aluminum atoms and carbon atoms.

Rundle also considers that there is nothing unique about the "protonated double bond" proposed by Pitzer except, possibly, the very small size of the hydrogen atoms which results from the extension of their bonding electrons over relatively long distances. It is difficult to conceive of the proton, which is a very strong electron acceptor, existing as such in a chemical bond. Indeed, the observation of "bridge" hydrogens in the decaborane structure by X-ray analysis would seem to be evidence against their existence in the structure as protons (see below). On the other hand, it is likely that the "bridge" hydrogens in diborane, as well as those in other borane structures, are more positive than the normal hydrogen atoms; therefore, they would be more easily attacked by electron-donor reagents, such as ammonia, hydroxyl ion, or halide ions.

This discussion of structure theories has been intended to serve only as a brief introduction to a very complex and controversial subject. The reader interested in forming his own opinions should consult the original literature references. It will be apparent, however, that the later theories are closely similar in concept, differing only in details which may be relatively minor. There is little point in speculating about structure until molecular configurations have been firmly established.

Comparative Chemistry. The chemistry of the hydrides of boron and their derivatives is quite complex. As a family of hydrides, these compounds probably are surpassed in extent only by the hydrocarbons. The boron hydrides were among the earliest of the volatile hydrides to be synthesized and investigated, and much research work has been done with them since. The hydrides of aluminum and gallium, on the other hand, have been known for only a short time, and knowledge of these compounds and their behavior is rather scanty.

Certain differences are observed in the chemical and physical properties of the Group III hydrides. There is, for example, the expected decrease in volatility with increasing molecular weight; diborane is more volatile than digallane. Although relatively little is known about the chemical reactivity of the hydrides of aluminum and gallium, it appears that these compounds are less stable toward thermal decomposition than the boron hydrides and are more reactive chemically, particularly in reactions involving attack by oxidizing agents, such as oxygen, halogen, and water. The order of reactivity in the formation of complex derivatives by donor-acceptor bonding appears to be reversed; the boron hydrides form such complexes more readily, and the complex compounds or ions are more stable than those of aluminum hydride or gallium hydride. This is because boron is a stronger electron acceptor than aluminum or gallium. The Group III hydrides form many complex compounds with electron-donor groups, such as ammonia, amines, and ethers, as well as with hydride ions in complex anionic hydrides like *lithium borohydride*, $LiBH_4$, *lithium aluminum hydride*, $LiAlH_4$, and *lithium gallium hydride*, $LiGaH_4$.

The hydrides of boron, aluminum, and gallium cannot be prepared by the direct reaction of these elements with molecular hydrogen. A general and useful method of synthesis is the metathetical reaction of a halide with a strong reducing hydride, such as lithium hydride or lithium aluminum hydride. Similarly, an alkyl derivative, such as trimethylgallium, may be converted to a hydride by reaction with an active hydride such as lithium aluminum hydride.

The Group III hydrides may also be prepared by subjecting a mixture of a chloride or bromide, for example, BCl_3, or a trialkyl, for example, $Al(CH_3)_3$, with hydrogen to the action of a high-voltage electric glow discharge.

The aqueous hydrolysis of metal borides has been used to prepare boron hydrides, but the great chemical reactivity of aluminum hydride and gallium hydride makes the synthesis of these compounds by hydrolysis reactions impossible.

REFERENCES

1. Pauling, *Nature of the Chemical Bond*, Cornell University Press, Ithaca, N.Y., 1940.
2. Schlesinger and Burg, *Chem. Rev.*, **31**, 1–41 (1942).
3. Bauer, *Chem Rev.*, **31**, 43 (1942).
4. Longuet-Higgins and Bell, *J. Chem. Soc.*, **1943**, 250 ff. Longuet-Higgins, *J. Chem. Soc.*, **1946**, 139 ff.
5. Pitzer, *J. Am. Chem. Soc.*, **67**, 1126 (1945).
6. Rundle, *J. Am. Chem. Soc.*, **69**, 1327, 1719 (1947). *J. Chem. Phys.*, **17**, 671 (1949).

BORON

B_2H_6—*diborane*.
Colorless gas, relatively stable
Melting point: $-165.5°$
Boiling point: $-92.5°$
Density: 0.438 g/cc at b.p.
Heat of formation: -6.7 Kcal/mole (1)

B_4H_{10}—*tetraborane*
Colorless gas, unstable
Melting point: $-120°$

Boiling point: 16°
Density: 0.56 g/cc at −35°

B_5H_9—*pentaborane*
Colorless liquid, relatively stable
Melting point: −46.8°
Boiling point: 58°
Density: 0.61 g/cc at 0°
Vapor pressure: 66 mm at 0°

B_5H_{11}—*unstable pentaborane* (*dihydropentaborane*)
Colorless liquid, unstable
Melting point: −123°
Boiling point: 65°
Vapor pressure: 52.8 mm at 0°

B_6H_{10}—*hexaborane*
Colorless liquid, relatively stable
Melting point: −65°

B_6H_{12}—*unstable hexaborane* (*dihydrohexaborane*)
Colorless liquid, unstable
Melting point: ca. −90°

$B_{10}H_{14}$—*decaborane*
White crystalline solid, stable
Melting point: 99.5°
Boiling point: 213°
Density: 0.94 g/cc at 25°
Vapor pressure: 19.0 mm at 100°

It will be observed that, on the basis of their formulas, the hydrides of boron can be divided into two different groups. The normal hydrides have the general formula B_nH_{n+4}; these compounds are relatively stable toward thermal decomposition, and several members of the series do not ordinarily exhibit spontaneous flammability. The hydrogen-rich boron hydrides have the general formula B_nH_{n+6}; these compounds are much less stable than the normal hydrides, they have much lower melting points, and they are spontaneously inflammable in air.

Norton recently has discovered a previously unknown borane, believed to be B_9H_{13}, in the course of examining the boron hydrides with the mass spectrometer (2). No volatile compounds higher than decaborane were observed, however.

In addition to the boron hydrides listed above, there are liquid and solid non-volatile polymeric boranes. Most of these compounds contain proportionately less hydrogen than the lower boranes, and they are of rather indefinite compositions ranging from $(BH_{1.5})_x$ to $(BH_{0.8})_x$ and to even lower hydrogen/boron ratios. Little is known about these highly condensed boranes, and no definite compounds have been isolated from this group as yet. The condensed boranes, however, appear to be similar to the lower boranes in some of their chemical properties.

Structure. Measurements made by X-ray diffraction, Raman spectroscopy, infrared spectroscopy, and by electron diffraction techniques suggest that, although the diborane molecule has the general shape of the ethane molecule, in some ways it is more analogous to the ethylene molecule; that is, rotation of the BH_3 units about the boron-boron bond is restricted rather than free, as would be expected from an ethane-like structure. There also is evidence that two of the six hydrogen atoms in the diborane molecule are located close in to the boron-boron bond structure and lie in a plane perpendicular to that of the two boron atoms and the other four hydrogen atoms (3). The boron-boron bond distance in diborane is 1.86 A. U.; this is significantly larger than the normal boron-boron bond distance of 1.76 A. U. The boron-hydrogen bond distance is 1.27 A. U. (4, 5).

In the higher boranes, the average boron-boron bond distance is smaller than in diborane. In pentaborane, the average value of 1.76 A. U. is very close to the expected value for a normal boron-boron bond. The average boron-hydrogen distance remains about 1.27 A. U., which is slightly larger than the normal boron-hydrogen bond distance of 1.18 A. U. (4).

Complete structures have been worked out in detail for two of the boron hydrides. Kasper, Lucht, and Harker (6) have shown that the *decaborane* molecule comprises a cage of ten boron atoms in which each boron atom is bonded normally to one hydrogen atom, the remaining four hydrogen atoms forming single-atom bridges between four pairs of the ten boron atoms. Most of the boron-boron bonds in the compound do not involve any hydrogen bridging. Although the average boron-boron bond distance in the molecule is 1.77 A. U., each boron forms part bonds at various bond distances with its boron atom neighbors. To quote the authors: "It is rather definite that the binding within the molecule is of the metallic type with a mobile system of electrons, and for which the bonds have directional properties different from those ascribed to normal covalent bonds" (6). (See frontispiece.)

Dulmage and Lipscomb (7) have published the structure of the *pentaborane* molecule, B_5H_9. The skeleton of the molecule comprises five boron atoms in a tetragonal pyramid. The boron atom at the apex of the pyramid is bonded to each of the other four boron atoms through boron-boron bonds, and to a single hydrogen atom. Four of the hydrogen atoms form single hydrogen-bridge bonds between the four boron atoms at the base of the pyramid, and each of these boron atoms also is linked to a single hydrogen atom by a normal boron-hydrogen bond. The boron-boron bond distances range from 1.66 to 1.77 A. U., depending upon the position of the bond in the molecule, and the boron-hydrogen bond distances similarly range from 1.20 to 1.35 A. U., depending upon whether the hydrogen is bonded normally to one boron atom or is acting as a bridge between two boron atoms. The authors (7) consider that the structure of this compound, like that of decaborane, involves some bonds of a "metallic" type; the structures of the two compounds appear to be closely related.

The delineation of the structures of the decaborane and the pentaborane molecules does not, of course, explain the electronic configuration of the diborane molecule, nor why two hydrogen atoms seem to be necessary to hold the two boron atoms together in this molecule. It does, however, remove any doubt about the necessity for two-atom hydrogen bridging, or even single-atom hydrogen bridging, for the existence of the boron-boron bonds in the higher boranes.

Preparation. The classical method for preparing the boron hydrides, and that used by Stock (8) in his monumental work on these compounds, is the hydrolysis of reactive metal borides, such as magnesium boride, in acid solutions. However, this synthesis gives poor yields at best, and then only of the relatively unstable tetraborane together with trace amounts of some of the higher hydrides. Any diborane that might initially be formed in a hydrolysis reaction of this type would be decomposed immediately by the solution and could not be isolated.

In 1931 Schlesinger and Burg (9) reported that when a mixture of boron trichloride and hydrogen was passed through a high-voltage discharge, a reduction reaction occurred and diborane was formed. Conversions of chloride to hydride as high as 30% per pass were obtained in this reaction, and the overall yields were as high as 75%. The major part of the diborane product was condensed in the cold traps following the reactor as the monohalide derivative B_2H_5Cl. This compound, *diborane monochloride*, is unstable at room temperature, however, and during the distillation of the reaction product it disproportionated readily into diborane and boron trichloride (9). A similar reaction will occur with boron tribromide and hydrogen (8).

In subsequent investigations, Schlesinger and H. C. Brown (10) discovered a new method whereby diborane can be prepared pure, in quantity, and in almost quantitative yields. This reaction, comprising the metathetical reaction in ether solution of boron trifluoride with lithium hydride or, preferably, a complex reducing hydride like lithium aluminum hydride, can be performed in simple glass laboratory apparatus at room temperature:

$$4BF_3 + 3LiAlH_4 \rightarrow 2B_2H_6 + 3LiF + 3AlF_3$$

The technique for preparing diborane by this reaction is quite simple. A solution of boron trifluoride in dry ether is added slowly to an ether slurry of finely powdered lithium aluminum hydride, and the diborane which is evolved is scrubbed free of ether by a reflux condenser and is collected in a trap cooled with liquid nitrogen. If lithium hydride is used as the reducing agent, the reaction mechanism appears to involve the formation of lithium borohydride as an intermediate; in fact, the reaction usually will not proceed smoothly unless some of this compound is added as an initiator (11).

A similar reaction occurs when the vapor of a boron halide is passed at elevated temperature over the hydride of an alkali or alkaline earth metal. With boron trifluoride and sodium hydride, for example, the metathesis reaction begins at about 180°. A carrier gas, such as nitrogen or hydrogen, is employed to sweep the diborane reaction product out of the heated reaction zone. The metal hydride is converted to the corresponding halide in this process (12).

It also has been found that when a boron halide together with an excess of hydrogen is passed through a heated bed of a finely divided electropositive metal, a reaction occurs with the formation of diborane and a halide of the metallic reducing agent. This reaction proceeds with metals such as sodium, lithium, calcium, magnesium, zinc, aluminum, and iron, although the best results are obtained with aluminum or sodium. The reaction does not proceed at temperatures much below 300° and may be run as high as 500°. The product, as collected in a cold trap, comprises a mixture of diborane, diborane monohalide, and unreacted boron halide (12). The mechanism of this reaction is obscure, although it is postulated that reactive metal hydrides may be formed as intermediates (13).

Thermal Stability of the Boranes. It is difficult to make generalizations about the thermal stability of the boranes, particularly in making comparisons with the thermal stabilities of other covalent hydrides. The boranes are unusual in that the decomposition of these compounds at moderate temperatures leads to more complex condensed systems of boron and hydrogen, although the ultimate pyrolysis products at high temperatures are elemental boron and hydrogen. Most of the covalent hydrides decompose directly to hydrogen and the parent element at elevated temperatures.

Diborane gas will decompose slowly at room temperature to form higher boranes and hydrogen. The hydrogen thus released appears to act as an inhibitor for the decomposition reaction, however, and, once some hydrogen is present in the diborane, the decomposition reaction is very slow. At temperatures above 300° diborane rapidly decomposes to elemental boron and hydrogen.

Tetraborane, B_4H_{10}, decomposes slowly at room temperature to form diborane and hydrogen in addition to some of the higher hydrides. Its complete pyrolysis to boron and hydrogen is rapid at 300°.

Pentaborane, B_5H_9, is one of the most stable of the volatile boranes. Its decomposition at room temperature is negligibly slow if the material is pure and not exposed to light. The decomposition of pentaborane at 300° to boron and hydrogen is much slower than that of diborane.

Unstable pentaborane, B_5H_{11}, decomposes fairly rapidly at room temperature to form both lower and higher boranes.

Hexaborane, B_6H_{10}, is believed to be less stable than diborane, but it certainly is more stable at room temperature than tetraborane and the unstable pentaborane. Its decomposition at 300° is rather slow.

Unstable hexaborane, B_6H_{12}, appears to be quite unstable at room temperature. Little is known about this compound.

Decaborane, $B_{10}H_{14}$, appears to be stable indefinitely at room temperature. It can be kept at 150° for extended periods without decomposition if air is excluded, and is only slightly decomposed in 48 hours at 200°. The decomposition of decaborane into boron and hydrogen at 300° goes very slowly. Decaborane appears to be the most stable of the boranes thus far characterized; the non-volatile condensed boranes may, of course, be very stable also.

It will be apparent that, although diborane is less stable toward thermal dissociation into its elements than silane, for example, the higher boranes as a group are probably more stable than any other polynuclear hydride systems except those of carbon. Since the boranes are endothermic compounds, this may seem surprising, but the "metallic"\type of structure known to be present in pentaborane and in decaborane may stabilize these compounds to a considerable extent.

Norton (14) has made quantitative measurements of the relative stability of several of the boranes in the course of his investigations of these compounds with the mass spectrometer. He finds that pentaborane is more stable than diborane by a factor of 100; diborane is more stable than the unstable pentaborane by a factor of 10; unstable pentaborane is more stable than tetraborane by a factor of 5.

Borane Conversion Reactions. At moderately elevated temperatures, most of the volatile boranes will undergo polymerization reactions to form boranes of higher molecular weight, although some thermal cracking reactions also may be observed. These conversion reactions appear to be quite complex, and the reaction mechanisms still are not completely understood. Furthermore, the nature of the products derived from a borane conversion reaction can be influenced to a considerable degree by the pyrolysis temperature as well as by the presence of various catalytic materials.

The experimental technique used in studying borane conversions generally involves passing the vapors of a borane through a heated tube and condensing the pyrolysis products from the vapor stream at the outlet end of the reaction tube. If desired, the vapors of the borane may be mixed with inert or catalytically active gases, and the reaction tube may be packed with catalytically active solids. It is possible to construct an apparatus for conversion reactions so that any unreacted borane will be continuously recycled back through the heated reactor until complete conversion is attained. A few reactions can be studied by heating the vapor of a borane in a sealed flask until the desired degree of conversion has been reached.

The early work on the conversion reactions of the boranes, which was largely qualitative in nature rather than quantitative, is summarized in the review article by Schlesinger and Burg on these compounds (9).

Work by Norton, McCarty, and Bragg (14, 15) has given considerable insight into some of the complex borane conversion reactions, and some investigations have been made on the kinetics of these reactions. In the pyrolysis of diborane, for example, the following reaction scheme has been found to account satisfactorily for the observed products and yields:

$$B_2H_6 \rightarrow 2BH_3$$

$$B_2H_6 + BH_3 \rightarrow \text{(intermediate products)}$$

$$\text{(Intermediate products)} + B_2H_6 \rightarrow B_5H_{11} + 2H_2$$

$$B_5H_{11} \rightarrow B_5H_9 + H_2$$

$$B_5H_{11} \rightarrow B_2H_6 + \text{higher hydrides}$$

Under the experimental conditions, that is, at temperatures of 100° to 120° and initial diborane pressures of 20 to 120 mm, the pentaborane products appeared to be relatively stable. The assumption of the initial cleavage of the diborane molecule into two borine units, followed by reaction of these units with diborane molecules, is predicated on the observation that the order of the reaction process involving the disappearance of diborane was 1.5. The nature of the intermediate products is not known, although tetraborane may be involved. It is known that diborane can condense reversibly to tetraborane and hydrogen:

$$2B_2H_6 \rightleftharpoons B_4H_{10} + H_2$$

Tetraborane decomposes at 60° to form the unstable pentaborane as a principal product; some hexaborane, diborane, and decaborane are formed also (14).

The higher hydrides formed in borane pyrolysis reactions almost always contain non-volatile solid or liquid condensed boranes in addition to decaborane, particularly at more elevated temperatures. At temperatures between for instance, 150° and 250° the conversion and pyrolysis reactions are exceedingly complex, and almost any of the boranes may be present in the reaction mixture as a transitory species.

Chemical Properties of the Boranes. In its normal valence state of tricovalence, the boron atom is electronically unsaturated. That is, the boron atom has orbitals to accomodate four pairs of bonding electrons, but it is normally associated with only three pairs. Consequently, it is possible for the boron atom in a normal covalent boron compound to accept a share in a pair of electrons from an electron donor to form a fourth covalent bond (we may say that the boron atom completes its octet of electrons in this fashion). Since boron is a very strong electron acceptor, and since there are many atoms which can serve as electron donors, the chemistry of boron is rich in the number of complex coordination derivatives. Many of these compounds are derivatives of the boron hydrides.

Many of the chemical reactions of the boranes are not difficult to interpret if one keeps in mind a few essential features of these compounds:

(*a*) The boron atom is a very strong electron acceptor and can form coordination complexes with a wide variety of electron donors.

(*b*) The establishment of a coordinate covalent link between a boron atom and an electron donor usually results in some degree of polarity or charge distribution in the complex, that is, "electrical strain," and affects the strength of the bond between boron and its attached hydrogen atoms.

(*c*) The boron-bonded hydrogen atoms can migrate fairly readily to relieve electrical strains in the complex, particularly toward positions of relative positive charge; the hydrogen atoms become more negative as a result of the complex formation and, often, the bond between boron and hydrogen may be weaker than the coordinate covalent bond between boron and the electron donor.

(d) With the higher boranes, an increasing degree of metallic character is noted in the boron-boron bonding; the boron-bonded hydrogen atoms become less reactive as well as sparsely distributed over the boron-atom structure.

(e) Since boron is a relatively electropositive element, considerable amounts of energy may be released when it forms chemical bonds with strongly electronegative elements like oxygen and the halogens.

OXIDATION. All the boranes will burn vigorously in air or oxygen if ignition occurs. With the more volatile boranes, such as diborane, the oxidation reaction can be explosive unless it is controlled. Judged from known thermochemical data, the oxidation of a borane should liberate considerably more energy than the oxidation of a corresponding amount of hydrocarbon, and very high flame temperatures should be observed in the combustion of diborane.

It is difficult to make any specific comments about the spontaneous inflammability of the various boranes since spontaneous inflammability depends on many factors, such as the presence of impurities in the hydride, moisture in the air, and the rate of mixing of the vapors of the hydride with air. Impure diborane containing traces of higher boranes usually will appear to be spontaneously inflammable, whereas pure diborane in dry air or oxygen does not ignite until a temperature of ca. 125° to 150° has been reached. Similarly, pure pentaborane may not ignite upon mixing with air under some conditions, whereas under other circumstances it may ignite spontaneously. Decaborane, if pure, does not ignite at room temperature and may be handled safely in air. Tetraborane and the unstable pentaborane always appear to ignite on mixing with air.

The products of complete combustion of a borane are boric oxide and water:

$$B_2H_6 + 3O_2 \rightarrow B_2O_3 + 3H_2O$$

HALOGENATION. Diborane reacts violently and spontaneously with free chlorine to form, as end products, hydrogen chloride and boron trichloride. Intermediate chlorine derivatives of diborane may be formed, but such compounds are known to disproportionate rapidly into boron trichloride and diborane (see below).

$$B_2H_6 + 6Cl_2 \rightarrow 2BCl_3 + 6HCl$$

Diborane reacts much more slowly with bromine or iodine, and these reactions can be controlled to yield the intermediate diborane monohalides, B_2H_5Br and B_2H_5I.

The reactivity toward free halogens appears to decrease as the boranes become condensed and more complex. Decaborane, for example, does not react spontaneously with chlorine at room temperature, and reacts only slowly with bromine or iodine to form di- and trihalide derivatives. The halogens differ in reactivity probably because bromine and iodine are better electron donors than chlorine.

Diborane monochloride, B_2H_5Cl, is a very unstable compound that can exist at temperatures above 0°C only in equilibrium with diborane and boron trichloride. It can, in fact, be formed most easily by allowing a mixture of diborane and boron trichloride to come to equilibrium:

$$5B_2H_6 + 2BCl_3 \rightleftharpoons 6B_2H_5Cl$$

Diborane monochloride also occurs as an intermediate in the reduction of boron trichloride with hydrogen in an electric discharge or over heated aluminum, although in the isolation of the diborane product from these reactions the monochloride is completely disproportionated. Diborane monochloride is known to be a spontaneously inflammable gas.

Diborane monobromide, B_2H_5Br, can be formed by the action of elemental bromine or hydrogen bromide on diborane at elevated temperatures, although a better method for obtaining this compound is to isolate it as an equilibrium reaction product from a mixture of diborane and boron tribromide. Diborane monobromide is not spontaneously inflammable. It melts at ca. −104°, and its extrapolated boiling point at atmospheric pressure is about 10°. It is considerably more stable against disproportionation than diborane monochloride although it does revert fairly rapidly at room temperature to form an equilibrium mixture containing diborane, diborane monobromide, and boron tribromide.

Diborane monoidide, B_2H_5I, can be formed by reactions similar to those for the formation of the monobromide. It is somewhat more stable than the monobromide and is not spontaneously inflammable. The compound melts at −110° and has a vapor pressure of 78 mm at 0°C. This compound is of particular interest since two molecules of diborane monoiodide can be condensed with sodium amalgam in a Wurtz type synthesis to form tetraborane.

In contrast to its reactions with free halogens, the reactions of diborane with the hydrogen halides are very slow, and usually require extended periods at elevated temperatures in the presence of a catalyst such as an aluminum trihalide. The reaction is a substitution reaction:

$$B_2H_6 + HBr \xrightarrow{AlBr_3} B_2H_5Br + H_2$$

Again, the unstable diborane monohalide products disproportionate rapidly into boron trihalide and diborane unless special precautions are taken to keep them. In general, the ease of this substitution reaction with the hydrogen halides decreases with the more complex boranes; pentaborane and decaborane do not react with hydrogen chloride even at 100° in the presence of a catalyst. The higher boranes, however, will undergo substitution reactions slowly with hydrogen bromide or hydrogen iodide. This, again, appears to illustrate the importance of the electron donor properties of the attacking group; the halogen atoms in hydrogen bromide and particularly in hydrogen iodide are better electron donors than the chlorine in hydrogen chloride.

HYDROLYSIS. The boranes vary greatly in the rate at which they are hydrolyzed by water to boric acid and hydrogen:

$$B_2H_6 + 6H_2O \rightarrow 2B(OH)_3 + 6H_2$$

For example, the complete hydrolysis of diborane occurs in a few seconds when the gas is brought into contact with water. A given sample of tetraborane will be hydrolyzed to the extent of ca. 50% in 2 hours at room temperature. Pentaborane hydrolyzes rather slowly at room temperature, and extended periods at ca. 90° to 100° are required for its complete hydrolysis. At room temperature and in contact with water, a sample of decaborane will be less than 10% hydrolyzed in 10 days; the hydrolysis of decaborane is slow even at 100°.

This difference in hydrolysis rate appears to be related to the relatively inert nature of the boron-atom skeletons of the higher boranes; the boron-boron linkages are broken only very slowly.

It is believed that a coordination of the oxygen in the water molecule with a boron atom is the first step in the hydrolysis of a borane. A migration of a relatively negative boron-bonded hydrogen to the relatively positive hydrogen in the water molecule then can follow with the splitting off of molecular hydrogen. A similar coordination and rearrangement can be postulated to explain the attack on the boranes of other electrophilic reagents, such as the halogens and the hydrogen halides. The reaction of a borane with an alcohol, or other oxygenated organic compound containing a readily replaceable hydrogen follows a course analogous to that of hydrolysis. Hydrogen is evolved, and an *alkoxy* or *acyl, etc.*, group is attached to boron through oxygen.

Most of the boranes are rather strong reducing agents and are capable of precipitating many heavy metals from solutions of their salts, for example, metallic silver from silver nitrate solution, as well as reducing solutions of oxidizing agents like the permanganates. Both these reactions have been used as tests for the presence of diborane in gas mixtures. It is of interest to note, however, that decaborane is not affected by concentrated nitric acid at room temperature (8).

Coordination Compounds of the Boranes. Diborane reacts readily with *ammonia* to form the stable, white solid *diborane-diammoniate*, $B_2H_6 \cdot (NH_3)_2$. The reaction is quite exothermic and usually is carried out at relatively low temperatures to avoid loss of diborane by pyrolysis. Diborane-diammoniate is not volatile and it appears to be somewhat ionic. It will react with water to liberate hydrogen, ammonia, and boric acid. If the complex is treated with an "acid" stronger than the borine molecule, for example, BF_3, the diborane will be displaced and can be partially recovered. In this respect, the behavior of the diborane-ammoniate complex is similar to that of other coordination compounds.

If diborane-ammoniate is heated, it loses hydrogen and forms more condensed boron-nitrogen systems, including *diborine imide*, $[(BH_3)_2NH]_x$, and *borazole*, $B_3N_3H_6$ (see page 89). On strong heating, these intermediate boron-nitrogen compounds presumably decompose to form boron nitride, $(BN)_x$, which has a structure similar to that of graphite except that the six-membered rings are composed of alternate boron and nitrogen atoms instead of carbon atoms.

Ammoniates of the other boranes are known: $B_4H_{10} \cdot (NH_3)_4$, $B_5H_9 \cdot (NH_3)_4$, and $B_{10}H_{14} \cdot (NH_3)_6$. These ammoniates are nonvolatile and are solid except the pentaborane derivative, which is an oil. With the exception of the decaborane derivative, they form borazole when they are heated; decaborane-ammoniate decomposes reversibly to form decaborane and ammonia. The ammoniate of tetraborane is unstable at room temperature and decomposes to more condensed systems.

Diborane also forms relatively stable coordination complexes with *organic amines*, including heterocyclic amines like pyridine as well as aliphatic amines. In contrast to the ammoniate complex, the diborane-amine complexes usually are liquids. Some of these compounds are hydrolyzed only very slowly in the presence of water.

Since the amine nitrogen atom is a better electron donor than the ammonia nitrogen, the amine complexes should be more polar than the ammonia complex, but steric factors undoubtedly play an important part in determining the properties of the molecules; they are more readily decomposed by "acids" to regenerate diborane than the ammonia complex. The pyrolysis of the diborane-amine complexes yields substituted borazoles (see page 90). The higher boranes similarly form coordination complexes with organic amines, but such compounds have not received much attention. If one considers the large number of organic amines, and the number of known boranes, it will be apparent that a great many borane-amine complexes are possible; only a few of these have been prepared and studied.

A very interesting coordination complex of borine is the unusual molecule *borine carbonyl*, BH_3CO, which forms and exists in equilibrium amounts in a mixture of diborane and carbon monoxide. The formation of this molecule is considered to be evidence for the existence of borine, in small amounts at least, in equilibrium with diborane. The chemical bond between boron and carbon in borine carbonyl undoubtedly involves the coordination of a pair of electrons from the carbon atom to the boron atom. This type of bonding is similar to that responsible for the chemical bonding in the metal carbonyls. Borine carbonyl is stable at room temperature only in the presence of both excess carbon monoxide and diborane. It can, however, be frozen out of a mixture of the two gases at $-80°$ and studied at low temperatures (m.p., $-137°$; b.p., $-64°$). The vapor density of borine carbonyl indicates that it is a derivative of borine rather than of diborane (16).

The formation of a coordinate covalent bond between a *borine* molecule and a *hydride ion* results in a *borohydride ion:*

$$H:^- + \begin{matrix} H \\ \cdot\cdot \\ B:H \\ \cdot\cdot \\ H \end{matrix} \rightarrow \left[\begin{matrix} H \\ \cdot\cdot \\ H:B:H \\ \cdot\cdot \\ H \end{matrix}\right]^-$$

This ion is relatively stable, and a considerable number of borohydride derivatives, such as *lithium borohydride*, $LiBH_4$, and *magnesium borohydride*, $Mg(BH_4)_2$, are known. Some of the borohydrides appear to be ionic salts; other borohydrides are covalent and presumably involve a type of hydrogen "bridge" bonding. (See Chapter 14.)

If we treat diborane with an amalgam of an alkali metal, such as sodium or potassium, solid non-volatile derivatives which appear to be ionic are formed.   These compounds dissolve in water with only a slight amount of hydrolysis.   They can be decomposed with hydrogen chloride to regenerate diborane.   We might postulate that the valence electrons from the alkali metal atoms complete the bonding between the boron atoms, making a complex ion with a normal covalent bond between boron atoms:

$$B_2H_6 + 2Na \rightarrow \begin{bmatrix} & H & H & \\ & \cdot\cdot & \cdot\cdot & \\ H & : B & : B & : H \\ & \cdot\cdot & \cdot\cdot & \\ & H & H & \end{bmatrix}^= \cdot 2Na^+$$

However, some hydrogen is formed in the reaction, and there is evidence to suggest that the solid compound contains sodium borohydride and is not simply a derivative of a complex $B_2H_6^=$ ion (17).   Tetraborane also forms a solid complex with sodium: $B_4H_{10} \cdot 2Na$.   This compound must contain some complex boronate ion since tetraborane can be regenerated from the complex by treatment with hydrogen chloride, although, in this case also, some borohydride appears to be present.

Diborane forms coordinate bonds with oxygen, such as the oxygen atom in an organic ether, but such bonds are relatively weak and the ether complexes are stable only at relatively low temperatures.   On warming, the diborane-ether complexes decompose to regenerate diborane and the ethers.

Since the formation of a coordination complex with a good electron donor shields the boron atom from chemical attack and satisfies it electronically, the coordination complexes of the boron hydrides are, in general, much less reactive toward chemical reagents than the boron hydrides themselves.   It should be remembered, however, that the coordinate bond between boron and the electron donor atom often is stronger than the boron-hydrogen bond, and intramolecular rearrangements and cleavages can occur rather easily.

The Reactions of Diborane with Hydrocarbons.   If diborane gas is mixed with an unsaturated hydrocarbon gas, such as ethylene or acetylene, the usual result is a violently exothermic reaction which yields a variety of highly polymeric products containing boron and carbon (8, 9).   However, if relatively small amounts of diborane are mixed with hydrocarbons at liquid air temperatures, and the mixtures are allowed to warm up gradually under pressure in sealed pressure vessels, the reactions will proceed smoothly and can easily be investigated. The experimental results that follow have been obtained in this fashion (18).

It has been found that diborane adds quite rapidly to the carbon-carbon double bond in olefins to form trialkyls of boron. It is convenient, although not necessary, to consider this as a reaction of borine:

$$BH_3 + 3RCH{=}CH_2 \rightarrow (RCH_2CH_2)_3B$$

Since the initial attack of the boron atom may be on either of the double-bonded carbon atoms, both the possible isomeric products are formed in the reaction. We have the choice of assuming that the borine molecule keeps adding to double bonds until all three hydrogens have been replaced, or that, after one alkyl group has been attached, the molecule disproportionates with similar molecules to form a trialkylborine and re-form borine. This latter process is known to occur readily with alkyldiborane molecules.

The ease with which diborane is added to olefins depends upon the nature of the olefin. The addition of diborane to ethylene goes rather slowly at temperatures up to 100°, whereas the addition to butylene goes rapidly at temperatures well below 0°. With some olefinic materials, for example, butadiene and vinyl chloride, the diborane catalyzes a polymerization of the olefin.

Diborane attacks benzene at 100° in a substitution reaction; we can consider again that the borine molecule is the reactive component:

$$3C_6H_6 + BH_3 \rightarrow (C_6H_5)_3B + 3H_2$$

We can assume either that stepwise substitution occurs or that an initially formed *phenylborine* disproportionates to triphenylboron and borine.

The reactions of diborane with paraffin hydrocarbons are more complex. At temperatures between 100° and 200°, diborane can catalyze all sorts of degradation and synthesis reactions of the hydrocarbon chains as well as form boron-containing substitution products. With methane at 180°, diborane causes the formation of ethane, propane, and butane in addition to solid polymers containing both boron and carbon. The action of diborane on a higher hydrocarbon, such as pentane, also forms methane and ethane in addition to solid polymeric products which contain boron in small amounts.

Although only a few investigations of this sort have been made with boranes other than diborane, it appears that the higher boranes will operate in a manner similar to that of diborane in their reactions with hydrocarbons. It is known, for example, that decaborane and pentaborane can cause the cross-linking and vulcanization of rubbers (see *Uses*, page 94); decaborane also will catalyse the polymerization of styrene monomer to polystyrene.

In many of its reactions with hydrocarbons, the borine molecule behaves like a very strong "acid," comparable to such materials as boron trifluoride and aluminum chloride. The first step in most of the reactions outlined above probably involves the formation of a coordination complex between the strong electron-acceptor boron atom in the borine molecule and a carbon atom in the hydrocarbon molecule. Borine differs from BF_3 and $AlCl_3$, however, in that the boron-bonded hydrogen atoms can readily migrate to relieve any electrical strain resulting from the formation of the coordination complex.

Substitution Derivatives of the Boranes. The *halogen-substituted* derivatives of diborane have been mentioned previously. Most of the known reactions of the halogen-substituted diboranes are similar in principle to those of diborane.

Alkyl-substituted diboranes can easily be prepared by allowing a mixture of diborane and a trialkylborine (BR_3) to come to equilibrium at room temperature. The mixture then is frozen and, by careful fractionation at low temperatures in a vacuum system, a series of mono-, di-, tri-, and tetraalkyl substitution derivatives can be isolated. It is significant that no substituted diboranes exist containing five or six alkyl groups. Low temperatures are necessary for the separation of the alkyl substitution derivatives of diborane since, at room temperature, they rapidly disproportionate to form an equilibrium mixture of products. Thus the existence of an alkyl diborane as a pure species at room temperature can be only transient. It may seem surprising, but the alkyl diboranes cannot be prepared by the reaction of a metal alkyl, such as zinc dimethyl, on a diborane monohalide; this usually is a reliable method for preparing alkyl-substituted derivatives of covalent hydrides.

The hydrolysis of an alkyldiborane yields boric acid, a *mono-organoboric acid*, and/or a *diorganoboric acid*, depending upon the particular compound being hydrolyzed:

$$B_2H_5R + 5H_2O \rightarrow B(OH)_3 \quad + RB(OH)_2 + 5H_2$$

$$B_2H_4R_2 + 4H_2O \rightarrow B(OH)_3 \quad + R_2BOH \quad + 4H_2$$

$$B_2H_3R_3 + 3H_2O \rightarrow RB(OH)_2 + R_2BOH \quad + 3H_2$$

$$B_2H_2R_4 + 2H_2O \rightarrow 2R_2BOH \qquad + \qquad 2H_2$$

As a result of such hydrolysis reactions it can be shown that the dialkyldiboranes, as normally prepared, have both alkyl groups attached to the same boron atom, and that the trialkyldiboranes have two alkyl groups on one boron atom and one alkyl group on the other boron atom. The symmetrical dimethyldiborane, with one alkyl group on each boron atom, can be prepared by special methods, but it gradually disproportionates to the unsymmetrical isomer (19).

Table II gives the physical properties of the methyl diboranes (20). These compounds can undergo many of the reactions characteristic of diborane, including the formation of complex coordination derivatives. Ethyl and propyl diboranes also are known.

TABLE II

Compound	Formula	Melting Point	Vapor Pressure	Calculated Normal Boiling Point
Monomethyldiborane	$BH_3BH_2CH_3$		55 mm at $-78.5°$	
sym-Dimethyl-	$BH_2(CH_3)BH_2CH_3$	$-124.9°$	7.6 mm at $-78.5°$	$4.9°$
uns-Dimethyl-	$BH_3BH(CH_3)_2$	$-150.2°$	10 mm at $-78.5°$	$-2.6°$
Trimethyl-	$BH_2(CH_3)BH(CH_3)_2$	$-122.9°$	123 mm at $0°$	$45.5°$
Tetramethyl-	$BH(CH_3)_2BH(CH_3)_2$	$-72.5°$	48 mm at $0°$	$68.6°$

Phenyl-substituted diboranes never have been isolated and identified as such. In view of the electronegative character of the phenyl group it is believed that the *phenyldiboranes* would be very unstable toward disproportionation into diborane and boron triphenyl (18).

Borazole, $B_3N_3H_6$, is a fascinating compound which sometimes is called "inorganic benzene." Indeed, the molecular structure of borazole is much like that of benzene except that the six-membered ring is composed of alternate boron and nitrogen atoms rather than six carbon atoms:

Upon consideration of this structure it will be apparent that, from the standpoint of molecular weight and number of valence electrons involved, the boron and nitrogen atoms comprising the ring are nearly the equivalent of six carbon atoms. Many of the physical properties of borazole are similar to those of benzene:

	Borazole	*Benzene*
Molecular weight	80.5	78
Boiling point	53°	80°
Melting point	−58°	6°
Heat of vaporization	7 Kcal/mole	7.4 Kcal/mole
Critical temperature	21.4°	21.1°
Vapor pressure at 0°C	85 mm	26.5 mm

The nature of the chemical bonding in the borazole ring is such that there is some degree of aromatic character, that is, resonant double-bond character. It has been observed that this degree of aromatic character increases if the nitrogen-bound hydrogen atoms are substituted by alkyl groups, but if the boron-bound hydrogens are substituted the degree of aromatic character decreases and the compound becomes less like the corresponding carbon analog. The normal bond distance for a boron-nitrogen bond is 1.48 A. U.; in borazole the boron-nitrogen bond distance is 1.44 A. U. (21).

Borazole is prepared by the pyrolysis of a borane-ammoniate in a sealed tube at 180° to 200°:

$$3B_2H_6 \cdot (NH_3)_2 \rightarrow 2B_3N_3H_6 + 12H_2$$

The yields of borazole from tetraborane-ammoniate or pentaborane-ammoniate are somewhat better than those from diborane-ammoniate (8).

Borazole appears to be quite stable at room temperature in sealed containers, although it is somewhat sensitive to moisture. The complete hydrolysis of the compound with water requires extended periods at elevated temperatures; the hydrolysis products are boric acid, hydrogen, and ammonia. Borazole is soluble in cold water although the solution gradually gives off hydrogen formed by a hydrolysis reaction. If borazole is dissolved in water at 0°C, and the excess water is removed at a low temperature by vacuum distillation, it is possible to isolate a trihydrate of borazole, $B_3N_3H_6 \cdot 3H_2O$. At temperatures higher than 200°, borazole decomposes into hydrogen and a non-volatile polymeric solid containing boron, nitrogen, and hydrogen. At very high temperatures, the end product of this decomposition is a white solid that appears to be boron nitride, $(BN)_x$.

Alkyl-substituted borazole compounds can be formed by pyrolyzing the coordination complex of an alkyldiborane and ammonia; the resulting compounds are the B-alkyl borazoles. If a coordination complex between diborane and an organic amine is pyrolyzed, an N-alkyl borazole may be formed. A considerable number of substituted borazoles are known and have been studied rather extensively (22).

Borazole can act either as an electron donor (through the nitrogen atoms) or as an electron acceptor (through the boron atoms). Thus, the compound can form a variety of coordination compounds with electron donor or electron acceptor groups.

A few substitution derivatives of the boranes are known in which an *oxygenated group* substitutes for hydrogen. Burg and Schlesinger (23) have prepared *dimethoxyborine*, $(CH_3O)_2BH$, by the reaction of diborane with methyl alcohol:

$$B_2H_6 + 4CH_3OH \rightarrow 2(CH_3O)_2BH + 4H_2$$

This reaction gives a general indication as to the nature of the reactions of the boranes with alcohols, although such reactions usually are quite complicated. The disproportionation of dimethoxyborine to diborane and trimethoxyborine occurs rapidly at room temperature and appears to be readily reversible:

$$6(CH_3O)_2BH \rightleftharpoons B_2H_6 + 4B(OCH_3)_3$$

Dimethoxyborine is not spontaneously inflammable. Its extrapolated boiling point at atmospheric pressure is 25.9°. It is very rapidly hydrolyzed by water to form boric acid and methyl alcohol.

Vapor-density measurements indicate that dimethoxyborine is not associated in the gas phase; that is, it is not a diborane derivative even though the hydrogen necessary for the formation of the boron-boron bond is present. The existence of this compound as a monomer illustrates how large groups attached to the boron atom can block the establishment of hydrogen "bridge" bonding. Evidence was found by Burg and Schlesinger for the brief existence of a very unstable monomethoxyborine as a polymeric white solid. Compounds containing complex *methoxyborohydride ions*, $(CH_3O)_3BH^-$, etc., also are known.

If any of the lower boranes are treated with solid alkali hydroxides, or concentrated solutions of alkali hydroxide, a partial decomposition occurs, with the formation of substances known as *hypoborates*, for example, $(KOBH_3)_x$. These compounds are relatively stable in strongly alkaline solutions, just as the borohydrides are, and are believed to result from the partial substitution of hydrogen by hydroxyl:

$$B_2H_6 + 2KOH \rightarrow B_2H_4(OH)_2^{=} \cdot 2K^+ + H_2$$

The hypoborates are very strong reducing agents which are capable of reducing a number of heavy metal salts to the free metals or, in a few cases, to metal borides. Cupric salts are reduced to copper hydride by potassium hypoborate. The hypoborate salts are very rapidly hydrolyzed by aqueous acids to form boric acid and' hydrogen. They are stable thermally at temperatures up to ca. 100°; above this temperature they decompose into hydrogen, water, and complicated borate salts (8). Potassium hypoborate prepared by dissolving decaborane in strong alkali is capable of initiating the polymerization of styrene monomer in an aqueous emulsion to polystyrene at 50° to 60°.

Substitution derivatives of diborane and borine have also been prepared in which hydrogen has been substituted by nitrogen. Diborane and dimethylamine react at 180° to 200° to form *dimethylaminoborine*. This compound is dimeric at room temperature but dissociates in the vapor phase to the monomeric form at elevated temperatures. This dissociation is 90% complete at 105°:

$$[H_2BN(CH_3)_2]_2 \rightleftharpoons H_2BN(CH_3)_2$$

The dimeric form is a crystalline white solid (m.p., 73.5°) which is insoluble in water and is not attacked by either water or hydrogen bromide. In view of this inertness, it is believed that the dimerization of the compound occurs through the nitrogen atoms (24).

If dimethylaminoborine is treated with additional dimethylamine at 200°, a liquid monomeric *bis-dimethylaminoborine*, $HB[N(CH_3)_2]_2$, is formed. This compound melts at $-45°$ and boils at 109°. It shows no tendency toward dimerization. Unlike the dimeric mono-substituted borine, bis-dimethylaminoborine is readily hydrolyzed by water at room temperature to form *bis-dimethylaminoboric acid*, $[(CH_3)_2N]_2BOH$, and hydrogen (25).

Applications of the Boron Hydrides

METAL COATING. As observed previously, the boron hydrides decompose at sufficiently elevated temperatures to form hydrogen and elemental boron. If a metal or ceramic object is heated in an atmosphere containing diborane gas or the vapor of a volatile boron hydride, and the pyrolysis conditions are carefully controlled, elemental boron may be deposited directly on the heated object in the form of a smooth adherent coating. Since elemental boron not only is extremely hard, about 9.3 on Mohs' scale, but also is quite resistant to oxidation and corrosion at elevated temperatures, such boron coatings may prove useful in a variety of applications where hard, abrasive, or corrosion-resistant surfaces are desired. Thin films of boron deposited by the pyrolysis of diborane also are employed in neutron counters (26).

The type of coating obtained depends upon the conditions under which the decomposition takes place. Relatively low temperatures, that is, 300° to 400°, and very low pressures of diborane (below a few centimeters absolute pressure) favor the deposition of very smooth shiny coatings of boron with a high degree of purity. Such coatings, however, are less firmly bonded to the base metal than coatings made at higher temperatures, that is, 800° to 1000°, at which a fairly rapid diffusion between the boron and the base metal can occur during the deposition. Coatings made at the higher temperatures are, in general, not as smooth as the low-temperature coatings. Higher pressures of boron hydride vapor also are less favorable for the production of very smooth coatings.

Boron coatings can be built up to any desired thickness by the successive deposition of thin layers. Coatings up to $\frac{1}{8}$ inch in thickness have been deposited on fine wires in this fashion. However, we must appreciate that, except for very thin coatings, the coefficient of expansion of the base metal must not be too different from that of boron over the temperature range encountered in the coating operation. Otherwise the large strains set up during the cooling will cause the coating to crack and flake off.

The diffusion coatings made on metals at high temperatures may not be pure boron, although the concentration of boron will be relatively high at the surface of the coating. In the case of diffusion coatings of boron on iron, for example, iron boride compounds can be identified in the coatings. Such coatings are much less resistant to corrosion by acids than pure boron, but they are very hard.

Boron coatings on base metals, usually iron, have been used successfully as knife sharpeners, bearings, dies, and as intermediates for bonding ceramics to iron. Boron coatings on graphite can be used for bonding ceramics to graphite. A layer of boron on iron or steel protects the base metal from oxidation at temperatures as high as 1000°, or higher.

It is possible to prepare elemental boron of a very high degree of purity from diborane by depositing relatively thick coatings on thin (5-mil) tungsten wires. The coated wires are crushed to a powder and the tungsten can then be leached out with a mixture of nitric and hydrofluoric acids.

HIGH-ENERGY FUELS. Since the elements boron and hydrogen both have very high heats of combustion, it is not surprising that the oxidation of a boron hydride should release a large amount of energy.

It can readily be calculated from thermochemical data that the complete reaction of a stoichiometric mixture of a boron hydride and oxygen should release approximately twice as much energy per pound as an equal weight of a mixture of hydrocarbon and oxygen. This high-energy release, together with the very rapid reaction of certain boron hydrides and boron hydride derivatives with water, makes these compounds of potential interest as fuels for certain specialized applications, such as underwater rockets (27).

USES IN POLYMER CHEMISTRY. It has been observed in the General Electric Laboratories that boron hydrides and certain of their derivatives can be used as vulcanizing agents for organic polymers, including natural and synthetic rubbers. The compound that has been most extensively studied is *decaborane*, $B_{10}H_{14}$, since this material is a stable and relatively non-volatile crystalline solid, is soluble in organic solvents, and is easily handled.

In the vulcanization of rubbers, decaborane has been used to replace the conventional sulfur in the compounding formulas. Generally, only a few tenths of 1% of decaborane are required to produce a cure equivalent to that obtained with 3% of sulfur. An added feature is that good vulcanization can be achieved in the borane-cured rubbers at somewhat lower temperatures than are necessary for good vulcanization of sulfur-cured rubbers. Good cures have been made at temperatures as low as 100°. The physical properties of certain borane-vulcanized rubbers are comparable with, and in some instances better than, those of similar elastomers cured with sulfur (28).

Decaborane is particularly suitable for vulcanizing silicone gum to silicone rubber; it imparts a remarkable increase in heat stability and improved aging properties to the cured material with no sacrifice in other physical properties. Decaborane also may be used to gel dimethyl silicone oil (polydimethylsiloxane) to silicone rubber gum stock as well as for the vulcanization of the gum to rubber (29).

Other boron hydride compounds that have been tried as vulcanizing and cross-linking agents are pentaborane and several of the solid complex amine compounds of diborane and of decaborane. Although these materials have not been investigated extensively, they appear to be somewhat less effective than decaborane.

REFERENCES—BORON HYDRIDES

1. Prosen, Johnson, and Pergiel, Paper presented at a meeting of the International Congress of Pure and Applied Chemistry, New York, September, 1951.
2. Norton, *J. Am. Chem. Soc.*, **72**, 1849 (1950).

3. Rundle, *J. Am. Chem. Soc.*, **69**, 1327, 1719 (1947); *J. Chem. Phys.*, **17**, 671 (1949).
4. Pauling, *Nature of the Chemical Bond*, Cornell University Press, Ithaca, N.Y., 1940.
5. Longuet-Higgins and Bell, *J. Chem. Soc.*, (1943), 250 ff. Longuet-Higgins, *J. Chem. Soc.* (1946), 139 ff.
6. Kasper, Lucht, and Harker, *Acta Crystallographia*, **3**, 436 (1950); *J. Am. Chem. Soc.*, **70**, 881 (1948).
7. Dulmage and Lipscomb, *J. Am. Chem. Soc.*, **73**, 3539 (1951).
8. Stock, *Hydrides of Boron and Silicon*, Cornell University Press, Ithaca, N.Y., 1933.
9. Schlesinger and Burg, *Chem. Revs.*, **31**, 1 (1942).
10. Schlesinger and Brown, U.S. 2,543,511; 2,544,472.
11. Boldebuck and Elliott, *Tech.* Report R49AO512, Declassified (General Electric Company for U.S. Army Ordnance), 1949.
12. Hurd, *J. Am. Chem. Soc.*, **71**, 20 (1949).
13. Price, General Electric Company Report 55223 to U.S. Army Ordnance, 1947.
14. Norton, Tech. Report R49AO512 (General Electric Company to U.S. Army Ordnance), March 10, 1949.
15. Bragg, McCarty, and Norton, *J. Am. Chem. Soc.*, **73**, 2134 (1951).
16. Schlesinger and Burg, *J. Am. Chem. Soc.*, **59**, 780 (1937).
17. Kasper, McCarty, and Newkirk, *J. Am. Chem. Soc.*, **71**, 2588 (1949).
18. Hurd, *J. Am. Chem. Soc.*, **70**, 2053 (1948).
19. Schlesinger, Flodin, and Burg, *J. Am. Chem. Soc.*, **61**, 1078 (1939).
20. Schlesinger and Walker, *J. Am. Chem. Soc.*, **57**, 621 (1935). Schlesinger, Horvitz, and Burg, *J. Chem. Soc.*, **58**, 407 (1936).
21. Rector, Schaeffer, and Platt, *J. Chem. Phys.*, **17**, 460 (1949).
22. Wiberg, *Naturwissenschaften*, **6**, 182; **7**, 212 (1948).
23. Burg and Schlesinger, *J. Am. Chem. Soc.*, **55**, 4020 (1933).
24. Wiberg, *Z. anorg. Chem.*, **256**, 287 (1948).
25. Wiberg, *Z. anorg. Chem.* **257**, 131 (1948).
26. Dodson and Russel, U.S.A.E.C. Declassified Document MDDC-384, 1944.
27. Sawyer, *Chem. Eng. News*, **27**, 2067 (1949). Leonard, *J. Am. Rocket Soc.*, **68**, 12 (1946).
28. Hurd and Safford, U.S. 2,558,561; 2,558,559.
29. Safford, U.S. 2,558,560.

ALUMINUM

$(AlH_3)_x$—*aluminum hydride, aluane*
Known only in polymeric form.

Structure. Aluminum hydride never has been isolated except in the form of a highly polymerized compound having the general formula $(AlH_3)_x$. The structure of this compound is believed to comprise chains of AlH_3 molecules held together by hydrogen bridge bonding, although in view of the very small size of the covalent hydrogen atom and the coordination number of the aluminum atom, 6, the structure may be three dimensional and involve six hydrogen bridge bonds, or "half bonds," to each aluminum atom.

It is probable that the same factors responsible for the type of bonding observed in the boron hydrides also are operative in the case of aluminum hydride since the aluminum atom is a very strong electron acceptor and, moreover, is larger than the boron atom. Thus the "protonated double bond" theory of Pitzer or the "half-bond" theory of Rundle well might apply to aluminum hydride as well as to the boron hydrides (see Chapter 2). It also may be pointed out that dimerization through a similar type of "bridge" bonding is observed in *aluminum chloride*, Al_2Cl_6, and in *aluminum methyl*, $Al_2(CH_3)_6$, owing to the ability of the aluminum atom to coordinate electrons from donating groups on neighboring molecules.

Preparation. Stecher and Wiberg first prepared hydride compounds of aluminum by reacting the vapor of aluminum methyl with an excess of hydrogen in an electric discharge at elevated temperatures (1). They observed no volatile aluminum hydride, but they were able to isolate a polymeric compound of the general formula $(AlH_3)_x$ from their reaction products by chemical means. Mixed aluminum methyl hydrides of the type $Al_2H_n(CH_3)_{4-n}$ also were obtained but, unlike the alkyl diborane and digallane derivatives, these aluminum compounds did not disproportionate at moderate temperatures to form a *dialuane*, Al_2H_6. The isolation of the aluminum hydride fraction from the reaction product was achieved through the preparation of amine coordination compounds to separate those atoms of aluminum bonded covalently only to hydrogen from those bonded to alkyl groups as well as to hydrogen.

The development of new synthetic methods for the preparation of hydrides, based on the metathetical reactions of lithium hydride, provides a more convenient method for preparing aluminum hydride. The most successful technique involves the reaction of aluminum chloride with an excess of lithium hydride. This reaction is performed in a medium of dry ether. The aluminum hydride, as it is formed, reacts further with the excess of lithium hydride present to form the complex hydride compound known as *lithium aluminum hydride*, $LiAlH_4$. Lithium chloride precipitates during the reaction. The formation of this compound may be represented by the following equations:

$$3LiH + AlCl_3 \rightarrow AlH_3 + 3LiCl$$

$$LiH + AlH_3 \rightarrow LiAlH_4$$

Lithium aluminum hydride is analogous to the complex borohydrides discussed previously and contains the complex hydride anion AlH_4^-, formed by the coordination of a negative hydride ion from the lithium hydride molecule to the acceptor aluminum atom in the aluminum hydride molecule.

Lithium aluminum hydride can then be reacted with aluminum chloride in ether solution to form lithium chloride and a solution of aluminum hydride in ether. This solution of aluminum hydride cannot be evaporated to obtain a volatile aluminum hydride, although it has been shown that a stable etherate, $3AlH_3 \cdot Et_2O$, exists (5). On standing, it deposits a high polymeric form of aluminum hydride as an insoluble white solid (3).

A solid compound, believed by some investigators to be an aluminum hydride, has been observed as a film on aluminum metal electrolyzed cathodically in a solution of potassium hydroxide (4). Considering the chemical reactivity of the aluminum-hydrogen covalent bond, this probably is only a solution of some of the hydrogen released at the cathode in the aluminum metal. Hydrogen is known to be somewhat soluble in aluminum.

The transient molecule (AlH) has been observed in the spectra of electrical discharges between aluminum electrodes in hydrogen as well as in the spectra of certain stars. This molecule has been the subject of a number of theoretical investigations.

Properties. Aluminum hydride is hydrolyzed quite rapidly by water or alcohol, with the evolution of hydrogen and the formation of aluminum oxide or oxide derivatives. It oxidizes spontaneously upon exposure to air or oxygen to form water and aluminum oxide. When freshly prepared by the reduction of aluminum chloride, aluminum hydride is soluble in ethyl ether as a low polymeric compound but, as the solution stands, polymerization proceeds and a high polymeric form is precipitated as a white solid. This solid material decomposes into its component elements at temperatures above 100°.

Aluminum hydride, which is a good reducing agent, may be used for the preparation of other hydrides by metathetical reactions. In general, however, it is less convenient for these purposes than its derivative lithium aluminum hydride.

Aluminum hydride will, like many other compounds of aluminum, form coordination compounds with donor atoms, such as the nitrogen atom in ammonia or amines. These compounds have not been studied to any appreciable extent, however.

Derivatives. Wiberg and his coworkers (1, 5) have isolated several methyl derivatives of aluminum hydride from the reduction of alu-

minum methyl with hydrogen in the electric discharge.   These include
the compounds $Al_2H_2(CH_3)_4$, $Al_2H_3(CH_3)_3$, and $Al_2H(CH_3)_5$.   These
compounds are spontaneously inflammable in air and react vigorously
with water to form methane, hydrogen, and aluminum oxide.   *Tetra-
methyldialuane*, $Al_2H_2(CH_3)_4$, does disproportionate at about 160° to
form aluminum methyl and aluminum hydride, but, at this temperature, the aluminum hydride is quite unstable and immediately
decomposes, with the evolution of hydrogen and the deposition of
aluminum, usually as a mirror of the metal.   This compound forms no
etherates at room temperature, in contrast to aluminum methyl,
but reacts with ether at higher temperatures to form alkoxy aluminum
compounds and methane.

With diborane, aluminum hydride forms the complex compound
aluminum borohydride, $Al(BH_4)_3$.   Unlike the alkali metal borohydrides this compound does not appear to be ionic.   (See Chapter 14.)

The most interesting and useful derivative of aluminum hydride
is the lithium aluminum hydride mentioned previously, a relatively
stable material that has been found to be exceedingly useful as a
chemical reducing agent for many types of chemical synthesis.   This
compound is also discussed in more detail in Chapter 14.

Uses.   Aluminum hydride as such is not used except as an intermediate in the preparation of lithium aluminum hydride and, possibly,
aluminum borohydride.   There is the possibility, however, that aluminum hydride may find a limited application as a specialized reducing agent in laboratory investigations.

REFERENCES—ALUMINUM HYDRIDE

1. Stecher and Wiberg, *Ber.*, **75B**, 2003 (1942).
2. Gibb, Banus, Bragdon, and Hinckley, Paper read at the American Chemical
   Society Meeting, April, 1951.
3. Finholt, Bond, and Schlesinger, *J. Am. Chem. Soc.*, **69**, 1199 (1947).
4. Parshad, *Nature*, **154**, 178 (1944).
5. Wiberg and Stecher, *Angew. Chemie* , **52**, 372 (1939).

GALLIUM

Ga_2H_6—*digallane*
Colorless liquid
Melting point: −21.4°
Boiling point: 139°
Vapor pressure at 0° C = 2.5 mm

Structure. The structure of digallane has not been determined, but it may be presumed to be similar to that of diborane. In digallane, gallium exhibits the same anomalous valence behavior that is observed for boron in the boron hydrides. Tricovalent gallium, like aluminum and boron, is electronically unsaturated and can act as an acceptor for electrons from donor atoms. Therefore, a structure for digallane based on hydrogen "bridge" bonding is a reasonable assumption. Unfortunately, higher hydrides of gallium have not been prepared as yet, so that it is unknown whether the formulas of such compounds would parallel those of the boron hydrides.

Preparation. Digallane was first prepared by Wiberg and Johannsen (1) by passing a mixture of trimethylgallium and hydrogen through an electric glow discharge. Under the conditions of this experiment, a partial replacement reaction occurred with the formation of *tetramethyldigallane*, $Ga(CH_3)_3GaH_2(CH_3)$. This compound was reacted with an excess of triethylamine at room temperature, and digallane was obtained by careful distillation. Digallane is formed according to the overall reaction:

$$3Ga(CH_3)_3GaH_2(CH_3) + 4N(C_2H_5)_3$$
$$\rightarrow 4Ga(CH_3)_3 \cdot N(C_2H_5)_3 + Ga_2H_6$$

Evidently the methylgallium hydride undergoes a disproportionation during this reaction. This disproportionation, in contrast to that of the methyldiboranes, apparently is quite slow at room temperature. At 130°, however, it must be more rapid since, at this temperature, the tetramethyldigallane decomposes into gallium methyl, gallium, and hydrogen. The temperature at which digallane itself begins to decompose is about 130°.

The most convenient synthesis of digallane probably would be from gallium chloride and lithium aluminum hydride (2).

It has been reported that the action of atomic hydrogen on metallic gallium for extended periods of time at 100° to 120° produced a surface coating on the metal of a white salt-like hydride of gallium. The compound thus formed reacted exothermically with water to liberate hydrogen. Gallium could be identified in the resulting solution by chemical analysis. The relationship of this compound to the normal covalent hydride, digallane, is not clear (3).

Properties. Digallane is described as a mobile colorless liquid. It is stable at temperatures up to about 130°, at which point the decomposition of the compound into metallic gallium and hydrogen begins.

Digallane undoubtedly is a strong reducing agent and should be hydrolyzed rapidly by water. It is expected that, in many of its reactions, digallane will behave much like diborane. The compound probably is spontaneously inflammable.

Derivatives. The only known alkyl derivative of gallium hydride is the tetramethyldigallane mentioned previously. This compound is described as a colorless, viscous liquid. Its vapor pressure at $0°$ was measured as 0.5 mm; its estimated boiling point at atmospheric pressure is about $172°$. The compound is spontaneously inflammable, and, like its boron analog, it is very sensitive to moisture (1).

From the scanty amount of information available on gallium it would appear that the chemistry of digallane derivatives may be quite similar to that of the diborane derivatives. Thus a number of alkyl derivatives should be possible. Digallane also should form coordination compounds with strong donor molecules such as ammonia and the amines.

Since gallium is, like boron and aluminum, an acceptor atom, it is capable of coordinating a negative hydride ion to the hypothetical *galline* molecule, GaH_3, to form a complex hydride anion. This behavior is exhibited in the formation of *lithium gallium hydride*, $LiGaH_4$, described by Finholt, Bond, and Schlesinger (2). Lithium gallium hydride is a white crystalline solid. Like lithium borohydride and lithium aluminum hydride, it is a strong reducing agent, but it is less stable thermally than either of these compounds. It cannot be kept at room temperature without decomposition occurring. At elevated temperatures it breaks down into metallic gallium, lithium hydride, and hydrogen.

REFERENCES—GALLIUM HYDRIDE

1. Wiberg and Johannsen, *Die Chemie*, **55**, 38 (1942).
2. Finholt, Bond, and Schlesinger, *J. Am. Chem. Soc.*, **69**, 1199 (1947).
3. Pietsch, Seuferling, Roman, and Lehl, *Z. Electrochem.*, **39**, 577 (1933).

CHAPTER

9

The Hydrides of the Group IV Elements

GENERAL CONSIDERATIONS

The elements in Group IV (and IVB), *carbon, silicon, germanium, tin, lead,* are quadricovalent; that is, in compound formation, they normally form four covalent bonds. Thus the simple hydrides of this group of elements have the general formula MH_4. However, the lighter elements in Group IV are unusual in their ability to form linked multi-atom structures, such as the carbon atom chains in hydrocarbons, and the simple hydrides comprise only a small fraction of the possible hydride compounds in this group.

The tendency toward the formation of complex structures is carried to an extreme in the element carbon. A carbon atom can form double or triple covalent bonds, as well as single covalent bonds, with other carbon atoms. As is well known, the compounds comprising only carbon and hydrogen are numbered in the thousands. In silicon and germanium, the ability to form covalent bonds between like atoms is much less well developed. Only a few polynuclear silanes and germanes are known, and there is no positive evidence for the existence of multiple covalent bonding between silicon atoms or germanium atoms. What is not readily appreciated, however, is that single covalent bonds between silicon and carbon are not difficult to form and are quite stable. Compounds with carbon-germanium bonds and carbon-tin bonds can also be made. It will be evident that, by the partial replacement of carbon atoms in known hydrocarbons by silicon atoms, for example, an astronomical number of mixed hydride compounds is theoretically possible. The hydrides of tin and lead, however, are known only as the simple compounds SnH_4 and PbH_4. Thus, for any reasonable comparisons between the Group IV hydrides, we should consider only the normal, or MH_4 forms.

The thermal stability of the Group IV hydrides decreases steadily as the atomic weights and sizes of the parent elements increase within the group. Whereas *methane* can exist in limited quantities in equilibrium with carbon and hydrogen at temperatures above 1000°,

101

monosilane decomposes irreversibly at about 400°, and lead hydride, or *plumbane,* is thermally unstable at room temperature.

Methane differs considerably from the other Group IV hydrides in its chemical properties. This difference is due in part to the greater electronegativity of carbon, but it also is related to the relatively small size of the carbon atom as compared to the other Group IV elements. The maximum coordination number of carbon is only four, whereas the maximum coordination number of silicon and germanium, for example, is six. This means that there is room for, at most, only four other atoms to be bonded chemically to one carbon atom. The silicon atom, on the other hand, is large enough to accommodate at least six other atoms, provided, of course, that these attached atoms are not too large. (A comparison of CO_2 with SiO_2 offers a good illustration of the effect of atomic size.)

Since the silicon atom in monosilane has only four attached hydrogen atoms, there is ample room for an attacking reagent, such as oxygen, halogen, and hydroxyl ion, to affect the valence electron structure of the silicon atom itself. The carbon atom in methane, on the other hand, is well shielded from chemical attack by its four attached hydrogen atoms. We observe, therefore, that under normal conditions of temperature the methane molecule is practically nonreactive toward many reagents that will react spontaneously and violently with monosilane. Once its molecular shield is broken by the removal of a hydrogen atom, the carbon atom in methane becomes highly reactive. In general, the chemical properties of monogermane, stannane, and plumbane resemble those of monosilane.

The hydrides of silicon are the only Group IV hydrides that show spontaneous inflammabi ity in air or oxygen at room temperature. This reaction is not at all well understood; it possibly may be catalyzed by traces of water, or by the presence of very unstable impurities, since such factors are known to be responsible for spontaneous inflammation in other hydrides.

Several of the general methods for the synthesis of volatile hydrides are applicable to the preparation of the Group IV hydrides. Perhaps the most convenient laboratory synthesis is the metathetical reaction of a halide with a strong reducing hydride such as lithium aluminum hydride (see page 64), although the hydrolysis of a binary "metal–non-metal" compound may also be employed. The process of direct union with elemental hydrogen to form a hydride can be applied only to carbon and is hardly a practical laboratory method. Presumably, all of the Group IV elements will react with atomic hydrogen. The hydrides of tin and lead have been prepared by electrolysis reactions; it is not known for sure whether this type of reaction is applicable to the preparation of the hydrides of silicon, germanium, or carbon.

CARBON

The large family of compounds comprising the hydride compounds of carbon, the hydrocarbons, is too well known to require at this point more than a discussion of the relationship of the hydrocarbons to the hydrides of other elements.

As a result of the unusual ability of the carbon atom to form single and multiple bonds with other carbon atoms, the various saturated and unsaturated hydrocarbon systems are exceedingly complex; most of the hydrocarbons have no counterparts among the hydrides of other elements and may best be considered within the domain of organic chemistry. However, *methane*, CH_4, the most simple hydrocarbon, can be considered as a typical covalent inorganic hydride for it is closely related to the inorganic hydrides and, in particular, to the hydrides of the other Group IV elements. This is true to a lesser extent for ethane, propane, and butane, counterparts for which are found among the hydrides of silicon and germanium.

Structure. The methane molecule comprises a central carbon atom with four hydrogen atoms situated about it at the corners of a regular tetrahedron. The bond distance C—H is 1.093 A. U., and the bond angle H—C—H is 109°28′. The higher members of the paraffin series are built on similar structural principles. Ethane, for example, may be visualized as two tetrahedra joined together, each having one corner in common with the other in the carbon-carbon bond and the remaining corners of the tetrahedra being occupied by hydrogen atoms.

Preparation. Methane, and certain other simple hydrocarbons such as acetylene and ethylene, may be synthesized by one or more of the general methods used for the preparation of covalent hydrides.

DIRECT UNION OF THE ELEMENTS. At elevated temperatures hydrogen and carbon will combine to form hydrocarbons. The particular compounds that may be isolated from this reaction will depend on the temperature of the reaction, the pressure, and the nature of catalytic materials which may be present (1). At temperatures between 500° and 1000° the primary product appears to be methane. The formation of methane is an equilibrium reaction:

$$C + 2H_2 \rightleftharpoons CH_4$$

in which the amount of methane in equilibrium with carbon and hydrogen decreases with increasing temperature. At much higher temperatures, such as those present in an electric arc, acetylene is the primary product. Although acetylene is unstable thermodynamically at room temperature toward decomposition into its component elements, it is stable at very high temperatures. A commercial method for producing acetylene involves the pyrolysis of cheap hydrocarbons, such as natural gas or oil, in an electric arc where recombination of the elements to form acetylene may take place.

It should be noted that methane and the lower paraffin hydrocarbons are much more stable toward thermal decomposition than their counterparts among the hydrides of silicon and germanium. This greater stability is in accord with the much higher energy of the chemical bonding in the hydrocarbon compounds.

BY HYDROLYSIS REACTIONS. A number of metal carbides will undergo hydrolysis and liberate hydrocarbons when they are treated with water or dilute acids. It has been shown that the nature of the hydrocarbon product obtained depends to a great extent on the crystal structure of the metal carbide and the grouping of the carbon atoms in the carbide lattice, as well as on the conditions of the hydrolysis reaction. (See *Hydrolysis Reactions*, page 63). The formation of methane by the hydrolysis of aluminum carbide appears to be analogous to the formation of silane, germane, or ammonia by the hydrolysis of a silicide, a germanide, or a nitride.

BY METATHETICAL REACTIONS. Simple hydrocarbons and certain of their derivatives can readily be prepared by the reduction of hydrocarbon halides with an active hydride such as lithium aluminum hydride. The general reaction is quite analogous to those described for the preparation of other hydrides by this technique. An example of the reaction is the preparation of methane from carbon tetrachloride:

$$CCl_4 + LiAlH_4 \rightarrow CH_4 + LiCl + AlCl_3$$

The replacement of halogen by hydrogen may be carried only part way if we desire to obtain the intermediate halomethanes.

Properties. The physical properties of methane are given here for comparison with those of other covalent hydrides:

> Melting point: $-184°$
> Boiling point: $-161.5°$
> Density at $-164°$: 0.415 g/cc
> Heat of formation: 20.34 Kcal/mole

It may be seen that these properties have about the values that would be expected by extrapolating from the values for the hydrides of the other Group IV elements. Methane and the lower paraffin hydro-carbons are more volatile than their analogs among the silanes and germanes. The compounds are insoluble in water and aqueous solutions. They are, within the limits imposed by their high vapor pressures, soluble in organic solvents.

The chemical reactions of methane and the lower paraffins differ from those of the related silanes and germanes principally in degree rather than in type. In the reactions of halogenation, oxidation, etc., there appears to be a great deal of similarity shown by methane and by silane if due allowance is made for the greater electronegativity of the carbon and the higher binding energy in the methane molecule; methane is much less reactive than silane.

Derivatives. It is only natural that the compounds of an element as important as carbon have been studied extensively. As a result, a large number of derivatives of even the most simple hydrocarbons are known. For example, alkyl derivatives with all the chemical elements except the inert gases and some transitional metals have been prepared (2). Many of these derivatives, such as the alkyl boranes, alkyl silanes, alkyl amines, and mercaptans, can be considered as *mixed*, or *molecular complex, hydrides* (see Chapter 14).

Certain features of the chemistry of methane and its derivatives may be of particular interest since they point to possibilities in the chemistry of other hydrides which have not been as thoroughly investigated. Carbon is a fairly electronegative element; thus the *methyl radical*, $CH_3 \cdot$, and the negative *methyl ion* or *methide ion*, $CH_3:$, appear to be definite entities. The existence of methyl radicals, as well as higher hydrocarbon radicals, has been well proved by the work of Paneth, Rice, and others on the pyrolysis of organic compounds, in particular the metal alkyls such as lead tetramethyl. As for the methide ion, we know that the methyl compounds of strongly electropositive elements like the alkali metals are salt-like compounds that behave as though they were ionic. Indeed, in this respect the methide ion resembles the hydride ion. Hydrolysis of the alkali methides yields methane. A reaction analogous to the formation of complex hydride anions further demonstrates the ionicity of the methide group. If an ether solution of aluminum trimethyl is treated with lithium methyl, a transfer of the methide ion with its free electron pair is made to the acceptor aluminum atom. The result is the formation of a new complex anion, $Al(CH_3)_4{}^-$, and the lithium salt, *lithium tetramethanoaluminate*, may be isolated. A complex derivative of boron trimethyl, *lithium tetramethanoborate*, $LiB(CH_3)_4$, may be formed similarly (3). Mixed anions also are known in which, for example, both hydrogen and methide groups are present, such as in $LiAlH_2(CH_3)_2$. Compounds of this type may be prepared by the interaction of the appropriate metal alkyl and metal hydride.

The possibility of ionic behavior of the alkyl radical decreases rapidly in going up the series of homologous groups; ethyl, propyl, butyl, etc., and the metal alkyls of these radicals are predominantly covalent.

Most methyl derivatives, including both mixed hydrides and metal alkyls, are covalent. It is doubtful, considering how strong an acceptor group the ion CH_3^+ would be, whether this ion ever exists as such, just as it appears that free protons do not appear in chemical compounds or take part in chemical reactions as such. It is postulated, however, in explaining the mechanism of certain organic reactions, that hydrocarbon groups do form transient *carbonium ions* in

which the terminal carbon atom assumes the configuration $R\!-\!\overset{\displaystyle |}{\underset{\displaystyle |}{C}}\!^{+}$

(4). In such cases, the attached groups may markedly influence the effective electronegativity of the terminal carbon and make possible the temporary existence of such an ion as a factor in a reaction mechanism.

REFERENCES—CARBON

1. Ipatieff, *Catalytic Reactions at High Pressures and Temperatures*, Macmillan, New York, pp. 228–235, 1936.
2. Krause and Grosse, *Die Chemie der Metallorganischen Verbindungen*, Borntraeger, Berlin, 1937.
3. Hurd, *J. Org. Chem.*, **13**, 711 (1948).
4. Remick, *Electronic Interpretations of Organic Chemistry*, Wiley, New York, 1949.

SILICON

SiH_4—*silane, (silicane, silicomethane)*
Melting point: $-185°$
Boiling point: $-111.8°$
Density: 0.68 at $-185°$
Heat of formation: 11.9 Kcal/mole

Si_2H_6—*disilane, (disilicane, silicoethane)*
Melting point: $-132.5°$
Boiling point: $-14.5°$

Si_3H_8—*trisilane, (trisilicane, silicopropane)*
Melting point: $-117.4°$
Boiling point: $52.9°$

Si_4H_{10}—*tetrasilane*, (*tetrasilicane*, *silicobutane*)
Melting point: $-93.5°$
Boiling point: $109°$

(Higher silane compounds are known but these are quite
unstable)
Colorless, spontaneously inflammable gases or volatile liquids.

Structure. The structures of the hydrides of silicon are similar
to those of the corresponding hydrocarbons, methane, ethane, propane,
butane, etc. In monosilane the four hydrogen atoms are arranged at
the corners of a tetrahedron about the central silicon atom. The
spacing Si—H is about 1.49 A. U. The bond angle H—Si—H is
about 109.5° (1). The polynuclear silanes may be visualized as chains
of silicon atoms, similar to the carbon-atom chains in the hydrocarbons, each with a tetrahedral disposition of four chemical bonds to
neighboring silicon atoms or to hydrogen atoms. There are, however,
no compounds of silicon in which a multiple bond between two silicon
atoms is known to exist; in this respect silicon differs considerably
from carbon.

Preparation. The earliest method employed to prepare silanes in
quantities sufficient for laboratory investigation was the hydrolysis
of a reactive metal silicide, *magnesium silicide*, Mg_2Si, being the compound generally used. This method can best be demonstrated on a
small scale by dropping small pieces of magnesium silicide into a
beaker of 6 N hydrochloric acid. The formation of silanes is made
evident by the pops, the flashes of light, and the puffs of silica smoke
as the gases evolved by the reaction ignite spontaneously upon contact with the air.

The gaseous product of the acid hydrolysis of magnesium silicide
comprises a mixture of silanes, generally about 40% SiH_4, 30% Si_2H_6,
15% Si_3H_8, 10% Si_4H_{10}, and 5% higher hydrides, but the overall
yields are relatively low and the product is mixed with hydrogen.
If the gas is to be collected for laboratory investigations, somewhat
better yields may be obtained by using concentrated phosphoric acid as
the hydrolysis medium since, in a solution of hydrochloric acid, a
considerable amount of the unstable silane product may be lost
through its hydrolysis in the strongly acid solution. Much better
yields (up to 80%) may be obtained by decomposing magnesium
silicide in a medium of liquid ammonia with ammonium bromide as an
acidic reactant (2).

Hurd observed that monosilane is formed in small amounts (2 to
3%) together with larger amounts of *monochlorosilane* (4 to 5%) and
dichlorosilane (30%) when the vapor of *trichlorosilane*, $SiHCl_3$, is

mixed with an excess of hydrogen and passed over a bed of granular aluminum or zinc heated to a temperature in the range of 300° to 400°. Aluminum chloride is formed in the process (3).

The most convenient laboratory synthesis of monosilane is the metathetical reaction of silicon tetrachloride or trichlorosilane with lithium aluminum hydride in ether solution. The reaction proceeds smoothly upon the slow addition of the silicon halide to a slurry of finely divided LiAlH$_4$ in ether. The silane evolved is passed through a trap or reflux condenser at $-80°$ to separate the ether entrained by the gas stream and is condensed in a trap cooled with liquid nitrogen (4). (WARNING. If this preparation is attempted, it is essential that the apparatus be flushed with nitrogen gas before the reaction is started, and that the apparatus and traps be protected against the entrance of air by a nitrogen sweep at the outlet. Solid monosilane and liquid oxygen comprise a highly explosive and easily detonated mixture, even at $-180°$.)

Disilane and higher silanes are found in the gaseous product resulting from the hydrolysis of magnesium silicide. It also is possible to prepare these compounds from the corresponding chlorosilanes, for example, Si$_2$Cl$_6$, Si$_3$Cl$_8$, etc., by allowing them to react with lithium aluminum hydride in ether solution.

Treatment of calcium silicide with hydrochloric acid forms a polymeric brown solid (SiH$_2$)$_x$ (5). This highly reactive material is decomposed by acids and alkalies, and is spontaneously inflammable. If heated in vacuum, it decomposes, with the formation of lower silanes. Its structure is unknown.

Properties. The silanes are colorless gases or volatile liquids which ignite explosively upon exposure to air to form water and silicon-oxygen compounds. The silanes are not appreciably soluble in water, but they are soluble in organic solvents, such as alcohol and benzene. In many respects they show a resemblance to the paraffin hydrocarbons. Chemically, they are similar in many ways to the boron hydrides (6, 7).

In comparison with the volatile hydrides in general, monosilane is a fairly stable compound. It is decomposed completely into silicon and hydrogen at a temperature of about 600°. The stability of the polysilanes, however, decreases with the higher members of the series. At room temperature, monosilane and disilane appear to be stable indefinitely. The higher silanes slowly decompose upon standing to form lower silanes, usually with the simultaneous formation of a non-volatile solid residue approximating (SiH)$_x$ in composition. At elevated temperatures this degradation or "cracking" process is accelerated. At 400° to 500° disilane decomposes into hydrogen, monosilane, and small amounts of solid siliconhydrogen compounds. These "cracking" reactions are analogous to those observed in the paraffin hydrocarbons, but they occur at much lower temperatures.

It can be shown that very pure water has no chemical effect on the silanes but that even the slightest trace of alkali is sufficient to catalyze a rapid hydrolysis reaction. The silane compounds are decomposed by hydrolysis into silicic acids and hydrogen. The hydrolysis of a silane also may be catalyzed by acids, although, in this case, much larger concentrations are needed to catalyze the hydrolysis reaction. In this connection it may be mentioned that alkaline hydrolysis causes cleavage of silicon-silicon bonds as well as the silicon-hydrogen bonds. Completely substituted polysilane derivatives, containing no silicon-hydrogen bonds, will evolve hydrogen upon treatment with aqueous alkali.

The silanes are strong reducing agents and are capable of precipitating a number of the heavy metals, such as mercury and silver, from solutions of their salts. Potassium permanganate in solution is reduced to brown manganese dioxide upon treatment with monosilane. Such reduction reactions may, in fact, be used as sensitive tests for the presence of silicon hydrides.

With the halogens, the silanes undergo explosively violent replacement reactions to form hydrogen halides and halogenated silane derivatives. The reaction of a silane with a hydrogen halide to yield partially halogenated silanes is, on the other hand, a mild reaction that requires a catalyst and is easy to control. The higher silanes are able to reduce and dechlorinate halocarbon compounds, such as chloroform and carbon tetrachloride, to form partially chlorinated polysilanes; such reactions may be quite violent. Surprisingly enough, however, monosilane does not appear to react with these chlorocarbon compounds under ordinary conditions.

The silanes do not react with ammonia at ordinary temperatures.

Derivatives. A large number of derivatives of the silanes have been prepared and studied. For the most part, these are derivatives of monosilane.

Halogen-substituted silanes may be prepared by the controlled reaction of a silane with a halogen or, better, with a hydrogen halide. The reaction of monosilane with hydrogen chloride, for example, occurs smoothly at room temperature or at a slightly elevated temperature to form the various chlorosilanes. This reaction will not proceed without the presence of a catalyst, such as aluminum chloride. A silane reacts somewhat more easily with hydrogen bromide than with hydrogen chloride.

The halogenated monosilanes may also be prepared by the partial reduction of silicon tetrachloride or silicochloroform with a hydride reducing agent, or with an active metal and hydrogen at an elevated temperature (3, 4). *Trichlorosilane* (*silicochloroform*), $SiHCl_3$, may be formed by passing dry hydrogen chloride over calcium silicide or ferrosilicon. If hydrogen is mixed with hydrogen chloride and passed over heated silicon powder containing 5 to 10% of copper, it is possible to obtain small amounts of *dichlorosilane*, SiH_2Cl_2, as well as trichlorosilane. Typical of the halogenated monosilanes are the chlorosilanes:

SiH_3Cl—*chlorosilane*   m.p. $-118.1°$; b.p. $-30.4°$

SiH_2Cl_2—*dichlorosilane*   m.p. $-122°$;   b.p. $-8.3°$

$SiHCl_3$—*trichlorosilane*   m.p. $-126.5°$; b.p. $-31.8°$
(*silicochloroform*)

Partially halogenated derivatives of some of the higher silanes have been prepared, but these have not been studied to any extent.

The partially halogenated monosilanes are, in general, not spontaneously inflammable. They are quite susceptible, however, to a hydrolysis of the silicon-halogen bond and they react readily with traces of water to form oxygenated silane derivatives. They react with ammonia to form *silylamines*.

The chlorosilanes readily undergo disproportionation reactions in the presence of catalysts such as aluminum chloride. Thus, for example, a mixture of *chlorosilane* and *trichlorosilane* will react to form equilibrium amounts of *dichlorosilane*. In the case of the fluorosilanes, however, the disproportionation reactions of the partially halogenated monosilanes yield the end products, monosilane and silicon tetrafluoride.

Attempts to synthesize polysilanes by condensing partially halogenated monosilanes, such as SiH_3Cl, with metallic sodium have not been successful, although the alkylhalosilanes will undergo a Wurtz condensation to form polysilane compounds (7).

Partially oxygenated derivatives of monosilane may be prepared by the hydrolysis of the chlorosilanes, although care must be taken in such reactions to avoid a concentration of acid (resulting from the hydrolysis) sufficient to catalyze the hydrolysis of the silicon-hydrogen bonds. The hydrolysis of *monochlorosilane*, SiH_3Cl, leads to the formation of *disiloxane*, $(SiH_3)_2O$, probably through the intermediate formation of an unstable *monosilanol*, SiH_3OH. Disiloxane is a gaseous compound (b.p. $-15.2°$) that is not spontaneously inflammable and is stable at temperatures as high as 400°C. It is quite susceptible to hydrolytic decomposition in water containing acids or alkalies.

The hydrolysis of *dichlorosilane*, SiH_2Cl_2, produces solid polymeric compounds of the general formula $(SiH_2O)_x$, probably through the intermediate formation of an unstable silandiol. This compound, $(SiH_2O)_x$, is less susceptible to hydrolytic decomposition than disiloxane, but is decomposed readily by alkaline solutions. It also may be prepared by the controlled oxidation of monosilane. It is of interest to note that a piece of paper or glass exposed to the vapor of dichlorosilane becomes quite effectively water-repellent. The hydrolysis of trichlorosilane forms a white, solid and highly cross-linked polymeric material, $(HSiO_{3/2})_x$.

The reaction of chlorosilane with ammonia at room temperature yields *trisilylamine*, $(SiH_3)_3N$, a compound formally analogous to trimethylamine. Trisilylamine is spontaneously inflammable. It melts at $-105.6°$ and boils at $52°$. It is not possible to isolate the intermediate *mono-* and *disilylamines*, analogous to methyl- and dimethylamine, since these compounds disproportionate into trisilylamine and monosilane. Dichlorosilane and trichlorosilane form solid polymeric amine compounds upon treatment with ammonia. The silylamine compounds can be converted back into the chlorosilanes by treatment with hydrogen chloride.

Alkyl derivatives of the silanes may be prepared by treating the halosilanes with reactive metal alkyls, such as zinc dimethyl and aluminum trimethyl. A more convenient synthesis of alkylsilanes is accomplished by the reaction of the appropriate alkylhalosilanes, with lithium aluminum hydride (4). The addition of monosilane to olefins, such as ethylene or isobutylene, also forms alkylsilane derivatives (8). A similar process in which an olefin or acetylene is added to the silicon-hydrogen bond in a halosilane derivative, such as trichlorosilane, is used for the preparation of silicone intermediates, such as *vinyltrichlorosilane* (7).

A considerable number of alkylsilane derivatives have been prepared and studied. These compounds are not spontaneously inflammable and are intermediate between the hydrocarbons and the silanes in many of their properties. Typical of the *alkylmonosilanes* are the *methyl silanes:*

CH_3SiH_3—*methylsilane*   m.p. $-156.5°$; b.p. $-56.8°$

$(CH_3)_2SiH_2$—*dimethylsilane* m.p. $-150°$;   b.p. $-20.1°$

$(CH_3)_3SiH$—*trimethylsilane*   b.p. $-9°$

The stability of the alkylsilanes toward alkaline hydrolysis appears to increase with the number of substituting groups attached to the silicon atom.   The hydrolysis of the alkyl silanes leads to the formation of silicone compounds, that is, *polyorganosiloxanes* (7).

It is possible to prepare organic derivatives of the silanes in which substitution of hydrogen has been made partially by halogen as well as by alkyl or aryl groups, and a number of such compounds are known.   A typical compound of this class is *methyldichlorosilane*, CH_3SiHCl_2 (b.p., 41°).   This compound, and others in the same category, may be prepared by the partial reduction of an organohalosilane with a reducing agent such as lithium aluminum hydride. Methyldichlorosilane also occurs as a by-product in the process of manufacturing methylchlorosilanes (silicone intermediates) by the Rochow reaction in which methylchloride reacts with elemental silicon in the presence of copper.   A cautious hydrolysis of methyldichlorosilane leads to the formation of a linear polymer, *methylpolysiloxane*, $(CH_3SiH(O))_x$.   This compound has found some commercial use in rendering various materials water-repellent (7).

Uses.   That the unsubstituted silicon hydrides have no commercial applications is not surprising in view of the difficulty of preparing these compounds, their instability, and their great chemical reactivity.

Certain derivatives of monosilane, such as *methyldichlorosilane*, CH_3SiHCl_2, and *dichlorosilane*, SiH_2Cl_2, have been found useful as vapor process treating agents to render various surfaces water-repellent; methyldichlorosilane is now in commercial use to a limited extent.   Both dichlorosilane and trichlorosilane are used as intermediates for the preparation of organochlorosilanes and silicone polymers.

REFERENCES—SILICON HYDRIDES

1. Stevenson, *J. Chem. Phys.*, **8**, 285 (1940).
2. Johnson and Hogness, *J. Am. Chem. Soc.*, **56**, 1252 (1934).
3. Hurd, *J. Am. Chem. Soc.*, **67**, 1545 (1945).
4. Finholt, Bond, Wilzbach, and Schlesinger, *J. Am. Chem. Soc.* **69**, 2692 (1947).
5. Schwarz and Heinrich, *Z. anorg. u. allgem. Chem.*, **221**, 277 (1935).
6. Stock, *Hydrides of Boron and Silicon*, Cornell University Press, Ithaca, N.Y., 1933.
7. Rochow, *Introduction to the Chemistry of the Silicones*, 2nd Ed., Wiley, New York, 1951.
8. Hurd, U.S. Patent 2,537,763.

GERMANIUM

GeH_4—*monogermane, germane*
Melting point: $-165°$

Boiling point: −88.5°
Density at −142°: 1.523 g/ml

Ge_2H_6—*digermane*
Melting point: −109°
Boiling point: 29°
Density at −109°: 1.98 g/ml

Ge_3H_8—*trigermane*
Melting point: −105.6°
Boiling point: 110.5°
Density at 20°: ca. 2.2 g/ml

Colorless gases or volatile liquids

Structure. The structures of the normal germanes are built on tetrahedral patterns like those of the corresponding carbon and silicon hydrides. The bond angle H—Ge—H is 109.5°, and the bond distance Ge—H is 1.54 A. U. (1). Compounds higher than trigermane have not been prepared as yet.

Preparation. The germanium hydrides, or germanes, have been prepared in a variety of ways. The classical method, in which the germanides of electropositive metals are hydrolyzed to form germanes, gives moderate yields. The hydrolysis of magnesium germanide in dilute hydrochloric acid, for example, gives a yield of 20 to 25% of germane and the higher germanes.

Germanium differs from silicon in that it is possible to prepare monogermane by the reduction of germanium compounds in aqueous solution. Thus the action of a metallic reducing agent such as zinc or magnesium on a solution of germanium dioxide in sulfuric acid yields small amounts of germane. Similarly, the reduction of germanium dioxide in aqueous potassium hydroxide with aluminum forms small amounts of germane. Low yields of germane also may be obtained when a solution of acid is electrolyzed in a cell having a cathode of metallic germanium.

The most convenient preparation of monogermane is by the metathetical reaction of germanium tetrachloride with a hydride reducing agent such as lithium aluminum hydride. This reaction may be accomplished conveniently in a medium of dry ethyl ether at room temperature, and the yields are quite good (2). The higher germanes similarly could be prepared from the corresponding halides.

Monogermane has also been prepared by the action of atomic hydrogen on elemental germanium.

Properties. Although the germanes have not been studied at all extensively, their chemistry appears to be similar in many ways to that of the silanes. The germanes are less stable than the silanes, however, and all the known germanes are decomposed into their component elements when they are heated. Monogermane decomposes into germanium and hydrogen at about 340° to 360°. It will be seen that this is quite a bit lower than the decomposition temperature of monosilane (ca. 600°). At a pressure of 200 mm, digermane begins to decompose at about 215°, and trigermane begins to decompose at about 195°. It has been observed that the presence of small amounts of hydrogen acts to inhibit the decomposition of monogermane. This behavior is similar to that observed with the boron hydrides.

Monogermane also is dissociated upon exposure to ultraviolet light (3).

Unlike monosilane, monogermane is not spontaneously inflammable upon exposure to air. It also is much more stable to hydrolysis by dilute alkaline or acidic solutions than monosilane. Monogermane, however, is a strong reducing agent, and it will react with solutions of heavy metal salts, such as silver nitrate; to precipitate the free metals. In some cases the metal may be precipitated as a metal germanide.

Monogermane will burn if ignited; the combustion products are water and germanium dioxide.

Derivatives. Several halogen derivatives of monogermane are known. *Trichlorogermane*, $HGeCl_3$, may be prepared by the cautious reaction of monogermane with elemental chlorine, or by the reaction of magnesium germanide with strong hydrochloric acid. This compound is a colorless liquid which melts at $-71°$ and boils at 75.2°. *Dichlorogermane*, H_2GeCl_2, and *monochlorogermane*, H_3GeCl, as well as *trichlorogermane*, $HGeCl_3$, may be prepared conveniently by the partial reduction of germanium tetrachloride with lithium aluminum hydride. Dichlorogermane melts at $-68°$ and boils at 69.5°. Monochlorogermane melts at $-52°$ and boils at 28°. A similar series of bromogermanes also is known. These halogen derivatives of germane resemble the chlorosilanes in many of their general properties. The halogermanes are hydrolyzed readily by water to form solid nonvolatile products. With ammonia, however, chlorogermane reacts to form ammonium chloride, monogermane, and a solid material, $(GeH)_x$. Dichlorogermane is decomposed by ammonia to form ammonium chloride and elemental germanium (4). The *germanyl amines*, if formed, are not stable.

Monogermane will react with a solution of sodium in liquid ammonia to liberate hydrogen according to the equation:

$$GeH_4 + Na \rightarrow NaGeH_3 + \tfrac{1}{2}H_2$$

The compound thus formed, *sodium germanyl*, is apparently a true salt of the GeH_3^- ion and can be crystallized from ammonia, usually with some ammonia of crystallization. Although it is analogous to sodium methyl, it is not very stable and it decomposes at temperatures above $-33°$ into hydrogen and *sodium germanide*, NaGe. If the solution of sodium germanyl in liquid ammonia is electrolyzed, the GeH_3^- ion reacts with ammonia at the anode to form germane and nitrogen:

$$6GeH_3^- + 2NH_3 \rightarrow 6GeH_4 + N_2 + 6e$$

Alkyl germanes may be prepared by reacting sodium germanyl with alkyl halides:

$$NaGeH_3 + RX \rightarrow RGeH_3 + NaX$$

With an *aryl* halide, such as bromobenzene, the reaction is altogether different:

$$NaGeH_3 + C_6H_5Br \rightarrow C_6H_6 + GeH_2 + NaBr$$

The *germanium dihydride* thus formed is soluble in liquid ammonia but it may be isolated as a white solid by evaporating the ammonia solution. It is quite unstable and rapidly disproportionates into monogermane and a brown solid hydride, $(GeH)_x$. This brown solid hydride also is relatively unstable and will decompose at moderately elevated temperatures into germanium and hydrogen. It may be prepared alternately by the action of ammonium bromide on sodium germanide in liquid ammonia (5) and by the hydrolysis of sodium germanide with water (6).

Alkyl germanes also may be prepared by the reduction of alkylhalo-germanes with lithium aluminum hydride (2). These compounds have not been studied extensively, however, and few have been reported. Their general properties are intermediate between those of the germanes and the germanium alkyls. *Triethylgermane*, $(C_2H_5)_3GeH$, is a liquid which boils at $125°$, is soluble in organic solvents, but is insoluble in water. The alkyl germanes may be hydrolyzed to form polymeric *organogermanium oxides*, analogs of the silicones.

Monoalkyl germanes will react with sodium in liquid ammonia to form alkyl derivatives of sodium germanyl. These, in turn, may be further alkylated by reaction with alkyl halides (5).

Uses. Although there are no commercial uses for the hydrides of germanium at present, the increasing use of metallic germanium as a crystal rectifier for electronic applications makes these compounds of potential interest as sources of very pure germanium. The proper operation of germanium diodes and Transistors requires that the purity of the elemental germanium be very carefully controlled. The preparation of elemental germanium by the pyrolysis of monogermane, prepared in turn from germanium tetrachloride, affords simple physical methods for the separation of germanium from its common impurities, both in the distillation of the tetrachloride and in the distillation of the hydride prior to thermal decomposition.

REFERENCES—GERMANIUM HYDRIDES

1. Stevenson, *J. Chem. Phys.*, **8**, 285 (1940).
2. Finholt, Bond, Wilzbach, and Schlesinger, *J. Am. Chem. Soc.*, **69**, 2692 (1947).
3. Romeyn and Noyes, *J. Am. Chem. Soc.*, **54**, 4143 (1932).
4. Dennis and Work, *J. Am. Chem. Soc.*, **55**, 4486 (1933).
5. Kraus, *J. Chem. Educ.*, **26**, 45 (1949).
6. Dennis and Skow, *J. Am. Chem. Soc.*, **52**, 2369 (1930).

TIN

SnH_4—*stannane*
Colorless, poisonous gas
Melting point: $-150°$
Boiling point: $-52°$

Structure. Tetrahedral; the tin atom is surrounded by four hydrogen atoms arranged at the corners of a tetrahedron. This is similar to the disposition of the atoms in the methane molecule. The bond distance Sn—H is about 1.72 A. U., and the bond angle H—Sn—H is 109.5° (1).

Preparation. Stannane has been prepared in a variety of ways. The direct action of atomic hydrogen on metallic tin or stannous chloride at a temperature of $-180°$ forms small amounts of SnH_4 (2). Similarly, an electric discharge between tin electrodes in hydrogen gas yields stannane (3). The actual yields of material from both these reactions are extremely small.

The electrolysis with a lead cathode of a solution of tin in sulfuric acid is reported to yield as much as 10% of stannane in the gas evolved at the cathode (4).

The reduction of stannic chloride in acid solution by active metals such as magnesium or zinc yields stannane. This synthetic procedure was used in the original investigations on stannane, and it gives relatively good yields considering the instability of the gaseous hydride (5). A modification of this method involves the action of an acid upon an intimate mixture of tin and magnesium or zinc.

A very convenient method for synthesizing stannane is the reaction of stannic chloride in ether solution with lithium aluminum hydride. This is by far the preferred method since it is very easy to do and it gives excellent yields (6).

Properties. Stannane is a rather unstable gaseous compound which decomposes at a fairly rapid rate at room temperature. It is decomposed immediately at a temperature of 150°. It may be detected in very small amounts by passing the gas, usually mixed with hydrogen, through a heated glass tube, where decomposition occurs with the formation of a mirror of tin metal on the glass.

Stannane does not appear to be affected by dilute acids or alkalies, but it is absorbed and decomposed by strongly alkaline solutions, by concentrated sulfuric acid, and by solid alkalies. It is decomposed in solutions of heavy metal salts, such as silver nitrate, with the formation of metallic precipitates.

The gas has an unpleasant odor and is considered to be very poisonous. (See Appendix B.)

Derivatives. A few derivatives of stannane have been prepared. Typical of the organic derivatives are the methylstannanes. They may be prepared by reducing the appropriate organotinhalides with lithium aluminum hydride (6): *methylstannane*, CH_3SnH_3 (b.p.,0°); *dimethylstannane*, $(CH_3)_2SnH_2$ (b.p., 35°); *trimethylstannane*, $(CH_3)_3$-SnH (b.p., 50°). These compounds are more stable toward thermal decomposition than stannane itself, and the stability increases with the number of alkyl groups attached to the tin atom. Trimethylstannane also has been prepared by the action of an ammonium salt on $(CH_3)_3SnNa$ in liquid ammonia (7).

Weeks (8) claimed to have prepared a lower hydride of tin corresponding to a formula of Sn_2H_2 by reducing an alkaline solution of stannous chloride with metallic aluminum. This material was described as a gray powder which decomposed into tin and hydrogen when heated, and which was readily oxidized by air to form metallic tin and water. When the compound was heated in a stream of hydrogen, small amounts of stannane were formed (8). The exact nature of this compound may be considered to be questionable.

The Raman spectrum of *trichlorostannane*, $SnHCl_3$, has been studied. In this case, the compound was prepared by saturating an aqueous solution of stannous chloride with hydrogen chloride. The compound itself was not isolated.

Uses. In view of its rarity and great instability there are no commercial uses for stannane, although it conceivably could be used in a vapor process for tin plating. It has been pointed out that the possible formation of stannane in spoiled canned goods may be a potential source of food poisoning (9).

REFERENCES—TIN HYDRIDE

1. Stevenson, *J. Chem. Phys.*, **8**, 285 (1940).
2. Vdovenko, *J. Gen. Chem.* (USSR), **15**, 581 (1945).
3. Foresti and Mascaretti, *Gazz. chim. ital.*, **60**, 745 (1930).
4. Paneth, *Z. Elektrochem.*, **29**, 97 (1923).
5. Alimarin and Arest-Yakubovich, *J. Applied Chem.* (*USSR*), **10**, 920 (1937).
6. Finholt, Bond, Wilzbach, and Schlesinger, *J. Am. Chem. Soc.*, **69**, 2692 (1947).
7. Kraus and Greer, *J. Am. Chem. Soc.*, **44**, 2629 (1922).
8. Weeks, *Rec. trav. chim.*, **45**, 201 (1926).
9. Vaubel, *Chem.-Ztg.*, **48**, 351 (1924).

LEAD

PbH_4—*plumbane*
Colorless gas, boiling point unknown

Structure. Plumbane presumably has a structure similar to that of the monomolecular hydrides of the other fourth group elements; that is, a tetrahedral configuration of hydrogen atoms about a central lead atom.

Preparation. Because of the instability of lead hydride, this compound has been prepared and studied only in trace amounts. Paneth and Norring (1) prepared the gas by electrolyzing a sulfuric acid solution with lead electrodes. The hydrogen evolved from this reaction contained a few percent of plumbane. Plumbane also has been prepared by the action of acids on a mixture of magnesium and lead pellets, as well as by the reduction of a dilute solution of lead acetate with metallic magnesium. It has been reported that plumbane can be formed by the action of atomic hydrogen on metallic lead (2), but more recent investigations have not confirmed this synthesis.

Properties. Plumbane is a very unstable compound. It decomposes into its component elements very rapidly at room temperature and deposits metallic lead on the walls of the containing vessel. Little is known about its chemical properties.

No *derivatives* of plumbane are known. Attempts have been made to prepare alkyl plumbanes by reducing alkyl lead halides with lithium aluminum hydride, but these reactions have not been successful (3).

Other Hydrides of Lead. Weeks (4) reported the synthesis of a gray solid hydride of lead, corresponding in formula to PbH_2, by the reduction of an alkaline plumbate solution with metallic aluminum.

As described, this solid compound reacted with hydrogen under the influence of heat to form plumbane. The existence of this subhydride compound was deduced mainly from the fact that it contained about the correct percentage of hydrogen. This amount, ca. 0.5%, well might be physically adsorbed hydrogen rather than hydrogen bound chemically in the form of a true compound.

REFERENCES—LEAD HYDRIDE

1. Paneth and Norring, *Ber.*, **53B,** 1693 (1920).
2. Schultze and Müller, *Z. physik. Chem.*, Abt. B, **6,** 267 (1930).
3. Finholt, Bond, Wilzbach, and Schlesinger, *J. Am. Chem. Soc.*, **69,** 2692 (1947).
4. Weeks, *J. Chem. Soc.*, **127,** 2845 (1925).

CHAPTER

10

The Hydrides of the Group V Elements

GENERAL CONSIDERATIONS

The simple hydrides of the elements in Group V (and VB), *nitrogen, phosphorus, arsenic, antimony,* and *bismuth,* have the general formula MH_3. With the exception of ammonia, which, though essentially covalent, shows the effect of hydrogen bonding between ammonia molecules in its physical properties, all the simple Group V hydrides are normal covalent compounds.

The general structure pattern for the Group V hydrides comprises three hydrogen atoms covalently bonded to, and surrounding, the parent element atom at three corners of a distorted tetrahedron or triangular pyramid. The fourth corner of the pyramid may conveniently be considered to represent the location of an unshared pair of electrons which may be used for bonding in the formation of coordination complexes with electron-acceptor groups.

Because of the type of bonding involved ("p" bonds), the normal bond angles between the element-hydrogen bonds would be expected to be close to 90°. The observed bond angles in all the Group V hydrides except ammonia are close to this value.* In the *ammonia* molecule, the repulsion of the three hydrogen atoms situated on the relatively small nitrogen atom causes a broadening of the bond angles to 108°. When a fourth hydrogen joins this molecule in the formation of an *ammonium ion,* NH_4^+, the structure of the complex becomes tetrahedral, and the bond angles assume a value close to the tetrahedral angle of 109°28'.

Several of the general preparative reactions will serve for the formation of the Group V hydrides. Perhaps the most general reaction is the hydrolysis of a "metal–non-metal" binary compound, such as a *nitride, phosphide,* or *arsenide,* to yield a hydride of the "non-metal" component. This reaction may be used to prepare any of the Group V hydrides.

Lithium aluminum hydride has been used successfully for the

* Stevenson, *J. Chem. Phys.,* **8,** 285 (1940).

preparation of hydrides from certain of the Group V halides. It is a particularly useful method if we wish to prepare organic derivatives, since organohalo derivatives of elements like arsenic and antimony can easily be converted to the corresponding hydride derivatives. Lithium aluminum hydride presumably could be used also for the reduction of halide or oxide derivatives of nitrogen and phosphorus, although it would not be a convenient laboratory reagent for preparing the simple hydrides of these elements.

Ammonia is the only compound in Group V that is prepared in large quantities by the direct reaction of the element with hydrogen. High pressures, elevated temperatures, and catalysts are needed in this reaction. At very high pressures, some phosphine may be formed from elemental phosphorus and hydrogen at ca. 300°, but this is not a convenient synthesis method.

Phosphorus is unusual in that it will react with water in the presence of alkali in a manner similar to that of chlorine. A disproportionation occurs, part of the phosphorus is reduced, and a corresponding amount is oxidized:

$$4P + 6H_2O \rightarrow PH_3 + 3H_3PO_2$$

The thermal stability of the Group V hydrides decreases rapidly with increasing atomic weight of the parent element, and, in general, these compounds appear to be less stable than the hydrides in Group IV or in Group VI. The amount of ammonia in equilibrium with nitrogen and hydrogen at any given temperature, assuming the presence of a catalyst, is a function of the pressure; at one atmosphere pressure, the equilibrium amount of ammonia is about 3% at 300°. Stibine and bismuthine, on the other hand, decompose slowly at room temperature.

There are differences in the chemical reactivity of the Group V hydrides. Here, as in other groups of related hydrides, the prototype hydride of the Second Period element (ammonia in this group) differs to the greatest extent from the other members of the group.

In spite of a greater electronegativity, ammonia is much the strongest electron donor of the Group V hydrides, owing to the small size of the nitrogen atom and, thus, its tendency to form covalent bonds. Ammonia readily coordinates its unshared electron pair to a proton to form the *ammonium ion*, NH_4^+, and in aqueous solution ammonia behaves as a base. The ammonium ion is sufficiently stable so that it can exist as an ion in such salts as *ammonium chloride*, NH_4Cl.

(At the risk of being repetitious, it might be pointed out that the action of a molecule or ion as an acid or as a base is entirely a relative matter, and one which depends on the other reactants involved. Under some conditions, ammonia can act as an acid, for example, during the solution of sodium in liquid ammonia to liberate hydrogen and form *sodamide*, $NaNH_2$).

Phosphorus is a much weaker electron donor than ammonia. *Phosphonium* compounds are known, such as PH_4Cl and PH_4Br, but these compounds are unstable in water solution against dissociation into phosphine, hydronium ion, and halide ion. In *arsine*, the tendency to form coordination complexes is not developed, and stable salts of the *arsonium* ion, AsH_4^+, are not known. It might be mentioned that *arsonium* and *stibonium* derivatives are known in which organic groups have replaced the hydrogen atoms.

In accordance with their decreasing tendency to associate protons in aqueous solution, there is a decrease in aqueous solubility down the series, ammonia, phosphine, arsine.

Ammonia and phosphine, as well as their organo-substituted derivatives, will also form coordination complexes with acceptor molecules, such as the boron hydrides, boron alkyls, and similar compounds of aluminum and gallium. This tendency is shown to a lesser extent by the higher hydrides in Group V. In any of these coordination compounds the physical and chemical properties will depend on the strength of both the electron donor and the electron acceptor. It should be mentioned that ammonia forms coordination complexes, or *ammoniates*, with a great many metal ions.

All the Group V hydrides are strong reducing agents. They all can be combusted with oxygen, and the ease of oxidation increases with the heavier members of the group. Ammonia is relatively difficult to ignite, but it can be burned in oxygen to form water and either nitrogen or nitrogen oxides. Phosphine ignites in air at ca. 150°. The remaining hydrides in the group are easily ignited and will burn, depending upon the amount of oxygen available, to form water and either the free element or its oxide. All the Group V hydrides will react with halogens to form hydrogen halides and either the free element or its halide, depending upon the particular compound and the reaction conditions. All of the Group V hydrides can reduce certain heavy metal salts to the free metals or metallic derivatives, although here, also, the higher members of the group are stronger reducing agents than ammonia and phosphine.

Most of the Group V elements form polynuclear hydrides in addition to the simple hydrides of the type MH_3. Such polynuclear hydrides are well defined only with nitrogen and phosphorus, for example, *hydrazine, triazine, hydrazoic acid, diphosphine*. The only Group V hydride known to be spontaneously inflammable is the compound *diphosphine*, which often accompanies phosphine as an impurity. Most of the complex hydrides of nitrogen are beyond the scope of this book.

It will be apparent that, since other groups may be substituted for hydrogen in the Group V hydrides, and groups may be added to these molecules in the formation of coordination complexes, there are a very large number of derivatives of the Group V hydrides which are possible. This is particularly true of the stronger electron donors ammonia and phosphine.

NITROGEN

NH_3—*ammonia*
Colorless gas
Melting point: $-77.7°$
Boiling point: $-33.35°$
Density: 0.817 g/cc at $-79°$
Heat of formation: 15.84 Kcal/mole (liquid);
10.94 Kcal/mole (gas)

N_2H_4—*hydrazine*
Colorless liquid, fumes strongly in air
Melting point: $1.4°$
Boiling point: $113.5°$
Density: 1.011 g/cc at $15°$
Heat of formation: -12 Kcal/mole (anhydrous N_2H_4)

Structure. The ammonia molecule comprises three hydrogen atoms covalently bonded to a nitrogen atom; the bond angle H—N—H is ca. 108° and the bond distance N—H is 1.01 A. U. (1). The structure of hydrazine has not been determined in detail, but all of the bond angles in this compound are believed to be close to 110° (2).

Preparation. Ammonia is prepared on an industrial scale by the direct reaction of hydrogen with nitrogen at elevated temperatures and high pressures in the presence of a catalyst. An alternative method of synthesis, used sometimes for the laboratory preparation of pure *deutero-ammonia*, is the hydrolysis of a reactive metal nitride, such as Mg_3N_2:

$$Mg_3N_2 + 6H_2O \rightarrow 2NH_3 + 3Mg(OH)_2$$

$$Mg_3N_2 + 6D_2O \rightarrow 2ND_3 + 3Mg(OD)_2$$

Ammonia can also be replaced from its complex coordination derivatives, such as the ammonium ion, by a stronger electron donor or "base":

$$NH_4Cl + NaOH \rightarrow NH_3 + NaCl + H_2O$$

Hydrazine, the analog in the ammonia system of hydrogen peroxide in the water system, is prepared by the oxidation of ammonia with a hypochlorite:

$$2NH_3 + NaOCl \rightarrow N_2H_4 + NaCl + H_2O$$

The reaction actually is more complex than this general equation indicates (3).

Chemical Properties. Since the ammonia molecule is a very strong electron donor, much of its chemistry is concerned with complex coordination derivatives, ions and compounds. In aqueous solution, the ammonia molecule coordinates a proton to form the *ammonium ion*, NH_4^+; because of the excess of hydroxyl ions left by the proton transfer, the solution is basic. This complex ion formation is responsible in part for the very large solubility of ammonia gas in water—ca. 1176 cc of ammonia gas per cubic centimeter of water at 0°; 706 cc per cubic centimeter of water at 20°. Ammonia forms a number of coordination compounds with strong electron acceptor molecules, such as the boron hydrides, boron halides, boron alkyls, and similar compounds of aluminum, gallium, etc. Ammonia also forms coordination complexes with various metal ions, including ions of copper, silver, zinc, chromium, manganese, iron, nickel, cobalt, in addition to many others. Liquid ammonia is a good solvent for many inorganic salts as well as the alkali metals. Like water, it is an ionizing solvent.

Hydrazine also forms coordination complexes. Since each of the two nitrogens has a pair of electrons available for sharing, two types of complex are possible, depending on whether one or both of the nitrogen atoms form coordinate bonds. Hydrazine is quite soluble in water and does form the *hydrazonium ion*, $N_2H_5^+$, to some extent. It is, however, a weaker base than ammonia (k_b $N_2H_4 = 3 \times 10^{-6}$), and the tendency of hydrazine to form coordination complexes is less than that of ammonia. Both ammonia and hydrazine are somewhat soluble in organic solvents.

Ammonia and hydrazine both are reducing agents, although hydrazine is much the stronger of the two compounds in this respect. This is undoubtedly due to the endothermic nature of hydrazine; ammonia is relatively stable. There are only a few reactions of importance in which ammonia acts as a reducing agent. One of these is the catalytic oxidation of ammonia at 300° to 500° to oxides of nitrogen and nitric acid:

$$4NH_3 + 5O_2 \xrightarrow{\text{catalyst}} 4NO + 6H_2O$$

Ammonia will ignite and burn in chlorine gas to form hydrogen chloride and nitrogen.

Hydrazine is readily oxidized even by relatively weak oxidizing agents like sulfur:

$$N_2H_4 + 2S \rightarrow N_2 + 2H_2S$$

It reacts readily and violently with strong oxidizing agents like the halogens, and it will burn vigorously in oxygen. Free hydrazine in contact with air is gradually oxidized to water and nitrogen. In contact with oxidizing agents such as the permangantes, hydrazine reacts with explosive violence. Hydrazine also is capable of precipitating a number of the heavy metals from solutions of their salts.

Since hydrazine is endothermic, it is rather unstable and can decompose into ammonia, nitrogen, and hydrogen, with the evolution of considerable amounts of energy. If it is quite pure, hydrazine may be distilled at its normal boiling point of 113.5°, but at about 140° it generally explodes. The temperature at which hydrazine will explode spontaneously is markedly lowered by the presence of trace amounts of impurities which act as catalysts for the decomposition.

Hydrazine forms a rather stable hydrate, $N_2H_4 \cdot H_2O$, which has a boiling point of ca. 118.5° and a melting point of ca. $-40°$. Since anhydrous hydrazine is so dangerous, it almost always is used in aqueous solution.

Derivatives. In addition to the coordination complex ions and compounds, there are several other types of derivative which ammonia can form. In common with a number of the covalent hydrides, ammonia can form derivatives of electropositive metals through the replacement of one or more of the hydrogen atoms. The derivatives with the alkali and alkaline earth metals are known as *amides* (not to be confused with the organic amides). These compounds, of the general types MNH_2 and $M(NH_2)_2$, are stable salt-like solids that may be prepared by reacting the metal with ammonia. The reaction proceeds slow'y in liquid ammonia or more rapidly at elevated temperatures with gaseous ammonia:

$$2Li + 2NH_3 \rightarrow 2LiNH_2 + H_2$$

The amides of strongly electropositive metals are analogous to the hydroxides in the water system. Since ammonia is a stronger electron donor than water, the metal amides are readily hydrolyzed by water to form ammonia and metal hydroxides through the mechanism of proton transfer from oxygen to nitrogen. If metal amides are heated, they lose ammonia to form *imides*, M_2NH or MNH, depending on the valence of the metal:

$$2LiNH_2 \rightarrow Li_2NH + NH_3$$

On stronger heating, the imides decompose to *metallic nitrides:*

$$3Li_2NH \rightarrow 2Li_3N + NH_3$$

Metal derivatives of hydrazine, such as NH_2NHNa, may be prepared by treating alkali metals with anhydrous hydrazine. Compounds of this type are exceedingly sensitive, however, and they explode violently if they are moistened.

Ammonia forms a great many mixed hydride compounds. The most common examples of this type of compound are the *organic amines*, RNH_2 and R_2NH. Similar compounds are known with other hydride systems besides that of carbon, for example, *disilylamine*, $(SiH_3)_2NH$, *borazole*, $B_3N_3H_6$, etc.

Hydroxylamine, NH_2OH, a mixed, or molecular complex hydride of nitrogen and oxygen, is formed by the electrolytic reduction of nitric acid:

$$HNO_3 + 6H^+ + 6e \rightarrow NH_2OH + 2H_2O$$

Hydroxylamine is a white crystalline solid which melts at 33.1°; its boiling point is 56.5° at 22 mm. Like hydrazine, it is a very unstable endothermic compound, and the anhydrous material can be kept for any reasonable length of time only if it is highly pure. If anhydrous hydroxylamine is heated, its decomposition may be explosive. Hydroxylamine is a very strong reducing agent, and, like hydrazine, it is capable of reducing a large number of heavy metal salts to the free metals.

Compounds containing derivatives of the ammonium ion also are known, for example, *methylammonium chloride (methylamine hydrochloride)*, $(CH_3)NH_3Cl$, *hydroxylammonium* salts like $(NH_3OH)Cl$, etc. There are a large number of such compounds known, and a much larger number of possible compounds are as yet unprepared.

Mixed hydride derivatives of hydrazine are known, mainly within the field of organic chemistry. Such compounds include *ethylhydrazine*, $(C_2H_5)NHNH_2$, *1,1-diphenylhydrazine*, $(C_6H_5)_2NNH_2$, *1,1,2-triphenylhydrazine*, $(C_6H_5)_2NNH(C_6H_5)$, etc.

REFERENCES—HYDRIDES OF NITROGEN

1. Stevenson, *J. Chem. Phys.*, **8**, 285 (1940).
2. Penney and Sutherland, *Trans. Faraday Soc.*, **30**, 898 (1934).
3. Audrieth and Ogg, *The Chemistry of Hydrazine*, Wiley, New York, 1951.

PHOSPHORUS

PH_3—*phosphine*
Colorless poisonous gas
Melting point: $-132.5°$
Boiling point: $-87.4°$
Density: 0.746 g/cc at $-90°$
Heat of formation: 2.3 Kcal/mole

Structure. The structure of the phosphine molecule is similar to that of the ammonia molecule except that the bond angle, 93°, is much closer to the theoretical value of 90° for the Group VB hydrides. The phosphorus-hydrogen bond length is about 1.42 A. U. (1).

Preparation. Phosphine may be prepared by the direct reaction of elemental phosphorus with hydrogen at elevated temperatures (ca. 300°), but very high pressures are necessary to obtain significant yields of phosphine.

The hydrolysis of metal phosphides, such as *calcium phosphide*, Ca_3P_2, is a convenient laboratory method for preparing phosphine in small amounts:

$$Ca_3P_2 + 6H_2O \rightarrow 2PH_3 + 3Ca(OH)_2$$

Phosphine prepared by such hydrolysis reactions usually contains diphosphine as an impurity and, therefore, is spontaneously inflammable.

If elemental phosphorus is reacted with hot water in the presence of an alkali, a disproportionation reaction occurs to yield phosphine and hypophosphorous acid:

$$4P + 6H_2O \rightarrow PH_3 + 3H_3PO_2$$

This synthesis also is used for the laboratory preparation of phosphine. The hypophosphorous acid can be disproportionated further to yield additional amounts of phosphine:

$$2H_3PO_2 \xrightarrow{\text{heat}} PH_3 + H_3PO_4$$

Consequently, care should be taken when hypophosphorous acid or hypophosphites are heated during the course of laboratory work, since inflammation may result.

Chemical Properties. Phosphine is a weaker electron donor than ammonia, and relatively few of its coordination complexes are known. Phosphine is much less soluble in water than ammonia, ca. 27 cc per 100 cc of H_2O at room temperature, and there is only a very slight tendency to form the *phosphonium ion*, PH_4^+, in the solution. *Phosphonium halides* can be prepared by the reaction of phosphine with hydrogen halides, but these compounds appear to be primarily covalent and are dissociated in the vapor phase. **Typical compounds are**

phosphonium bromide, PH_4Br, a solid which sublimes at ca. 30°, and *phosphonium iodide*, PH_4I, which sublimes at 80°. In water, these compounds are almost completely hydrolyzed to phosphine, halide ion, and hydronium ion.

Phosphine is a stronger reducing agent than ammonia. Although pure phosphine is not spontaneously inflammable, it ignites readily in air at about 150°, and it reacts spontaneously with chlorine at room temperature. Phosphine will reduce many heavy metal salts, such as silver nitrate, to the free metals or to metallic phosphides.

Derivatives. Analogous to hydrazine, there exists a *diphosphine*, P_2H_4. This compound often accompanies phosphine as a product of hydrolysis reactions. It is a colorless spontaneously inflammable liquid whose melting point is −99° and whose boiling point is 51.7°. Diphosphine decomposes readily, especially on heating, to form phosphine and elemental phosphorus:

$$3P_2H_4 \rightarrow 2P + 4PH_3$$

Diphosphine is a strong reducing agent, and it appears to be analogous to hydrazine in most of its known chemical properties.

It has been suggested from time to time that higher hydrides of phosphorus may exist. Evidence for this lies in the fact that the solid material produced by the thermal decomposition of diphosphine often contains hydrogen. It is believed now, however, that this solid hydrogen-containing material comprises small amounts of phosphine adsorbed on elemental phosphorus rather than any definite higher hydrides.

Some organic substituted phosphines, analogous to the organic amines, are known, for example, *methylphosphine*, CH_3PH_2, which boils at 25° and is spontaneously inflammable, *diethylphosphine*, $(C_2H_5)_2PH$, which boils at 85°, and *phenylphosphine*, $(C_6H_5)PH_2$, which boils at 160°. Complex *organophosphonium* compounds are also known (2).

REFERENCES—HYDRIDES OF PHOSPHOROUS

1. Stevenson, *J. Chem. Phys.*, **8**, 285 (1940).
2. Kosolapoff, *Organophosphorous Compounds*, Wiley, New York (1950).

ARSENIC

AsH_3—*arsine*
Colorless, poisonous gas

Melting point: $-113.5°$
Boiling point: $-55°$
Heat of formation: -43.49 Kcal/mole

Structure. The structure of arsine is similar to that of ammonia and phosphine except that, with the greater size of the arsenic atom, the bond angles, H—As—H, are close to the value of 90° expected on theoretical grounds. The bond distance, As—H, is about 1.53 A. U. (1). Like nitrogen and phosphorus, tricovalent arsenic has an unshared pair of electrons which may be used for bonding to acceptor atoms in the formation of coordination complex compounds

Preparation. A number of methods are available for the preparation of arsine and its derivatives. These include many of the general methods for the synthesis of covalent hydrides.

Arsine can be made by the direct combination of arsenic with atomic hydrogen, but the compound is not sufficiently stable to be prepared by the combination of arsenic with elemental hydrogen at elevated temperatures (except, possibly, at exceedingly high pressures of hydrogen).

The arsenides of electropositive metals are a convenient source of arsine since their hydrolysis usually is effected easily with water or dilute non-oxidizing acids. Calcium arsenide, prepared by the direct union of calcium metal with arsenic, can be hydrolyzed in water to produce arsine in a yield of about 14%. If sodium arsenide is treated in liquid ammonia with ammonium bromide, yields of arsine as high as 90% can be obtained (2). For the convenient generation of arsine, an alloy of sodium arsenide with lead may be used since it is more easily handled than sodium arsenide (3).

Arsine may also be prepared by the reduction, electrolytic or chemical, of arsenic compounds in solution. The reducing action of zinc metal on an acid solution of arsenic oxide forms arsine, and other reducing agents, for example, Mg and Al, can exert a similar action. This type of reaction can be extended to the preparation of organic derivatives of arsine; for example, the reduction of $(CH_3)_2AsOH$ with zinc and hydrochloric acid yields *dimethyl arsine*, $(CH_3)_2AsH$. Various electrolytic processes, in which pieces of metallic arsenic are used as electrodes, yield small amounts of arsine.

It has been reported that small yields of arsine (12 to 17%) have been obtained by heating arsenic or sodium arsenate with sodium formate at a temperature of 400° (4).

The formation of organic derivatives of arsine by the action of specific strains of bacteria or fungi on arsenic compounds has been observed (5). (Some investigations on this subject have been prompted by the detection of volatile arsenic compounds released in dwellings by the action of bacteria on wallpaper in whose manufacture arsenic compounds had been employed!)

Properties. In common with the other Group V hydrides, arsine has an unpleasant odor and is an exceedingly poisonous gas.

The compound, which is relatively unstable thermally, may be decomposed at 300° by passing the gas through a heated tube. The decomposition of the arsine leaves a mirror of metallic arsenic on the tube wall. This phenomenon is the basis of the famous Marsh test for traces of arsenic, in which the arsine formed by the chemical reduction of the suspected material is lead through a heated glass tube, where it is detected by the formation of the mirror-like film of free arsenic.

Arsine is soluble in water to the extent of about 20 cm^3 per 100 cm^3 of water at room temperature. The solution formed is very slightly basic. At low temperatures ($-10°$), or under pressure, arsine forms a hydrate $AsH_3 \cdot 6H_2O$.

Arsine, a strong reducing agent, can precipitate a number of the heavy metals from solutions of their salts. For example, arsine will precipitate metallic silver from a solution of silver nitrate; arsenious acid is formed simultaneously. This reaction has been used for the detection and estimation of very small quantities of arsenic. Arsine may also be oxidized by reagents such as hydrogen peroxide or nitric acid.

Arsine will react with metallic sodium or potassium dissolved in liquid ammonia. A replacement of hydrogen occurs with the formation of metallic derivatives of arsine, $NaAsH_2$ or $KAsH_2$. Arsine may be regenerated from these compounds by treating the solution with ammonium bromide. The derivatives can be isolated, but they are decomposed by air. If the potassium derivative is heated to above 115° it decomposes, with the evolution of hydrogen and the formation of a potassium polyarsenide. If $KAsH_2$ is treated with methyl chloride, an alkylation reaction occurs with the formation of CH_3AsH_2 and KCl. CH_3AsH_2 will react further with potassium in liquid ammonia to form CH_3AsHK (2).

The direct action of chlorine on arsine at low temperatures leads to the formation of the yellow, solid *chloroarsines*, AsH_2Cl and $AsHCl_2$. These compounds are quite unstable, and are less stable than the corresponding derivatives of phosphine (6). At higher temperatures chlorine attacks arsine to form HCl and either free arsenic or $AsCl_3$.

Arsine will burn in air if ignited. The products of combustion are water and either free arsenic or arsenic oxides, depending on the combustion conditions and the supply of air.

Derivatives. Although a very large number of completely sub-stituted organic derivatives of arsine are known, the number of compounds containing hydrogen bonded to arsenic is not large.

As a typical example of the organic derivatives of arsine, *methyl arsine*, CH_3AsH_2, may be prepared by the alkylation of arsine in liquid ammonia via the potassium derivative (2), or by the reduction of methyl arsenic halides or oxides. Methyl arsine melts at $-143°$ and boils at $2°$. *Diethyl arsine*, prepared by reducing diethylarsenic compounds with zinc in acid solution, boils at $96.5°$. It is spontaneously inflammable in air. The organoarsines are exceedingly poisonous. They are more stable toward thermal decomposition than arsine. They may be oxidized to form organic-substituted arsenic acids.

Arsine can form coordination complexes by virtue of its unshared pair of electrons. Such complexes that are known, however, are much less stable than the corresponding derivatives of ammonia. Arsine forms a coordination compound with boron trichloride, for example, at low temperatures; but, upon being warmed, the compound dissociates at about $-40°$. In a sealed tube, it decomposes at room temperature to liberate hydrogen, arsenic, and boron trichloride (7). The compound with boron tribromide appears to be more stable. The arsine in this compound can easily be replaced by ammonia.

Solid Arsenic Hydride. If arsenic trichloride is reduced with stannous chloride in a solution of hydrochloric acid, a brown amorphous powder is obtained. The composition of this compound corresponds to a formula of As_2H_2. This material is insoluble in water, alkalies, and acids, with the exception of nitric acid. It is decomposed in boiling water; hydrogen is evolved, and arsenic oxide is formed. The compound is a reducing agent and, like arsine, it reduces solutions of silver nitrate or the salts of other heavy metals. Halogens attack it and form arsenic halides. If the solid arsenic hydride is heated in a vacuum, it decomposes to metallic arsenic, with the formation of some arsine (8).

The solid arsenic hydride has also been prepared by the partial oxidation of arsine in air, by the oxidation of arsine with stannic chloride, and by the electrolytic reduction of a sodium hydroxide solution with a cathode of arsenic metal.

Uses of Arsine. Because of its high toxicity, and because it is a relatively heavy gas, arsine has been used to some extent as a fumigant. A number of patents are on record describing various alloys for generating arsine by hydrolysis reactions.

The ease with which arsine may be liberated by hydrolysis reactions, or by electrolytic reactions, makes this gas a toxicity problem in certain industrial operations. Cases of arsenic poisoning have resulted from the action of water on iron alloys which have contained traces of arsenic and phosphorus. The contact of hot aluminum dross with water in certain metallurgical operations has also been observed to liberate toxic compounds of arsenic and antimony. The formation of arsine in electrolytic processes, such as electrolytic refining, can be suppressed by the addition of copper salts.

REFERENCES—ARSENIC HYDRIDES

1. Stevenson, *J. Chem. Phys.*, **8**, 285 (1940).
2. Johnson and Pechukas, *J. Am. Chem. Soc.*, **59**, 2065 (1937).
3. Blumenberg, U.S. Patent 1,338, 279.
4. Vournas, *Ber.*, **43**, 2264 (1910).
5. Huss, *Chem. Abstr.*, **7**, 3142.
6. Stock, *Ber.*, **53**, 837 (1920).
7. Stieber, *Compt. rend.*, **195**, 610 (1932).
8. Weeks and Druce, *Chem. News*, **129**, 31 (1924).

ANTIMONY

SbH_3—*stibine*
Melting point: $-88.5°$
Boiling point: $-17.0°$
Density: 2.204 g/cc at b.p.
Heat of formation: -34.27 Kcal/mole (1)

Structure. The structure of stibine is pyramidal like the structures of the other Group V hydrides. The bond distance Sb—H has been calculated to be about 1.73 A. U., and the bond angle H—Sb—H appears to be close to 90° (2).

Preparation. Although stibine may be prepared by several methods, the best synthesis appears to be the hydrolysis in dilute acid of an alloy of antimony with a reactive metal such as zinc or magnesium. Several alloys, including a zinc-antimony alloy and a complex alloy of antimony with lead and sodium, have been patented for the generation of stibine, since the gas has been used to some extent as a fumigant (3).

Stibine may also be prepared by the electrolysis of acid or alkaline solutions with a cathode of metallic antimony. Yields of stibine as high as 15% by volume in the gas evolved at the cathode have been reported, but this method of preparing stibine is not considered practical (4).

Small amounts of stibine may be formed by the action of atomic hydrogen on metallic antimony. Traces of hydrocarbon appear to be necessary as catalysts for this reaction (5). Stibine also has been prepared by reducing antimony pentoxide with hydrogen at high pressure (6).

Properties. Stibine is a colorless gas with a disagreeable odor. It is quite poisonous and, in fact, it is considered to be slightly more toxic than arsine and phosphine. The gas is slightly soluble in water and is very soluble in organic solvents, such as alcohol and carbon disulfide. Liquid stibine does not appear to be associated.

Stibine is less stable thermally than arsine and decomposes slowly on standing at room temperature. The rate of decomposition increases with increasing temperature, and the compound is very quickly destroyed at a temperature of 200° (7). The decomposition products are metallic antimony, generally deposited in the form of a mirror, and hydrogen. The gas may be decomposed by strong solutions of acid or alkali although it appears to be relatively stable in dilute solutions of such reagents. Stibine is decomposed rapidly in solution by oxidizing agents, such as permanganates, and it reacts with heavy metal salts like silver nitrate to form black metallic precipitates. Elemental chlorine attacks stibine, even at low temperatures, to form free antimony and antimony pentachloride.

Derivatives. Weeks and Druce claimed to have prepared a solid hydride of antimony, Sb_2H_2, by the reaction of stibine with concentrated aqueous sodium hydroxide as well as by the electrolysis of aqueous alkali with an antimony cathode (8). Later investigators were not able to confirm this preparation, however.

It should be possible to prepare organic derivatives of stibine by the reduction of organohalostibines with lithium aluminum hydride.

Applications. Since stibine is a highly poisonous gas it has been used as a fumigating agent. Occasionally there have been reports of accidental poisonings by stibine in metal refineries where water has come into contact with hot dross containing antimony together with a metal such as aluminum. Stibine has also been considered a hazard in submarines, where it may be generated electrolytically from antimony impurities in the lead of the storage batteries during charging.

REFERENCES—ANTIMONY HYDRIDES

1. Stock and Wrede, *Ber.*, **41**, 540 (1908).
2. Stevenson, *J. Chem. Phys.*, **8**, 285 (1940).
3. Blumenberg, U.S. Patent 1,338,279.
4. Sand, Weeks, and Worrell, *J. Chem. Soc.*, **123**, 456 (1923).
5. Paneth, Matthias, and Schmidt-Hebbel, *Ber.*, **55**, 775 (1922).
6. Ipatiev and Nikolaiev, *Ber.*, **59B**, 1423 (1922).

7. Stock, Echeandra, and Voigt, *Ber.*, **41**, 1309 (1908).
8. Weeks and Druce, *J. Chem Soc.*, **127**, 1069 (1925).

BISMUTH

BiH₃—*bismuthine*
Boiling point: 22°

Structure. Although it has not been investigated, the structure of bismuthine presumably is pyramidal like that of the related hydrides of nitrogen, phosphorus, arsenic, and antimony. The bond angle H—Bi—H, probably is close to 90°.

Preparation. The first preparation of bismuthine was made by Paneth, who hydrolyzed an alloy of magnesium and the radioactive isotope of bismuth, Thorium C. The minute amounts of volatile bismuth hydride thus formed could be traced and studied by the radio-activity of the gas (1). Paneth later found that bismuthine could be prepared from normal bismuth by treating a finely divided mixture of bismuth and magnesium with acid. It was not necessary to alloy the two metals for this synthesis. Surprisingly enough, an alloy of bismuth and sodium, Na₃Bi, yielded no bismuthine on hydrolysis (2). Bismuthine also may be prepared by treating acid solutions of bismuth salts with an active metal such as magnesium.

Attempts to prepare bismuthine by the action of atomic hydrogen on elemental bismuth have not been successful.

Properties. Little is known about the physical and chemical properties of bismuthine since the gas is very unstable and has been prepared only in small amounts. At room temperature, about 20% of a given sample of bismuthine will decompose into the component elements bismuth and hydrogen in one hour. The compound obviously is quite endothermic. The thermal decomposition proceeds rapidly at temperatures above 150°. If bismuthine is passed through a heated glass tube, it is possible to observe the formation of mirrors of metallic bismuth on the walls of the tube.

Bismuthine is completely destroyed upon being passed through a dilute solution of silver nitrate, and a precipitate of silver bismuthide is formed. A similar behavior would be expected with solutions of other heavy metal salts. Bismuthine is absorbed by strong alkaline solutions and by concentrated sulfuric acid. The gas appears to be slightly soluble in water. It undoubtedly would be rapidly destroyed by aqueous oxidizing agents, such as permanganates.

Bismuthine is considered to be somewhat more toxic than arsine and stibine.

Derivatives. A solid hydride of bismuth has been reported, but the existence of this compound has not been substantiated (3).

REFERENCES—BISMUTH HYDRIDES

1. Paneth, *Ber.*, **51**, 1704 (1918).
2. Paneth, Johannesen, and Matthias, *Ber.*, **55**, 769 (1922).
3. Weeks and Druce, *Rec. trav. chim.*, **44**, 970 (1925).

CHAPTER

11

The Hydrides of the Group VI Elements

GENERAL CONSIDERATIONS

With the exception of water, the hydrides of the Group VI (and VIB) elements, *oxygen, sulfur, selenium, tellurium,* and *polonium,* are typical covalent hydrides, both in their chemical reactions and in their physical properties. For example, it will be apparent by reference to Figures 2 and 3 in Chapter 7 that the boiling and melting points of these compounds are in a proper relationship to the physical properties of the other covalent hydrides. Only water is unusual in that it is polymerized by hydrogen bonds between water molecules. Since most of the elements in Group VI are more electronegative than hydrogen, their hydrides are commonly named as derivatives of hydrogen rather than as "hydrides," for example, *hydrogen sulfide,* and *hydrogen telluride,* although tellurium and polonium actually are less electronegative than hydrogen.

The general structure pattern of the simple hydrides, MH_2, comprises two hydrogen atoms covalently bonded to the parent atom, with a 90° angle between the two chemical bonds. Only in the water molecule is a departure from essentially covalent bonding noticed; the oxygen-hydrogen bond has been estimated by Pauling (1) to have 39% ionic character. Because of the mutual repulsion of the two relatively positive hydrogen atoms on a rather small parent atom, the bond angle between the two oxygen-hydrogen bonds in the water molecule is stretched to ca. 105°. The bond angle between hydrogen atoms in the hydrogen sulfide molecule is 92°20′, and the bond angle is very close to 90° in the remaining members of the series (2).

The Group VI hydrides may be prepared by several of the general methods for synthesizing covalent hydrides. These include the direct reaction of the parent element with hydrogen (with oxygen, sulfur, and selenium); the hydrolysis, or equivalent reaction, of a "metal-nonmetal" binary compound (with oxygen, sulfur, selenium, tellurium, polonium); the metathetical reaction of a halide with an active reducing hydride like lithium aluminum hydride (with tellurium,

136

polonium, possibly selenium), or the similar conversion of an oxide (with oxygen, sulfur, selenium); and electrolysis reactions in solution (with polonium and tellurium).

There are considerable variations in chemical reactivity among the Group VI hydrides, owing both to the rather large differences in electronegativity of the elements within the group and the effect of atomic size of the parent element on the strength of the covalent bonds to hydrogen. Water differs most from the rest of the group in this respect also.

The thermal stability of the hydrides decreases rapidly down the series H_2O, H_2S, H_2Se, H_2Te, H_2Po. H_2O, for example, is only 4% dissociated thermally at 2000°; H_2S is 25% dissociated at 1000°; H_2Te decomposes slowly into its component elements at room temperature.

The strength of a Group VI hydride as a reducing agent and its susceptibility to attack by oxidizing agents also increase down the group. H_2S and H_2Se can slowly oxidize in aqueous solution in the presence of light:

$$2H_2S + O_2 \rightarrow 2H_2O + 2S$$

H_2Te will rapidly oxidize in the presence of moist air to form water and free tellurium, and H_2Po acts similarly. All Group VI hydrides are attacked by halogens to form hydrogen halides and either the free parent element or halides of the parent element, depending on the particular compound and the reaction conditions.

In view of the decreasing electronegativity of the heavier elements in Group VI, it may seem surprising that the acid strength of aqueous solutions of the hydrides increases somewhat in the series H_2O, H_2S, H_2Se for the process:

$$H_2Y + H_2O \rightarrow H_3O^+ + HY^-$$

An important factor here, however, is the effect of increasing size of the parent atom on the strength of the covalent bond between hydrogen and the parent element. All the acid strengths of the Group VI hydrides are rather low and, in fact, are several orders of magnitude lower than those of the hydrogen halides.

At least two of the Group VI hydrides, water and hydrogen sulfide, are known to act as electron donors to electron acceptor groups, and they can form coordination complexes in this way. The reaction of this type that is most generally observed occurs in the ionization of an acid in aqueous solution when a hydronium ion, H_3O^+, is formed by the coordination of an electron pair by the oxygen atom in the water molecule to a proton. Water similarly can form coordination complexes with other strong electron acceptor groups, such as compounds like boron fluoride:

$$2H_2O + BF_3 \rightarrow H_3O^+ + (BF_3OH)^-$$

The *hydration* of certain metallic ions may be a similar phenomenon, in which water molecules are coordinatively bonded to the metal ions. As in the Group V hydrides, the ability of the Group VI hydrides as electron donors decreases rapidly with the increasing size of the parent element atoms.

Both oxygen and sulfur can form polynuclear hydrides in addition to the simple, or MH_2, hydrides; this is particularly true of sulfur.

Since the hydrides of oxygen and sulfur are adequately described in readily available chemical literature, it is considered that the present discussion of these compounds should be limited to those features which demonstrate their relationship to the other covalent hydrides.

REFERENCES

1. Pauling, *Nature of the Chemical Bond*, Cornell University Press, Ithaca, N.Y., 1940.
2. Stevenson, *J. Chem. Phys.*, **8**, 285 (1940).

OXYGEN

H_2O—*water*
Colorless liquid
Melting point: 0°C
Boiling point: 100°
Density: 1.000 g/ml at 4°
Heat of formation: 68.3 Kcal/mole (liquid);
57.8 Kcal/mole (gas)

H_2O_2—*hydrogen peroxide*
Colorless liquid, bluish in thick layers
Melting point: −1.7°
Boiling point: 157.8°
Density: 1.465 g/cc at 0°C
Heat of formation: ca. 45 Kcal/mole (liquid)

Although its widespread abundance and its vital role in living processes make water unique in importance among the inorganic compounds of hydrogen, its chemistry can be correlated nicely with that of the other covalent hydrides. Its reactivity as an oxidizing or reducing agent, or as an electron donor or electron acceptor, is determined by considerations of electronegativity and atomic size just as are the reactivities of other covalent hydrides. As described in the previous section, the structure of water is similar to the general structural pattern of the Group VI hydrides; the bond distance O—H is 1.01 A. U., and the bond angle H—O—H is 105°.* Water can be prepared by several of the general methods for the synthesis of covalent hydrides.

A very large number of derivatives of water are known, and these derivatives exhibit a wide variety of chemical properties. There are, for example, organic derivatives like the *alcohols*, ROH, and *acids*, RCOOH; derivatives with positive metals, such as the *alkali hydroxides*, MOH; intermediate metal derivatives which may act either basic or acidic, such as aluminum hydroxide; derivatives in which substitution of hydrogen has been made by an electronegative group, as in the *oxy-acids*, $HO \cdot SO_2 \cdot OH$, $HO \cdot NO_2$, HOCl, etc.; and coordination complexes, such as the *hydronium ion*, H_3O^+. Although this array of diverse derivatives may appear confusing, on consideration it will be apparent that many other compounds in the covalent hydride groups can form some, if not all, of these types of derivatives. Again the concept of chemical relativity must be stressed. The reaction of water as an electron donor or electron acceptor, or as an oxidizing or reducing agent, will depend not only on the water molecule but also on the particular system with which it is reacting and on the nature of the group, if any, that may be substituted for one of the hydrogen atoms in the molecule. The same considerations apply to other hydride systems.

Hydrogen peroxide is an unstable compound that comprises two covalently bonded oxygen atoms, each bonded to one hydrogen atom.

Hydrogen peroxide may be prepared by the hydrolysis of a metal peroxide:

$$Na_2O_2 + 2H_2O \xrightarrow{ice} H_2O_2 + 2NaOH$$

or by electrolysis reactions:

$$2H_2SO_4 \xrightarrow{\text{(anodic oxidation)}} H_2S_2O_8 + H_2$$

$$H_2S_2O_8 + 2H_2O \longrightarrow H_2O_2 + 2H_2SO_4$$

$$(\text{Net reaction: } 2H_2O \rightarrow H_2O_2 + H_2)$$

Although its heat of formation is positive, hydrogen peroxide is quite unstable against decomposition into water and oxygen. The compound usually is prepared and used in the form of dilute aqueous solu-

* Stevenson, *J. Chem. Phys.*, **8**, 285 (1940).

tions. Concentrated solutions of hydrogen peroxide are dangerous oxidizing agents, and very strong solutions may decompose almost explosively, with the liberation of large amounts of energy. The material can be concentrated to almost pure hydrogen peroxide by a cautious fractional distillation in vacuum of its aqueous solutions if care is taken to avoid overheating or the presence of any of the various agents which will catalyze its decomposition. Such catalytic agents include metals, alkalies, activated carbon, manganese dioxide, potassium iodide, and certain organic compounds such as enzymes.

The principal use of hydrogen peroxide is as an oxidizing agent. It is a ready source of oxygen, and in many of its reactions it behaves similarly to ozone. It also is used to a considerable extent as a bleaching agent.

$$H_2O_2 \rightarrow H_2O + (O)$$

Hydrogen peroxide also will act as a reducing agent with very strong oxidizing agents, such as the permanganates;

$$(O) + H_2O_2 \rightarrow H_2O + O_2$$

The manganese in the permanganate ion is reduced to the manganous valence state.

In aqueous solution, hydrogen peroxide acts as a weak acid; $K_a = 1.5 \times 10^{-12}$ at 20°.

Organic derivatives of hydrogen peroxide are known. These are the *organic hydroperoxides* that are extensively used as catalysts for the polymerization of organic resins. They usually are prepared by electrolysis reactions. A typical example is *tert-butyl hydroperoxide*, $(CH_3)_3C$—O—O—H. Hydrogen peroxide, itself, is used to some extent as a polymerization initiator in aqueous emulsion systems.

SULFUR

H_2S—*hydrogen sulfide*
Colorless gas, odor of rotten eggs
Melting point: −82.9°
Boiling point: −60.8°
Density: 0.96 g/cc at b.p.
Heat of formation: 4.8 Kcal/mole

Structure. The structure of the hydrogen sulfide molecule is similar to that of the water molecule except that the bond angle is much nearer the theoretical value of 90°. The actual value for the angle H—S—H is 92°28′. The bond distance H—S is 1.35 A. U. (1).

Preparation. The two common methods for preparing hydrogen sulfide are the direct reaction of the element with hydrogen and the acid hydrolysis of metal sulfides. It is of interest to note that sulfur can dehydrogenate paraffin hydrocarbons at moderate temperatures to form hydrogen sulfide. Others of the general preparative methods can be used, but these are not convenient except for the preparation of special derivatives.

Chemical Properties. Primarily because of its larger size, the sulfur atom in the hydrogen sulfide molecule is somewhat weaker as an electron donor than the oxygen atom in the water molecule. Thus in aqueous solution some transfer of protons to water molecules will occur, and hydrogen sulfide will behave as a weak acid ($K_a = 9.1 \times 10^{-8}$). In effect, this proton transfer proceeds only to the removal of one hydrogen atom from the ionized molecule; the negative ion formed is the *hydrosulfide ion*, HS^-, which remains practically unionized in solution ($K_a = 1.2 \times 10^{-15}$). Hydrogen sulfide is soluble in water to the extent of about 2.61 cc per cubic centimeter of water at 20°.

Hydrogen sulfide is a stronger reducing agent than water. It will, for example, reduce sulfur dioxide to free sulfur:

$$2H_2S + SO_2 \rightarrow 3S + 2H_2O$$

On exposure to light, an aqueous solution of hydrogen sulfide will slowly be oxidized to free sulfur by atmospheric oxygen:

$$2H_2S + O_2 \rightarrow 2H_2O + 2S$$

Derivatives. Since it is a weaker electron donor than water, hydrogen sulfide does not form coordination complexes to the same extent as water, and very few compounds of this type are known. In part, however, this may be because the reactions of hydrogen sulfide have not been investigated as extensively as those of water.

Hydrogen sulfide does form some substituted derivatives analogous to those of water. Such compounds include the *thioalcohols*, or *mercaptans*, RSH, and the *hydrosulfides* of electropositive metals, MSH.

Polynuclear Hydrides of Sulfur. Several polynuclear hydrogen sulfides are known. The sulfur atom in a sulfide is able to form coordinate bonds with other sulfur atoms, and by dissolving elemental sulfur in an alkaline sulfide solution (for example, sodium sulfide solution), *polysulfide ions* or *radicals* can be formed. These ions include $S_2^=$, $S_3^=$, $S_4^=$, $S_5^=$, $S_6^=$, and are believed to be linear chains of sulfur atoms.

By careful acidification of the alkali polysulfide solutions, we can obtain a yellow oil comprising a mixture of *hydrogen polysulfides*. A cautious distillation procedure will separate this mixture into its individual components, H_2S_4, H_2S_5, H_2S_6. By strong heating, the higher hydrogen polysulfides can be cracked to form lower members of the series. All the hydrogen polysulfides are endothermic compounds:

H_2S_2 pale yellow mobile liquid; vapor corrosive to eyes and nose; m.p. $-89.6°$, b.p. $70.7°$; density 1.376 g/cc.

H_2S_3 yellow liquid; m.p. $-52°$; decomposes before b.p. ca. 90°; density 1.496 g/cc.

H_2S_4 yellow liquid; sharp odor; m.p. ca. $-85°$; density 1.588 g/cc; soluble in benzene.

H_2S_5 yellow oil; dec. ca. 40°; density 1.660.

H_2S_6 viscous dark yellow oil; density 1.699 g/cc.

The hydrogen polysulfides are exceedingly sensitive to traces of alkali which catalyze their rapid decomposition into hydrogen sulfide and elemental sulfur (2).

REFERENCES—HYDRIDES OF SULFUR

1. Stevenson, *J. Chem. Phys.*, **8**, 285 (1940).
2. Ephraim, *Inorganic Chemistry*, Nordeman, New York (1939).

SELENIUM

H_2Se—*hydrogen selenide*
Colorless gas, poisonous, has a very unpleasant odor
Melting point: $-64°$
Boiling point: $-42°$
Heat of formation: -15.8 Kcal/mole

Structure. The structure of hydrogen selenide is similar to that of hydrogen sulfide. The bond angle H—Se—H is about 90°, and the bond length H—Se is 1.49 A. U. (1).

Preparation. Hydrogen selenide may be prepared by the direct union of hydrogen and selenium at temperatures of 250° to 650°. Similar to the reaction of hydrogen with sulfur, the formation of hydrogen selenide is an equilibrium reaction. The best yield, about 60%, is obtained at about 500°.

A good method for preparing hydrogen selenide on a laboratory scale is the hydrolysis of a metal selenide, such as aluminum selenide, in water or a dilute non-oxidizing acid. The metal selenide for this preparation usually can be made by the direct combination of the metal with selenium at an elevated temperature (2).

Hydrogen selenide may also be prepared by heating finely powdered elemental selenium in a hydrocarbon oil at 300° to 400° (3). This synthesis is similar to that used occasionally for the laboratory preparation of hydrogen sulfide in which sulfur is heated with a paraffin. In this connection it also may be mentioned that selenium occasionally is used in synthetic organic chemistry for the dehydrogenation of hydrocarbon compounds.

Properties. Hydrogen selenide begins to decompose into its component elements at a temperature of about 160°. However, since the formation and decomposition of hydrogen selenide at elevated temperatures is an equilibrium reaction, the gas will not be decomposed entirely unless the hydrogen evolved by the decomposition is removed.

Hydrogen selenide is soluble in water to the extent of about 1800 ml of gas per liter of water at room temperature. It is considerably more soluble in alkaline solutions, and it resembles hydrogen sulfide in this respect. Aqueous solutions of hydrogen selenide decompose if they are exposed to air, and the red form of elemental selenium is precipitated. It is reported that if the gas is dissolved in water under pressure and at a temperature below 30°, a crystalline hydrate of the composition $H_2Se \cdot 6H_2O$ is formed (4). Hydrogen selenide will precipitate heavy metals, such as silver and lead, as metal selenides from solutions of their salts. The compound is a mild reducing agent.

Hydrogen selenide will burn if the gas is ignited. The products of combustion are water and selenium dioxide. Although hydrogen selenide is stable in air or in oxygen if the gases are dry, the presence of moisture will catalyze a rapid oxidation of the compound into water and elemental selenium. Thus, under ordinary conditions, it is not very stable in air.

Hydrogen selenide will react with selenium dioxide to form elemental selenium, a reaction analogous to that between hydrogen sulfide and sulfur dioxide. If hydrogen selenide is treated with elemental sulfur, a replacement reaction occurs, with the formation of hydrogen sulfide and elemental selenium. This reaction is analogous to the replacement reactions of the halogen compounds. In this connection it is of interest to note that, at an elevated temperature, selenium can replace iodine in hydrogen iodide to form hydrogen selenide.

Derivatives. Very little is known concerning monosubstituted derivatives of hydrogen selenide, although it should be possible to prepare such compounds.

144   The Hydrides of the Group VI Elements

REFERENCES—HYDROGEN SELENIDE

1. Stevenson, *J. Chem. Phys.*, **8**, 285 (1940).
2. Waitkins and Shutt, *Inorganic Syntheses*, **II**, 183 (1946).
3. Green and Bradt, *Proc. Indiana Acad. Sci.*, **43**, 116 (1934).
4. Mellor, *Comprehensive Treatise on Inorganic and Theoretical Chemistry*, Vol. X, p. 763, Longmans, London.

TELLURIUM

H_2Te—*hydrogen telluride, tellurium hydride*
Colorless gas with extremely unpleasant odor
Melting point: $-51°$
Boiling point: $-4°$
Density of liquid: 2.70 g/cc at $-18°$
Heat of formation: -33.93 Kcal/mole

Structure.   The structure of hydrogen telluride is formally similar to that of hydrogen sulfide.   It comprises a tellurium atom bonded to two hydrogen atoms, the bond angle H—Te—H being very close to 90°.   The bond distance H—Te is 1.69 A. U. (1).

Preparation.   The best method of preparing hydrogen telluride is by the hydrolysis of a metal telluride, such as aluminum telluride, in water or a dilute non-oxidizing acid.   Metal tellurides for this purpose may be prepared by heating finely divided metals with tellurium. Aluminum telluride will evolve H_2Te upon treatment with water or, in fact, on contact with moist air.   The tellurides of zinc and iron are stable toward water, but may be hydrolyzed with dilute acids to yield H_2Te.   A yield of 80% may be obtained from the hydrolysis of aluminum telluride in 4 N hydrochloric acid (2).

Hydrogen telluride can be prepared by the action of atomic hydrogen on tellurium metal, but the compound is too unstable to be prepared by the direct union of the elements at an elevated temperature.   It also can be prepared by electrolyzing a cold solution of concentrated sulfuric or phosphoric acid with a cathode of tellurium metal (3).

Properties.   Hydrogen telluride is quite unstable thermally and decomposes into its component elements even at 0°, with the deposition of mirrors of metallic tellurium.   Liquid and solid hydrogen telluride are decomposed by light, although in the gaseous state, if dry, the compound is stable toward light.

Hydrogen telluride is decomposed instantly by dry oxygen at pressures below 10 cm, with the formation of water and the deposition of tellurium mirrors.   This reaction probably is autocatalytic as H_2Te

readily is decomposed by air in the presence of moisture (2). If ignited in air, it burns to form water and TeO_2. The compound is decomposed if it is bubbled through solutions of heavy metal salts such as lead nitrate or silver nitrate. It will reduce iron from the ferric to the ferrous state.

Hydrogen telluride has a frightful stench which has been compared to that of rotten horseradish. It is considered to be very poisonous. Investigators working with tellurium and its compounds develop a very unpleasant condition of body odor which may persist for some time.

With the exception of completely substituted compounds, few, if any, derivatives of hydrogen telluride have been prepared.

REFERENCES—HYDROGEN TELLURIDE

1. Stevenson, *J. Chem. Phys.*, **8**, 285 (1940).
2. Moser and Ertl, *Z. anorg. u. allgem. Chem.*, **118**, 269 (1921).
3. *Z. anorg. Chem.*, **25**, 313 (1900).

POLONIUM

PoH_2—*polonium hydride, hydrogen polonide*
Colorless gas, radioactive

Structure. Since polonium is a member of the Group VI elements, along with oxygen, sulfur, selenium, and tellurium, it may be presumed that polonium hydride is similar in structure to the other hydrides of this group and that the bond angle H—Po—H is approximately 90°.

Preparation. The existence of a volatile hydride of polonium was first suggested by Lawson, who noted a significant increase in the alpha ray activity from a sample of polonium in hydrogen gas when a thin metal window isolating the polonium from the electroscope chamber was removed. Lawson also observed that the volatile polonium compound presumed to be responsible for this effect was rapidly decomposed by air (1).

Paneth (2) succeeded in preparing and studying polonium hydride by electroplating microgram quantities of polonium onto a thin foil of magnesium, treating the coated foil with acid, and following the volatile polonium hydride thus formed by observing its radioactivity. The polonium hydride was, of course, highly diluted with hydrogen gas, which acted as a carrier for the exceedingly small amounts of the hydride actually obtained.

In a later modification of this technique, Paneth (3) first deposited the polonium onto a platinum foil by electrolysis, then vaporized the metal from the platinum onto magnesium powder, which subsequently was treated with acid to generate the polonium hydride. The polonium hydride thus formed could be condensed and collected in a trap cooled with liquid air.

Properties. There is little in the way of definite information on the physical properties of polonium hydride. This is not surprising, considering the extreme rarity of the element polonium. It has been reported, however, that polonium hydride is more volatile than bismuthine, BiH_3.

The chemical properties of polonium hydride have been studied by following the radioactivity of dilute solutions of the gas in a carrier of hydrogen gas. This technique of studying the compound has some disadvantages, however, since its thermal decomposition usually leaves a coating of highly radioactive polonium metal on the electroscopes or particle counters.

Polonium hydride is quite unstable thermally against decomposition into its component elements. At room temperature approximately 50% of a given sample of the gas will decompose in 4 minutes. The compound is almost completely destroyed upon bubbling it through a 0.1 N solution of silver nitrate, and is destroyed to a considerable extent upon being bubbled through a 0.1 N solution of sodium hydroxide. It is completely decomposed when it is passed over dry phosphorus pentoxide, and is partially destroyed in contact with dry calcium chloride. Like hydrogen telluride, polonium hydride is destroyed by air in the presence of moisture, presumably with the formation of water and elemental polonium. If the gas is thoroughly dried, it is considerably more stable in the presence of air. Paneth (3) considered that polonium hydride is less stable thermally than either bismuthine or tellurium hydride.

In studying the thermal decomposition of polonium hydride it has been observed that as the decomposition procedes, the decomposition rate becomes smaller (4). This behavior suggests that the decomposition process may be equilibrium reaction, that is:

$$PoH_2 \rightleftharpoons Po + H_2$$

The observation of Lawson (see above) would appear to confirm this contention.

REFERENCES—POLONIUM HYDRIDE

1. Lawson, *Monatsh.*, **36**, 845 (1915).
2. Paneth, *Ber.*, **51**, 1704 (1918).
3. Paneth and Johanneson, *Ber.*, **55B**, 2622 (1922).
4. Adler, *Chem. Abstr.*, **33**, 9098.

CHAPTER

12

The Hydrides of the Group VII Elements
F, Cl, Br, I

The hydrogen compounds of the elements in Groups VII and VIIB, the *halogens*, are considered by many as not properly belonging to the family of hydrides. As has been pointed out previously, this is entirely a question of where we draw the line between hydrides and other hydrogen compounds. It is the opinion of the author that the hydrogen halides certainly do belong to the family of hydrides, and in particular to the group of covalent hydrides. If considered in their normal states and apart from their solutions in water, these compounds are predominantly covalent (hydrogen fluoride is the only exception and even it is only slightly more ionic than covalent). The hydrogen halides may be formed by general reactions used to prepare other covalent hydrides, and their physical and chemical properties represent the terminus of the progressive changes in the character of the element hydrogen in its combinations with the various elements across the Periodic Table.

Since so much information on the hydrogen halides is readily available in the chemical literature, it is beyond the scope of this book to give more than a brief résumé to fit them into perspective with the other covalent hydrides. The physical properties of the hydrogen halides are listed below for reference and for comparison with the properties of other hydrides.

$(HF)_x$—*hydrogen fluoride*
Colorless gas or volatile liquid
Melting point: $-83.1°$
Boiling point: $19.5°$
Density of liquid: 0.991 g/cc at b.p.
Heat of formation: 64.2 Kcal/mole HF

HCl—*hydrogen chloride*
Colorless gas
Melting point: $-114.8°$
Boiling point: $-84.9°$
Density of liquid: 1.194 g/cc at $-86°$
Heat of formation: 43.8 Kcal/mole HCl

147

HBr—*hydrogen bromide*
Colorless gas
Melting point: −86.9°
Boiling point: −66.8°
Density of liquid: 2.77 g/cc at b.p.
Heat of formation: 23.2 Kcal/mole HBr

HI—*hydrogen iodide*
Colorless gas
Melting point: −50.7°
Boiling point: −35.4°
Density of liquid: 2.85 g/cc at −47°
Heat of formation: 2.5 Kcal/mole HI

Structure. With the exception of hydrogen fluoride, the hydrogen halides are simple diatomic molecules. The hydrogen to halogen bond distances for the several compounds are: H—Cl, 1.28 A. U.; H—Br, 1.42 A. U.; H—I, 1.62 A. U. (1). Hydrogen fluoride is strongly associated, not only in its condensed phases but also in the vapor phase; under normal conditions of temperature and pressure its average molecular weight corresponds to about (HF)$_3$, and there is good evidence for the existence of stable ring structures of (HF)$_6$ (2). The degree of polymeric character in the gas phase decreases with increasing temperature, and the gas is monomolecular at 100°. The normal bond distance H—F is 0.92 A. U. (1).

Preparation. Several of the general methods for the preparation of covalent hydrides are applicable to the synthesis of the hydrogen halides. It will be understood, however, that some of the general methods are not practical for the preparation of a particular hydrogen halide and are of academic interest only. Two methods that may be used are:

1. *The hydrolysis of a binary metal–non-metal compound.* Examples are the hydrolysis of phosphorous tribromide with water to yield hydrogen bromide; the hydrolysis of sodium chloride with aqueous sulfuric acid to form hydrogen chloride; the hydrolysis of calcium fluoride with sulfuric acid to form hydrogen fluoride. The usual syntheses of HF or HCl, in the laboratory as well as on an industrial scale, are those given as examples. Since HBr and HI are strong reducing agents and are decomposed by sulfuric acid, it is impractical to prepare these compounds by the hydrolysis of their common salts. The usual technique of preparing HBr or HI in the laboratory is the water hydrolysis of the corresponding phosphorous trihalide; other water-hydrolyzable halides can be used, but the phosphorus compounds are probably the most convenient.

2. *The direct union of the elements.* This synthesis is applicable to
the preparation of all the hydrogen halides, but for HF and HCl it is
less convenient than the method of hydrolysis reactions. HBr and
HI can easily be prepared on a laboratory scale by this method. With
HI the direct reaction is easily reversed, and we obtain an equilibrium
mixture of reactants and products whose composition depends on the
temperature of the reaction. At 300°, about 19% of a given amount
of HI will be dissociated at equilibrium. This reaction has been
extensively studied as a convenient laboratory example of an equilibrium reaction.

Properties. The one feature that sets the hydrogen halides apart
from the other hydrides is their high solubility in water and the fact
that they will ionize in water solutions to act as acids (see "Acids
and Bases," Chapter 13). It will be apparent that this reaction, as
well as the neutralization of a hydrogen halide solution with a base, is
formally analogous to the base-catalyzed hydrolysis of other covalent
hydrides. Most of the other chemical reactions of the hydrogen
halides can be correlated fairly well with those of the other covalent
hydrides. For example, hydrogen iodide, like hydrogen telluride, is
susceptible to decomposition by air oxidation:

$$2HI + O_2 \rightarrow H_2O + I_2$$

REFERENCES

1. Pauling, *Nature of The Chemical Bond*, 2nd Ed., Cornell University Press, Ithaca, N.Y., 1940.
2. Simons and Hildebrand, *J. Am. Chem. Soc.*, **46**, 2183 (1924).

CHAPTER

13

Acids and Bases

It is a characteristic of the hydrides of the strongly electronegative elements that they become more or less dissociated into positive and negative ions when they are dissolved in an ionizing solvent such as water or liquid ammonia. The water solutions of these hydrides belong to the class of compounds that we know familiarly as the *acids* and *bases*. In fact, most of our common acids and bases are hydrides or derivatives of hydrides in a general sense.

It will be appreciated that the terms *acid* and *base* are used here in an elementary sense. We consider "acid" a solution that has a sour taste, turns red litmus blue, or dissolves metals with the evolution of hydrogen; these properties are associated with the presence of positive hydrogen ions in concentrations greater than that of pure water. Similarly, we consider "basic" a solution which exhibits those chemical properties associated with appreciable concentrations of hydroxyl ion. The terms *acid* and *base*, however, may be extended to cover much more than the old familiar compounds like sulfuric acid and sodium hydroxide. For example, the classification of substances as acids or bases according to whether they are *proton donors* or *proton acceptors*, that is, sources or sinks for positive hydrogen ions, has aided considerably in understanding many chemical reactions. The development of the very general concepts of G. N. Lewis, in which chemical groups, molecules, and ions are classified as *acids* or *bases*, depending upon their *relative* strengths as *electron acceptors* or *electron donors*, has been of immeasurable importance in the development of chemistry as a whole. The discussion of common acids and bases that follows is derived largely from these concepts.*

Ionization. It must be admitted that the concept of ionization in which an acid is visualized as dissociating into an anion and a positive hydrogen ion, or proton, is useful for teaching purposes as well as for

---

* The reader is referred to the excellent textbook by W. F. Luder and S. Zuffanti, *The Electronic Theory of Acids and Bases*, Wiley, New York, 1946, for a detailed explanation of the Lewis concepts.

writing equations. However, in the light of present knowledge it seems unlikely that free positive hydrogen ions can ever exist as such in solution. Let us examine in more detail the mechanism whereby an "acid," hydrogen chloride, for example, becomes ionized in aqueous solution.

The hydrogen chloride molecule, HCl, comprises a relatively negative chlorine atom and a relatively positive hydrogen atom bonded together primarily by the covalent sharing of a pair of electrons. The relative negativity and positivity of the atoms comprising the molecule is a result of the difference in *electronegativity* of the two elements. The chlorine atom has a stronger affinity for the pair of bonding electrons than the hydrogen atom; consequently, the hydrogen and the chlorine do not share equally in the bonding electron pair, but the electron density is greater at the chlorine. Thus the hydrogen chloride molecule is partially ionic since the difference in electron density causes a difference in the electrical charges of the two atoms. However, the chemical bond as a whole still is predominantly covalent. Pauling* has estimated that the bond between hydrogen and chlorine in hydrogen chloride is about 35% ionic and 65% covalent. It will be apparent that all covalent compounds are at least partially ionic except in those rare cases where the electronegativities of the component elements happen to be equal, for example, in diatomic gases like N_2, H_2, O_2, Cl_2, etc.

As an illustration of the predominantly covalent nature of hydrogen chloride, we observe that it is quite soluble in non-polar, non-ionizing solvents such as dry benzene. In such a solution hydrogen chloride does not behave at all as it does in water solution. A solution of hydrogen chloride in dry benzene will not conduct electricity, will not turn red litmus blue, will not react with metals, nor, in fact, will it exhibit any of the properties commonly associated with acids or with ions in solution.

Despite the fact that the chlorine atom in hydrogen chloride has a stronger affinity for the pair of bonding electrons, the hydrogen atom still is a fairly strong electron acceptor. Thus, when a hydrogen chloride molecule is dissolved in water, the hydrogen nucleus, or proton, is able to acquire a larger share in a pair of valence electrons from the oxygen atom in a water molecule since this atom, associated with two hydrogen atoms and two extra electrons, is effectively less electronegative than the chlorine atom. (It will be recalled that substituent groups play an important role in determining the effective electro-

---

* Pauling, *Nature of the Chemical Bond*, Cornell University Press, Ithaca, N.Y., 1940.

negativity of an atom.) Consequently a transfer is effected; the proton leaves the chlorine atom and associates with a water molecule to form a *hydronium ion*, H_3O^+. It is the concentration of this ion that we measure in determining the strength, or pH, of an acidic solution. The chlorine atom finds no real competition from any strong electron acceptor and remains in possession of its complete octet of valence electrons as a chloride ion, Cl^-. The electrical charge on the negative chloride ion is balanced by the surrounding positive hydronium ions, and vice versa, so the solution as a whole is neutral. In the case of a very dilute solution of hydrogen chloride in water, the proton transfer becomes essentially complete, and the solution of hydronium ions and chloride ions is referred to as dilute hydrochloric acid. Since the new situation represents a lower energy state, considerable amounts of heat are evolved in the process of solution:

$$HCl + H_2O \rightarrow H_3O^+ + Cl^-$$

At this point several important features of the reaction between hydrogen chloride and water should be pointed out. Although the transfer of protons from chlorine to oxygen is essentially complete for *dilute* solutions, it is not necessarily final; the reaction is an equilibrium reaction and is reversible. The equilibrium point will depend, among other things, on the relative concentrations of free water molecules, hydronium ions, and chloride ions. If free water molecules become relatively unavailable, the tendency for proton transfer from chlorine to oxygen becomes less (Law of Mass Action). As the concentration of hydrogen chloride is increased, it will be evident that larger amounts of unionized hydrogen chloride will be present in the solution in equilibrium with ionized hydrochloric acid. Since unionized hydrogen chloride is a volatile covalent gas, its solubility as such in the aqueous solution will be small, and a definite gas pressure of hydrogen chloride will exist over the solution. It will be clear at this point that the acid strength, or pH, of a water solution of a hydride of an electronegative element will depend not only on the concentration of the compound but also on the electronegativity of the negative element as compared to that of oxygen. In hydrogen sulfide, for example, the sulfur atom has a much smaller electronegativity than chlorine, and thus the compound is more covalent and less ionic than hydrogen chloride. As a consequence, not only is hydrogen sulfide less soluble than hydrogen chloride in water but also the hydrogen atoms in dissolved H_2S molecules have only a very slight tendency to transfer to oxygen atoms in the water molecules. The equilibrium is far over on the side of unionized hydrogen sulfide, and only very small concentrations of hydronium ion are formed. We can say, then, that aqueous solutions of hydrogen sulfide are only weakly acidic.

Pure water itself is very slightly ionized, about one molecule in 10^7 is dissociated under normal conditions. Since the dissociation forms an amount of hydroxyl ion, OH^-, equal to that of hydronium ion, H_3O^+, the liquid is neutral according to the customary definitions of acids and bases. The product of the concentrations of hydroxyl ion and hydronium ion in pure water is thus about 10^{-14}; this value is known as the *ion product constant* of water. Hydroxyl ion and hydronium ion cannot coexist in concentrations such that the product of their concentrations exceeds 10^{-14}. It follows, therefore, that when a solution containing an excess of hydroxyl ions (a basic solution) is added to a solution containing an excess of hydronium ions (an acidic solution) the hydroxyl and hydronium ions will neutralize to form water molecules until the concentration product of the two ions is reduced to 10^{-14}.

It will be apparent from the earlier discussion that the process of neutralization is, in effect, a proton transfer. We might guess, therefore, that the hydroxyl ion is a better electron donor than the water molecule. This probably is the case, and the process of reaction is assisted electrically by the neutralization of the highly negatively charged hydroxyl ion by the positive proton.

The less electronegative elements in the covalent hydride group, including selenium and tellurium, are good electron donors, and their hydrides have practically no tendency to form hydronium ions in water solution. In liquid ammonia, however, this situation is altered somewhat since nitrogen is a better electron donor than oxygen. A compound, such as H_2Te, which does not ionize to any appreciable extent in water will behave as an acid in liquid ammonia. The process of ionization and acid formation in liquid ammonia is analogous to that in water. For example, if we dissolve hydrogen chloride in liquid ammonia, a proton transfer occurs with the formation of the *ammonium ion*, NH_4^+, which is the ammonia analog of the hydronium ion in water systems:

$$HCl + NH_3 \rightarrow NH_4^+ + Cl^-$$

The solution, therefore, has acidic properties. The counterpart of the hydroxyl ion is the *amide* ion, NH_2^-. Basic liquid ammonia solutions can be obtained by dissolving a metal amide, such as *sodium amide*, $NaNH_2$, in liquid ammonia. Because nitrogen is a better electron donor than oxygen, the complex ammonium ion is more tightly bound than the hydronium ion. Thus the ammonium ion is less effective as an acidic reagent (proton donor) than the hydronium ion. Acids in the ammonia system are weaker chemically than those in water systems.

Ammonia added to water forms a basic solution. Since the nitrogen atom in ammonia is a better electron donor than the oxygen atom in water, there is some transfer of protons from water molecules to the nitrogen in ammonia molecules, with the formation of ammonium ions. This process leaves an excess of hydroxyl ions in the solution and, since the ammonium ion holds the proton somewhat more tightly than the hydronium ion (see above), the solution as a whole exhibits basic properties. The formation of ammonium ion is, of course, an equilibrium reaction. If a large excess of hydroxyl ions is added to the solution, the process will be reversed, and ammonium ions will be decomposed to form ammonia.

The hydrides of the Group IV elements, such as methane, silane, and germane, would not be expected to form acidic solutions in pure water, and would be expected to have only a limited solubility in water. Certain of the Group IV hydrides, *monogermane*, GeH_4, for example, will act as acids in liquid ammonia, however.

Oxy-acids and Hydroxides. Only a few of the common acids and bases are binary hydrides, for example, HCl, HF, NH_3. Most of our acids and bases are *oxy*-compounds, that is, derivatives of water in which one of the hydrogens has been replaced by another chemical group.

In the *oxy-acids* the groups substituting for hydrogen in the water molecule are strongly electronegative, that is, they have a large affinity for electrons. This large electronegativity of the attached group acts to increase the effective electronegativity of the central oxygen atom and, thus, to affect the electron distribution in the bond between the oxygen and the hydrogen. The bond is made more ionic. Consequently, it becomes relatively more easy for the hydrogen to be lost by proton transfer to a water molecule when the compound is dissolved in water, and the solution is acidic.

Conversely, in the hydroxide of a highly electropositive metal, such as in sodium hydroxide, the lack of any group strongly competing for valence electrons results in an increase in the covalent nature of the bond between the oxygen and the hydrogen, that is, the bond is less ionic. This situation obtains also in solution; in both the solid hydroxides and in their water solutions the hydroxyl ion acts as an entity.

It will be seen that if a salt containing a strong electron donor group, such as the cyanide ion in sodium cyanide, is added to water, a transfer of protons from water molecules to the electron donor groups will occur, and the water solution will be basic, because of the excess of hydroxyl ions thus formed.

In this discussion of acids and bases the primary emphasis has been on the effect of relative electronegativity in determining how various hydride compounds act in solution. Admittedly, this treatment is an oversimplification since other factors, such as the sizes and charge densities of the various ions, are of considerable importance. It is believed, however, that the discussion, as presented, will be of some use as a general guide for predicting the properties of hydride compounds.

It will be seen that the behavior of acids and bases in aqueous solution is a rather specific example of a very general type of reaction between electron donor elements and electron acceptor elements. Many substances which do not contain hydrogen, such as boron trifluoride, may be considered "acids" in the Lewis sense because they are strong electron acceptors. Many substances, such as trimethylamine, may be considered "bases" because they are strong electron donors. Therefore, for example, the chemistry of complex coordination compounds, such as those discussed in the following chapter, may also be considered as examples of "acid-base" reactions.

CHAPTER

14

Complex Hydrides

There are a large number of compounds that contain more than one element in combination with hydrogen. These compounds are derivatives of the *simple, or binary, hydrides* and are designated *complex hydrides*. It should be noted that the term *complex hydride* is normally applied only to those compounds in which all the different parent element atoms are bonded to hydrogen; this is to distinguish the complex hydrides from simple hydride derivatives, such as the halides and oxides, of the binary hydrides. There are, however, important compounds containing *complex hydride ions* that should be discussed with the complex hydrides, both for convenience and because such compounds usually are formed by the reaction and combination of hydrides.

The complex hydrides and compounds containing complex hydride ions may, for more convenient discussion, be classified into several groups:

I. Normal molecular complex hydrides or mixed hydrides.
II. Donor-acceptor coordination complexes between binary hydrides.
III. Compounds containing complex hydride anions.
IV. Compounds containing complex hydride cations.

These various classes of hydride compounds will be considered in the order given.

I. Normal Molecular Complex Hydrides. The *normal molecular complex hydrides*, or *mixed hydrides*, are compounds in which two or more different elements other than hydrogen are united by normal covalent bonds, and in which the remaining valences of each of these elements are satisfied by bonding to hydrogen atoms. A good example of a molecular complex hydride is *methyl silane*, CH_3SiH_3, in which the carbon atom and the silicon atom are bonded together by a single covalent bond; the remainder of their normal valence bonds are occupied with hydrogen atoms.

The mixed hydrides comprise by far the largest class of complex hydride compounds. Organic derivatives of the binary hydrides should logically be included in this group, and in addition there are countless possibilities for mixed hydrides with three or more "parent" elements, for example, *methyl silyl germane*, $(CH_3)GeH_2(SiH_3)$. Surprisingly enough, the present state of hydride chemistry is such that only a very few mixed hydrides are known outside those containing carbon as a component element. A few representative examples are *hydroxylamine*, NH_2OH, *silyl amine*, SiH_3NH_2, and *borazole*, $B_3N_3H_6$.

For the most part, experimental techniques for the preparation of particular mixed hydrides have not been worked out. There are, however, general methods useful for the preparation of organic derivatives that may be applicable with modification to such syntheses. One of these is the reaction of a halide with a reactive metal alkyl or Grignard reagent:

$$ClSiH_3 + CH_3MgCl \rightarrow CH_3SiH_3 + MgCl_2$$

However, outside of a few compounds such as, for example, *lithium amide*, $LiNH_2$, and *potassium germanyl*, GeH_3K, very little is known about hydride compounds analogous to the metal alkyls that might be used in such synthesis. A Wurtz type reaction also might be generally useful:

$$CH_3Cl + ClSiH_3 + 2Na \rightarrow CH_3SiH_3 + 2NaCl$$

Since the mixed hydrides are essentially covalent compounds, their chemical and physical properties can, in most cases, be predicted fairly well from a knowledge of the component hydrides. A few of the mixed hydrides have been described in the preceding chapters on the hydrides of the various elements.

II. Donor-Acceptor Coordination Complexes. It was pointed out in Chapter 2 that *electron-donor* elements, such as nitrogen, are distinguished by having an extra, or unshared, pair of electrons that are not used in fulfilling the normal valence bonding in compound formation. *Electron-acceptor* elements, such as boron, may lack sufficient electrons in their normal valence bonding to occupy all the available valence shell orbitals; that is, to complete closed octets of electrons. If a pair of electrons is made available by an electron-donor atom, an electron-acceptor atom may be able to incorporate this pair of electrons into its valence electron structure with the formation of a coordinate covalent bond between the two atoms. Thus a tendency exists for molecules containing donor atoms to react with, and form compounds with, molecules containing acceptor atoms:

$$
\begin{array}{ccc}
\text{H} & \text{Cl} & \text{H . Cl} \\
\overset{\cdot\cdot}{} & \overset{\cdot\cdot}{} & \overset{\cdot\cdot}{}\;\overset{\cdot\cdot}{} \\
\text{H : N :} \quad + & \text{B : Cl} \quad \rightarrow & \text{H : N : B : Cl} \\
\underset{\cdot\cdot}{} & \underset{\cdot\cdot}{} & \underset{\cdot\cdot}{}\;\underset{\cdot\cdot}{} \\
\text{H} & \text{Cl} & \text{H   Cl}
\end{array}
$$

Although the bonding electron pair is shared by the two combining atoms, the formation of a chemical bond between neutral molecules by this type of electron sharing results in a partial negative charge on the acceptor atom and leaves a partial positive charge on the donor atom. This polarity may be reflected in the properties of the complex compound; many complex coordination compounds formed from volatile covalent molecules appear to resemble ionic solids. Both the strength and the polarity of the coordinate bond will depend on the relative abilities of the electron-donor and electron-acceptor atoms as such, as well as on the presence of any large attached groups which might hinder the close approach necessary for the electron transfer between the two atoms. In some instances, the bond may be so weak that the complex is stable only at low temperature, and dissociation of the complex into its component parts occurs quite readily. In other cases, the bond may be so strong that the complex compound will disintegrate at elevated temperatures into decomposition products without dissociating the coordinate bond between the electron-acceptor atoms.

Most of the few known examples of complex hydride compounds formed by the donor-acceptor bonding of binary hydrides involve boron hydrides as the electron acceptor molecules. A common example is the *diborane-ammonia complex*, a non-volatile white solid (see page 84).

It has been postulated that donor-acceptor complexes are the first intermediate steps in the hydrolysis of a boron hydride, or the reaction of a boron hydride with a hydrogen halide, etc. (1). The reaction may be written generally:

$$
BH_3 \xrightarrow{HX} BH_3HX \xrightarrow{-H_2} BH_2X \xrightarrow{HX} BH_2XHX
$$
$$
\xrightarrow{-H_2} BHX_2 \xrightarrow{HX} BHX_2HX \xrightarrow{-H_2} BX_3
$$

(where X = Cl, OH, OR, NH_2, NHR, NR_2, etc.). Similar mechanisms may be responsible for the hydrolysis, etc., of other hydrides, depending on the particular compound and the reaction conditions.

Many of the more negative elements, such as F, O, N, Cl, P, and

C, are capable of acting as donors to such a strong electron acceptor as boron. Atomic and molecular dimensions must, of course, be taken into consideration as the boron atom is rather small. Aluminum and gallium, the other hydride-forming elements in Group III, can also act as electron acceptors, but these elements are not as strong in this respect as boron. Many of the possible donor-acceptor complex hydrides have not as yet been prepared. (See *Boron* and *Aluminum* in Chapter 8 for some examples of donor-acceptor compounds of the hydrides of these elements.)

III. Compounds Containing Complex Hydride Anions. The complex hydride anions are formed by a process similar to that by which coordination complexes, or donor-acceptor compounds, are formed. The process of forming a complex hydride anion, however, involves a negative hydride ion as the electron donor rather than a neutral covalent molecule.

The most well-defined examples of complex hydride anion formation are those in which alkali metal hydrides serve as the source of hydride ion. In the process of complex ion formation, the hydride ion coordinates, or donates a share in its pair of electrons to the central atom of the acceptor molecule:

$$
\text{Li}^+ : \text{H}^- \quad + \quad
\begin{matrix} \text{H} \\ \overset{..}{\text{B}} : \text{H} \\ \overset{..}{\text{H}} \end{matrix}
\quad \rightarrow \quad
\left[\begin{matrix} \text{H} \\ \text{H} : \overset{..}{\text{B}} : \text{H} \\ \overset{..}{\text{H}} \end{matrix} \right]^-
\quad + \quad \text{Li}^+
$$

It should be pointed out that this type of reaction normally is an equilibrium reaction. The complex as a whole assumes the one negative charge of the hydride ion and, once the complex is formed, all the covalent bonds to the hydrogen atoms are equivalent. The compound formed in the example given is actually an ionic salt made up of lithium ions and *borohydride* ions.

We find that the phenomena of complex hydride anion formation is confined for practical purposes to the Group III elements, boron, aluminum, and gallium, since it is only in these elements that really strong properties as electron acceptors are developed. The hydride ion is not a particularly strong electron donor, and thus the acceptor component must necessarily be strong if compound formation is to take place. The three types of complex hydride anions that are formed are the *borohydride ion*, BH_4^-, the *aluminum hydride ion*, AlH_4^-, and the *gallium hydride ion*, GaH_4. (These names reflect the lack of a systematic nomenclature for such relatively new compounds.

See Chapter 17, "Nomenclature.") Of these ions, the borohydride ion is by far the most stable and the least chemically reactive; this is not surprising since, of the three elements mentioned, boron is the strongest electron acceptor. For example, the borohydride ion is stable in water solution if the concentration of positive hydrogen ion is kept low. The AlH_4^- ion and the GaH_4^- ion are rapidly decomposed by water.

The stability of a complex hydride salt depends not only on the strength of the electron acceptor but also on the strength of the metallic component as an electron acceptor. The alkali metal borohydrides are fairly stable since the alkali metal ion can offer very little competition to the BH_3 group for the electrons associated with the hydride ion. However, if a stronger electron acceptor is substituted for the alkali metal ion, the reaction:

$$H^- + BH_3 \rightleftharpoons BH_4^-$$

may more easily be reversed, or may not go to completion. Thus a compound such as beryllium borohydride appears to be much less stable toward thermal decomposition than, for example, lithium borohydride. Aluminum borohydride is even less stable. A similar reaction accounts for the decomposition of a complex hydride anion in water, since the positive hydrogen ion, or hydronium ion, is a strong electron acceptor:

$$BH_4^- + H_3O^+ \rightarrow BH_3 + H_2 + H_2O$$

Therefore, although the borohydride ion normally is stable in neutral or alkaline solution, it is destroyed by acids since the borine thus reformed is rapidly hydrolyzed.

Although the process of complex anion formation is clear-cut with the ionic hydrides as reactants, some of the borohydrides with less electropositive metals appear to be more or less covalent. Beryllium borohydride is a solid, but it is slightly volatile and it is quite soluble in organic solvents. Aluminum borohydride is a very unstable and highly reactive liquid that seems to be entirely covalent. It is very difficult to make any assertions about the presence of borohydride ions as such in this compound although its formula, $Al(BH_4)_3$, is that which would be predicted from normal valence considerations. It is possible that covalent borohydrides such as those of aluminum and uranium, for example, have a type of chemical bonding involving *hydrogen bridges* and closely related to that responsible for the unique structures of the boron hydrides. (See page 69 ff.)

Since aluminum and gallium are poorer electron acceptors than boron, we should expect that it would be more difficult for the hydrides of these elements to form complex anionic derivatives with the hydrides of less electropositive elements, such as boron does.   This appears to be substantiated by experimental fact.

Since the complex anionic hydrides are relatively important compounds we shall consider them in more detail.   Most of our knowledge concerning complex anionic hydrides has been obtained from the pioneer work by Professors H. I. Schlesinger and H. C. Brown and their coworkers at the University of Chicago.*

THE BOROHYDRIDES.   As an example of the formation of a borohydride we may consider the reaction between lithium hydride and diborane in a medium of ethyl ether:

$$2LiH + B_2H_6 \rightarrow 2LiBH_4$$

For this type of reaction, it appears to be necessary that the reactants have at least some solubility in the reaction medium, or, in the absence of a reaction medium, a certain degree of mutual solubility.   Other methods may be more useful for the preparation of certain borohydrides, including those in which diborane or borohydrides are used as reducing agents as well as combining reactants:

$$3NaOCH_3 + 2B_2H_6 \xrightarrow{\text{ether}} 3NaBH_4 + B(OCH_3)_3$$

$$ThF_4 + 2Al(BH_4)_3 \rightarrow Th(BH_4)_4 + 2AlF_2(BH_4)$$

$$3(CH_3)_2Be + 4B_2H_6 \rightarrow 3Be(BH_4)_2 + 2B(CH_3)_3$$

A considerable number of borohydrides are known, including mixed salts of the type $MXBH_4$, illustrated in the second equation above, in which other anions may be present in addition to the borohydride ion, as well as compounds in which one or more of the hydrogens in the borohydride ion may be substituted by other groups such as CH_3, OCH_3, etc.

Sodium borohydride, $NaBH_4$, is a white crystalline ionic solid which is surprisingly stable in a number of respects.   Its decomposition temperature is above 300°, and, unlike most ionic hydrides, it is very soluble with only slight decomposition in cold water.   In fact, the compound may be recrystallized from aqueous solutions.   Since sodium borohydride is ionic, it is insoluble in most organic solvents; it is, however, soluble in liquid ammonia and certain primary amines.

* Publication of much of this work has been delayed by security requirements. Consult *J. Am. Chem. Soc.* for 1952 and 1953 for specific papers.

The density of sodium borohydride is reported to be 1.074 g per cc. Its crystal structure is face-centered cubic (a = 6.15 A. U.) (1). Its heat of formation is 43.83 kcal/mole (2).

The remarkable stability that sodium borohydride exhibits when it is dissolved in water is due, in part at least, to the alkalinity of the solution that results by an initial hydrolysis of a small amount of the material. When the concentration of positive hydrogen ion, or hydronium ion, is reduced, the existence of the borohydride ion in solution is no longer threatened by any strong electron acceptor. (Na^+ is a very weak electron acceptor.) An attack of the BH_4^- ion by a proton or other strong electron acceptor to remove the extra hydride anion from the complex is necessary before the BH_3 unit can be attacked and decomposed by water.

Sodium borohydride in aqueous solution can be hydrolyzed by acidification of the solution. Certain metallic salts also can catalyze the hydrolysis of the BH_4^- ion:

$$NaBH_4 + 4H_2O \rightarrow 4H_2 + NaOH + B(OH)_3$$

The complete hydrolysis of sodium borohydride yields 2.4 liters of hydrogen gas per gram of solid compound; for this reason, the compound found some use during the second World War as a portable source of hydrogen for filling signal balloons, etc.

Sodium borohydride, which is a strong reducing agent, may be of use in various analytical and synthetic reactions. For example, it is capable of reducing organic aldehydes, ketones, and acid chlorides to alcohols (3). It does not, however, reduce organic acids, nitro compounds, or unsaturation in organic compounds. For some purposes, therefore, it may be more useful as a reducing agent than the more powerful lithium aluminum hydride (see below). In quantitative analysis, sodium borohydride may be used as a reagent for reducing ferric iron to the ferrous state, etc.

Sodium borohydride also may be used as a convenient laboratory source of diborane. A non-aqueous "acid," that is, proton donor or electron acceptor, is used for the decomposition. The reaction is performed in a medium of anhydrous diethyl ether, with the usual precautions to exclude air:

$$3NaBH_4 + BF_3 \quad \rightarrow \quad 2B_2H_6 + 3NaF \text{ (or } NaBF_4)$$

Lithium borohydride is also a white crystalline non-volatile solid (4). The density of this compound is 0.66 g per cc. and its crystal structure is orthorhombic with these unit cell dimensions: a, 6.81 A. U.; b, 4.43 A. U.; c, 7.17 A. U. (5). Its heat of formation is 44.15 Kcal/mole

(2).   In most of its chemical properties, lithium borohydride resembles sodium borohydride, except that it is rapidly decomposed by water or alcohols. The compound appears to be relatively stable toward thermal decomposition and is reported to melt at over 275°, although some decomposition occurs at this temperature.   It is soluble to the extent of about 3.2% by weight in diethyl ether at room temperature. Like sodium borohydride, lithium borohydride is a strong reducing agent and may be used in a number of organic reduction reactions (6).

Lithium borohydride may be used as a convenient laboratory source of diborane.   It is particularly attractive as a solid source of hydrogen since it comprises almost 19% by weight of hydrogen.   The complete hydrolysis of one pound of lithium borohydride yields 66 cubic feet of hydrogen at S.T.P.   Lithium borodeuteride and borotritide would, of course, contain proportionately more hydrogen isotope by weight than lithium borohydride; lithium borotritide would comprise almost 40% of tritium.

Magnesium borohydride has been prepared by Wiberg and Bauer (7) through the reaction in ether solution between a magnesium dialkyl and diborane:

$$3MgR_2 + 4B_2H_6 \rightarrow 3Mg(BH_4)_2 + 2BR_3$$

The presence of the ether solvent appears to be necessary if good yields are to be obtained in the reaction.   The reaction proceeds at room temperature.

Magnesium borohydride appears to be a white crystalline solid that is slightly soluble in ether.   It undoubtedly is a strong reducing agent but, as yet, its properties have not been extensively investigated. *Zinc borohydride*, $Zn(BH_4)_2$, white, solid, and non-volatile, has been prepared similarly by the reaction of zinc dimethyl with diborane.   Its properties are expected to resemble those of magnesium borohydride.

Beryllium borohydride is a solid material, but one that shows a considerable degree of covalent character; it appears to be more covalent than ionic (8).   The vapor pressure of beryllium borohydride at 0°C is ca. 0.5 mm; its normal sublimation temperature is 91.3°.   The compound is soluble in organic solvents including non-polar solvents like benzene.

Beryllium borohydride is much more reactive than lithium borohydride.   It is spontaneously inflammable in air, and it reacts very vigorously with water and other reducing agents.   It is decomposed by hydrogen chloride at −80°.   It is less stable toward thermal decom-

Complex Hydrides

position than lithium borohydride and begins to decompose at temperatures as low as 123°. Unlike lithium borohydride, beryllium borohydride forms addition compound with tertiary amines; this compound formation is reversible.

Several intermediate compounds have been observed in the preparation of beryllium borohydride from dimethylberyllium and diborane:

$$Be(CH_3)_2 \xrightarrow{(B_2H_6)} (CH_3)BeBH_4 \xrightarrow{(B_2H_6)} HBeBH_4 \xrightarrow{(B_2H_6)} Be(BH_4)_2$$

These mixed compounds have not been extensively studied, however.

The covalent character of beryllium borohydride is believed to be due to the small size and relatively high charge of the beryllium ion (8). The compound contains approximately 21% of hydrogen by weight.

Aluminum borohydride is an unstable covalent liquid (9). The compound melts at −64.5° and has a vapor pressure of 119.5 mm at 0°C. Its boiling point is estimated to be 44.5° by extrapolation from vapor pressure data. It is very soluble in organic solvents, including benzene.

Aluminum borohydride is an exceedingly reactive compound. It ignites spontaneously on exposure to air and burns with a brilliant flame.* Its reaction with water is explosively violent. It is decomposed by hydrogen chloride at −80°, with the formation of diborane:

$$6HCl + 2Al(BH_4)_3 \rightarrow 6H_2 + 3B_2H_6 + Al_2Cl_6$$

Aluminum borohydride forms addition compounds with amines, but, unlike beryllium borohydride, its compounds with tertiary amines cannot be reversibly decomposed to yield the borohydride again. Since it is a strong reducing agent, aluminum borohydride may be used as a reagent for preparing other borohydrides or hydride compounds.

Derivatives of aluminum borohydride are known in which one or two of the borohydride groups are substituted by other groups, such as halogen or alkyl groups. These compounds generally disproportionate at elevated temperatures into the normal borohydride and aluminum trihalide or trialkyl.

Borohydrides of *titanium, zirconium, hafnium,* and *thorium* have been prepared by Hoekstra and Katz (11) by reacting the correspond-

---

* It has been found that aluminum borohydride is not spontaneously inflammable at room temperature in dry air or oxygen. This indicates that traces of water, and an initial hydrolysis, are necessary for spontaneous inflammation (10).

ing metal halides with aluminum borohydride:

$$ThF_4 + 2Al(BH_4)_3 \rightarrow Th(BH_4)_4 + 2AlF_2(BH_4)$$

Because of the reactivity of aluminum borohydride toward air and moisture, such syntheses must be done in a vacuum manipulation system.

Titanium tetrachloride is reduced to the trivalent state in the synthesis reaction, and the borohydride compound isolated is the deep blue, slightly volatile mixed compound $TiCl(BH_4)_2$.

Zirconium and *hafnium borohydride* are crystalline solids which melt slightly above room temperature, and which have vapor pressures of about 15 mm at room temperature.

Thorium borohydride appears to be ionic. It is a crystalline white solid which melts at 204° and has a vapor pressure of about 0.2 mm at 150°. Its chemical behavior is much like that of the alkali metal borohydrides, and it is not spontaneously inflammable in air. It decomposes at 300° in the vapor phase to form hydrogen and thorium boride. Thorium borohydride is soluble in diethyl ether to the extent of ca. 20 g per 100 ml; in this respect it differs from the borohydrides of sodium and lithium.

Hoekstra and Katz (11) also prepared borohydrides of *neptunium* and *plutonium* by the reactions of their fluorides with aluminum borohydride. These compounds appear to be solids of relatively low volatility.

A volatile borohydride of *uranium*, $U(BH_4)_4$, has been prepared by Schlesinger and Brown (12) by the metathetical reaction of uranium tetrafluoride with aluminum borohydride. Uranium borohydride appears to be a covalent borohydride in which much of the chemical bonding is through hydrogen bridges. It is slightly volatile and has a vapor pressure of 0.19 mm at room temperature. On heating, the compound sublimes, but it will melt at ca. 126°, with decomposition. Uranium borohydride is very reactive chemically and will react vigorously with a variety of compounds, such as water, alcohols, and hydrogen chloride; it is reported to oxidize slowly in dry air. Uranium borohydride is soluble in diethyl ether to the extent of about 2 g per 100 ml, and it forms stable etherates. It is slightly soluble in nonpolar solvents. Partially methylated derivatives of uranium borohydride also have been prepared.

Undoubtedly, many borohydride compounds eventually will be prepared and studied.

COMPLEX ALUMINUM HYDRIDES. The discovery of the complex aluminum hydrides by Finholt, Bond, and Schlesinger (13) has made a very powerful and unique reducing agent, *lithium aluminum hydride*, $LiAlH_4$, available to chemical technology.

Lithium aluminum hydride results from the reaction of lithium hydride with aluminum chloride in solution in diethyl ether at room temperature:

$$4LiH + AlCl_3 \xrightarrow{\text{Et}_2\text{O}} LiAlH_4 + 3LiCl$$

The reaction is analogous to the formation of lithium borohydride, and, like that reaction, it can be carried a step further to produce a hydride:

$$3LiAlH_4 + AlCl_3 \rightarrow 3LiCl + 4AlH_3$$

Lithium aluminum hydride is a non-volatile crystalline solid. When it is pure, it is white; but the article of commerce usually is a gray powder. Although it is not spontaneously inflammable in air, lithium aluminum hydride powder may generate enough heat by hydrolysis upon exposure to moist air to ignite and burn. It does not ignite in dry air at 130°.

At 120° lithium aluminum hydride begins to decompose slowly into hydrogen, lithium hydride, and metallic aluminum:

$$2LiAlH_4 \rightarrow 2LiH + 3H_2 + 2Al$$

If heated rapidly, the compound melts at ca. 150°, but at that temperature thermal decomposition is quite rapid. The heat of formation of lithium aluminum hydride is 24.08 Kcal/mole (2).

Lithium aluminum hydride is soluble in a number of organic solvents. In diethyl ether it dissolves to the extent of 30 g per 100 ml, and in tetrahydrofurane to the extent of about 13 g per 100 ml. This solubility, together with its unusual abilities as a reducing agent, makes lithium aluminum hydride a valuable tool for preparative and analytical chemistry. This is particularly true in view of its ready availability in quantity from Metal Hydrides, Inc., of Beverly, Massachusetts.

The use of lithium aluminum hydride in metathetical reactions for the preparation of volatile hydrides already has been mentioned:

$$4MX + LiAlH_4 \rightarrow 4MH + LiX + AlX_3$$

Hydrides of boron, aluminum, silicon, germanium, tin, arsenic, and antimony have been prepared by this reaction. In addition, a large number of organic derivatives of these and other hydrides can be made by the reaction of the corresponding halide derivatives with $LiAlH_4$:

$$2(CH_3)_2SiCl_2 + LiAlH_4 \rightarrow 2(CH_3)_2SiH_2 + LiCl + AlCl_3$$

Lithium aluminum hydride also may react with metal alkyls to form hydrides, such as those of zinc, beryllium, and magnesium. Mixed alkyl hydride compounds of elements in Groups II and III may be formed in this way also.

A sizable volume of literature describing the uses of lithium aluminum hydride in organic chemistry has been developing in the few years since the discovery of this compound. Unlike many reduction and hydrogenation reagents, lithium aluminum hydride does not hydrogenate carbon-carbon double bonds except under a few special conditions. Lithium aluminum hydride is unique in its tendency to avoid side reactions, cleavages, or condensations such as are caused by ionic hydrides like sodium hydride. Sterically hindered compounds which are difficult to reduce by other methods usually may be reduced with lithium aluminum hydride. The reduction reactions generally are almost quantitative, and the products have a high degree of purity. Lithium aluminum hydride is a rapid and convenient reagent for converting oxygenated compounds, such as aldehydes, ketones, acids, anhydrides, esters, and acid halides, to the corresponding alcohols. Nitriles can be reduced to primary amines, and hydrocarbon halides can be reduced to the corresponding hydrocarbons without reducing unsaturation that may be present in the molecules.

Some general examples of reductions that can be effected with lithium aluminum hydride are:

a. Oxygenated compounds:

$$4CH_3COOH + 3LiAlH_4 \rightarrow LiAl(CH_3CH_2O)_4 + 2LiAlO_2 + 4H_2$$

$$LiAl(CH_3CH_2O)_4 + 4H_2O \rightarrow 4CH_3CH_2OH + LiOH + Al(OH)_3$$

Similar equations can be written for the reduction of aldehydes, ketones, esters, acid chlorides, etc., including some amides.

b. Nitriles:

$$2CH_3CN + LiAlH_4 \rightarrow LiAl(CH_3CH_2N)_2$$

$$LiAl(CH_3CH_2N)_2 + 4H_2O \rightarrow CH_3CH_2NH_2 + LiOH + Al(OH)_3$$

Amides are generally reduced to amines by lithium aluminum hydrides; a few are reduced to alcohols as in example *a* above.

c. Hydrocarbon halides:

$$4CH_2{=}CH{-}CH_2Br + LiAlH_4 \rightarrow 4CH_2{=}CH{-}CH_3 + LiAlBr_4$$

A partial list of general references to reductions with lithium aluminum hydride is appended in the footnote below.*

Magnesium aluminum hydride (14) has been prepared by the reaction of magnesium bromide with lithium aluminum hydride in ether solution:

$$MgBr_2 + 2LiAlH_4 \rightarrow Mg(AlH_4)_2 + 2LiBr$$

Lithium aluminum hydride appears to react with Grignard reagents in an analogous fashion to form mixed compounds:

$$RMgX + LiAlH_4 \rightarrow MgR(AlH_4) + LiX$$

Magnesium aluminum hydride also may be prepared by the action of excess magnesium hydride on aluminum chloride in ether:

$$4MgH_2 + 2AlCl_3 \rightarrow Mg(AlH_4)_2 + 3MgCl_2$$

As yet, magnesium aluminum hydride has been studied only in ether solutions of the material, but it appears to resemble lithium aluminum hydride in its chemical properties. It is decomposed by water with the evolution of hydrogen. It will reduce acetone to

* "Reduction of Organic Compounds by Lithium Aluminum Hydride. I. Aldehydes, Ketones, Esters, Acid Chlorides and Acid Anhydrides." Robert F. Nystrom and Weldon G. Brown. *J. Am. Chem. Soc.*, **69**, 1197 (1947).

"Reduction of Organic Compounds by Lithium Aluminum Hydride. II. Carboxylic Acids." Robert F. Nystrom and Weldon G. Brown. *J. Am. Chem. Soc.*, **69**, 2548 (1947).

"Reduction of Organic Compounds by Lithium Aluminum Hydride. III. Halides, Quinones, Miscellaneous Nitrogen Compounds." Robert Nystrom and Weldon G. Brown. *J. Am. Chem. Soc.*, **70**, 3738 (1948).

"The Preparation and Some Properties of Hydrides of Elements of the Fourth Group of the Periodic System and of Their Organic Derivatives." A. E. Finholt, A. C. Bond, Jr., K. E. Wilzback, and H. I. Schlesinger. *J. Am. Chem. Soc.*, **69**, 2692 (1947).

"Eine Neue Methode zur Reduktion Eines Amids zum Amin mit der Gleichen Anzahl von Kohlenstoffatomen." A. Uffer and E. Schlittler. *Helv. Chim. Acta*, **31**, 1397 (1948).

"Hydrogenolysis of Alkyl Halides by Lithium Aluminum Hydride." J. Enoch Johnson, Ronald H. Blizzard, and Homer W. Carhart. *J. Am. Chem. Soc.*, **70**, 3664 (1948).

"Lithium Aluminum Hydride, Aluminum Hydride and Lithium Gallium Hydride and Some of Their Applications in Organic and Inorganic Chemistry." A. E. Finholt, A. C. Bond, Jr., and H. I. Schlesinger. *J. Am. Chem. Soc.*, **69**, 1199 (1947).

A considerable number of specific syntheses with LiAlH₄ are described in the chemical literature. Such references may be found through *Chemical Abstracts*. Volume VI of *Organic Reactions* (Wiley, New York, 1951) contains a chapter on reductions with lithium aluminum hydride by W. G. Brown.

isopropyl alcohol. Propargylaldehyde is reduced to propargylalcohol by magnesium aluminum hydride; as in similar reductions with lithium aluminum hydride, the carbon-carbon triple bond is not reduced in this synthesis.

Lithium aluminum hydride and magnesium aluminum hydride are the only compounds of this type that have been studied so far.   It is likely, however, that other complex aluminum hydrides will eventually be synthesized.

LITHIUM GALLIUM HYDRIDE.   At present, the only known complex gallium anionic hydride is *lithium gallium hydride* (13).   This compound has been prepared by the reduction of gallium chloride with lithium hydride in diethyl ether:

$$4LiH + GaCl_3 \rightarrow LiGaH_4 + 3LiCl$$

Lithium gallium hydride is a white solid when freshly prepared, but it is relatively unstable and it rapidly turns dark on standing at room temperature. Its properties have not been investigated in detail.

IV. Compounds Containing Complex Hydride Cations.   A complex positive ion, or cation, is formed when a positive hydrogen ion, or proton, accepts a share in an electron pair from an electron donor atom and becomes associated with this atom through the formation of a coordinate covalent bond. Common examples of complex hydride cations formed in this way are the *ammonium ion*, NH_4^+, and the *hydronium ion*, H_3O^+:

$$\begin{array}{cc} H & H \\ \ddot{} & \ddot{} \quad\quad\quad\quad \ddot{}\; + \quad\quad \ddot{} \\ H:N: + H:O:H \rightarrow H:N:H + :O:H^- \\ \ddot{} & \ddot{} \quad\quad\quad\quad \ddot{} \quad\quad\quad \ddot{} \\ H & H \end{array}$$

$$\begin{array}{cc} H & H \\ \ddot{} & \ddot{} \quad\quad\quad\quad\quad \ddot{}\; + \quad\quad \ddot{} \\ H:O: + \; H:Cl: \rightarrow H:O:H + \quad :Cl:^- \\ \ddot{} & \ddot{} \quad\quad\quad\quad\quad \ddot{} \quad\quad\quad\quad \ddot{} \end{array}$$

In the formation of the positive ion, the positive charge of the proton is assumed by the ion as a whole; the hydrogen atoms surrounding the central atom are equivalent as are the covalent bonds linking them to the central atom.

The formation reaction is reversible, and the amount of complex cation present will depend on several factors, including the reaction conditions and the relative strength of the electron donor group. For example, the familiar ammonium hydroxide is, in actuality, a solution of ammonia gas in water in equilibrium with ammonium ions and hydroxyl ions in the solution and with the gas pressure of ammonia above the solution. If the solution is heated, ammonia gas escapes from the solution and, consequently, ammonium ions release protons (to hydroxyl ions to form water molecules) to become ammonia molecules again. If a stronger electron donor is added to a solution containing complex hydride cations, a proton transfer may occur from the complex cation to the stronger electron donor. Thus, if ammonia is added to a solution containing hydronium ions, such as a dilute solution of HCl, ammonium ions will be formed by proton transfer from the hydronium ions:

$$NH_3 + H_3O^+ + Cl^- \rightarrow NH_4^+ + H_2O + Cl^-$$

Complex hydride cation formation is extensive only with ammonia and water. Of these, only the ammonium derivatives can be isolated in the form of stable salts, for example, *ammonium chloride*, NH_4Cl. *Phosphine*, PH_3, can form *phosphonium* derivatives:

$$PH_3 + HCl \rightarrow PH_4Cl$$

Judged from their properties, these compounds appear to be more covalent than ionic, however, and they are decomposed by water. Because of its larger size, the phosphorus atom in phosphine is less capable of forming a coordinate covalent bond to a proton than is the oxygen atom in a water molecule; thus phosphine shows only a slight tendency to form phosphonium ions in water solution. This tendency would be even less against the stronger competition of an ammonia molecule in liquid ammonia, but would be greater in, for instance, liquid hydrogen fluoride or hydrogen chloride.

It is of interest to note that carbon is believed to form complex *carbonium* ions with protons in the course of certain organic reactions.

REFERENCES

1. Soldate, *J. Am. Chem. Soc.*, **69**, 987 (1947).
2. Davis, Mason, and Stegeman, *J. Am. Chem. Soc.*, **71**, 2775 (1949).
3. Chaikin and Brown, *J. Am. Chem. Soc.*, **71**, 122 (1949).
4. Schlesinger and Brown, *J. Am. Chem. Soc.*, **62**, 3429 (1940).
5. Harris and Meibohm, *J. Am. Chem. Soc.*, **69**, 1231 (1947).
6. Nystrom, Chaikin, and Brown, *J. Am. Chem. Soc.*, **71**, 3245 (1949).
7. Wiberg and Bauer, *Z. Naturforschg.*, **5b**, 397 (1950).
8. Schlesinger and Burg, *J. Am. Chem. Soc.*, **62**, 3425 (1940).
9. Schlesinger, Sanderson and Burg, *J. Am. Chem. Soc.*, **62**, 3421 (1940).

10. Badin, Hunter, and Pease, *J. Am. Chem. Soc.*, **71**, 2950 (1949).
11. Hoekstra and Katz, Declassified Document AECD 1894, Oak Ridge, Tennessee. See also *J. Am. Chem. Soc.*, **71**, 2488 (1949).
12. Schlesinger and Brown, Declassified Document MDDC 1341, Oak Ridge, Tennessee. See also entry in Katz and Rabinowitch, *The Chemistry of Uranium*, McGraw-Hill, New York, 1951.
13. Finholt, Bond, and Schlesinger, *J. Am. Chem. Soc.*, **69**, 1199 (1947).
14. Wiberg and Bauer, *Z. Naturforsch.*, **5b**, 398 (1950).

CHAPTER

15

The Hydrides of the Transitional Elements

The behavior of the transitional elements with hydrogen is a subject about which there has been much argument. Some of the transitional metals react vigorously with hydrogen to form products that not only contain large amounts of hydrogen but obviously are also different in appearance and properties from the original metals. Are these substances hydrides? Are they true compounds, or are they hydrogen-metal alloys? Others of the transitional metals may absorb large volumes of hydrogen, but they suffer no change in appearance and very little change in their physical and chemical properties. Are these substances to be considered hydrides?—interstitial compounds?—alloys? Some of the transitional metals are relatively inert to hydrogen and may occlude only small amounts of hydrogen by physical adsorption. Where do we draw the line?

Much of the argument regarding the transitional metals and their reactions with hydrogen is largely a matter of *definition*, and arises from differences in opinion about "what is a compound and what is not." The simplest and most satisfactory course we can adopt in considering the transitional metal hydrides, whatever their particular characteristics may be, is to abandon fixed definitions, to remember that most chemical phenomena are best described in relative rather than in absolute terms, and to look for systematic differences between the transitional metals in their reactions with hydrogen. In considering the various groups of the transitional elements that are discussed in the following pages, several features will become apparent.

1. The capacity of the various metals to absorb, occlude, adsorb or otherwise react with hydrogen decreases progressively across the Periodic Table from left to right. The elements in Group IIIA, the *rare earth metals*, rank highest in their capacity to absorb hydrogen. The Group VIII metals, on the other hand, are relatively inert to hydrogen. (Palladium is the one notable exception to this rule.)

2. The amount of heat liberated by the reaction of the various transitional elements with hydrogen decreases progressively across

172

the Periodic Table from left to right. In fact, after *chromium* in Group VIA the heat of reaction becomes negative for the succeeding elements in Groups VIA, VIIA, and VIII. That is, the elements in these groups react *endothermically* with hydrogen. The reactions of the IIIA and IVA elements with hydrogen are very *exothermic;* the heats of formation of the hydrides of these elements are comparable to the heats of formation of the ionic hydrides.

3. An expansion of the crystal structures of the transitional metals always occurs during the process of hydrogen absorption or occlusion, that is, the hydrides are less dense than the metals from which they are derived. This lattice expansion may be sufficient with some metals to cause a rearrangement of the basic metal structure into new structures or phases. Some of the transitional metal hydrides, therefore, have structures differing in type as well as in size from those of the metals from which they are derived. This expansion is roughly proportional to the capacity of the element to absorb hydrogen, and will therefore decrease with successive elements across the Periodic Table from left to right. With the ionic hydrides, hydride formation always is accompanied by a shrinking of the structure and an increase in density over that of the original metal.

4. The absorption of hydrogen by a transitional element appears to cause a partial loss of the metallic character of the element. The loss in metallic character is related to the amount of hydrogen that the element has been able to absorb and is most marked in the hydrides of the rare earth metals.

5. The diffusion of hydrogen into and through a transitional metal occurs primarily, and most rapidly, through *intergranular rifts* or minute cracks and defects in the structure of the metal. All the transitional elements appear to be similar in this respect. *Alloying* (and this term is used advisedly) then may occur with some, but not with all, of the transitional metals. This alloying may be the formation of a *solid solution* of *metallic hydrogen** in the metal; the formation of an *interstitial alloy* or *compound* in which hydrogen atoms or protons occupy the interstices between metal atoms in the crystal lattice of the metal; or the establishment of a structure such as that now known to exist in uranium hydride (see below) in which hydrogen atoms form

---

* If hydrogen behaves as a metal, as it is believed to do in some cases, the valence electrons become a part of the general electron system of the metal as a whole and become relatively mobile. The hydrogen nucleus, or proton, assumes a fixed position in the metal structure. However, it should be pointed out that the proton is, at any given time, associated with a certain electron density and thus is not ionized in the usual sense of the word.

"bridge" bonds between metal atoms and take the place of the normal metal atom–metal atom bonds. Various transitional metals appear to behave somewhat differently in this respect. However, in view of the large expansions observed during hydrogen absorption by the more electropositive transitional metals (those in the lower numbered groups), the third type of bonding may be more common than heretofore has been considered.* The tendency to form *alloys*, or *compounds*, is strongest with Groups IIIA and IVA elements and decreases with the succeeding groups. (Again palladium is the notable exception.) However, whether alloying does or does not occur there still is a possibility for hydrogen to be physically adsorbed in rifts in the metal structure. In many of the transitional metals, the adsorption and absorption of hydrogen, and the resulting lattice expansion, may open up new rifts where none existed in the metal prior to hydrogenation. Thus a hydrided transitional metal may contain hydrogen both by alloying (that is, by compound formation—again a matter of definition) and by physical adsorption.

6. The formulas of the transitional metal hydrides are indefinite. That is, they do not correspond to nice even stoichiometric formulas. In view of the remarks in the above paragraph, it is not difficult to see at least one reason for this; analytical methods seldom are able to differentiate between physically adsorbed hydrogen and alloyed, or compound, hydrogen.†

With the above discussion in mind, the reader should be prepared to consider the following discussion of the individual transitional elements with an open mind. If the question is asked, "*Do any of the transitional elements form hydride compounds?*," the answer should be, "*Yes; and what is meant by 'hydride compounds'?.*" There is little doubt that many of the transitional elements do enter into chemical combination and form chemical bonds with hydrogen. A few of the transitional elements obviously do not. However, since the transitions in behavior within the group as a whole are so gradual, there is little point in trying to draw classifying boundary lines between the transitional elements. One natural line that may be drawn is between the *exothermic* occluding elements and the *endothermic* occluding elements. Actually, this line is not sharply defined either.

---

* Rundle, *J. Am. Chem. Soc.*, **69**, 1327, 1719, 2075 (1947).

† For that matter, many of the ionic hydrides are difficult to prepare and keep with a 100% stoichiometric content of hydrogen. As ordinarily manufactured and sold, ionic hydrides usually fall short of the stoichiometric content of hydrogen, and the formulas are conventions rather than representing actual compositions.

THE GROUP IIIA ELEMENTS AND THE RARE EARTH METALS

Several of the more common rare earth metals are known to form hydride compounds. *Lanthanum, cerium, praseodymium,* and *neodymium,* for example, will react quite exothermically with hydrogen, and the heats of formation of their hydrides are comparable to those of the alkali metal and alkaline earth metal hydrides. The rare earth metal hydrides, however, are of rather indefinite composition, and they do not have exact formulas. Also, considerable expansions of the metal crystal structures occur during the absorption of hydrogen and the formation of hydrides by these metals. In these respects, the rare earth metal hydrides differ from the ionic hydrides.

The rare earth metal hydrides are considerably more stable against thermal decomposition than are the hydrides of metals in the following groups of transitional elements. They also appear to be more reactive chemically. However, the rare earth metals follow closely the general pattern of the transitional metals in their reactions with hydrogen. The metal is penetrated by hydrogen diffusing through intergranular rifts, the metal structure is expanded and opened up as hydrogen is absorbed by the metal, and an alloying or solution of hydrogen into the solid metal occurs. The volume expansion that accompanies the formation of a rare earth metal hydride usually is sufficient to convert solid metal into brittle friable powder. With the rare earth metals, as with certain other metals in the transitional group, there is the possibility that hydrogen may be absorbed in excess of the amounts required by alloy formation. Thus compositions will be indefinite, and it will be difficult to determine what the normal formula for a particular compound may be (1). The crystal structures of the rare earth metal hydrides probably are different from those of the metals from which they are derived (2). The rare earth metal hydrides are rather reactive chemically; they are soluble in acids, and are decomposed by alkalies.

The normal Group IIIA elements, *scandium, yttrium,* and *actinium,* are so rare that the hydrides of these elements have not been prepared. Such compounds should resemble the rare earth metal hydrides in many of their properties.

LANTHANUM

LaH_3(?)—*lanthanum hydride*
Black powder of indefinite composition
Density: 5.83 g/cc for $LaH_{2.76}$
Heat of formation: 40.09 Kcal/mole H_2 for $LaH_{2.76}$

Lanthanum hydride is prepared by heating lanthanum metal in hydrogen (3). The absorption of hydrogen by lanthanum will occur at room temperature if the metal has been activated by heating it to a high temperature, but fresh samples of lanthanum usually are inert to hydrogen at temperatures below 300°. The density of lanthanum metal drops by about 13% when the metal is converted to lanthanum hydride (3). Lanthanum hydride is not pyrophoric. It has about the same thermal stability as cerium hydride.

CERIUM

CeH_3 (?)—*cerium hydride*
Black pyrophoric powder of indefinite composition
Density: 5.5 g/cc for $CeH_{2.69}$
Heat of formation: 42.26 Kcal/mole H_2 for $CeH_{2.69}$

Cerium metal heated in hydrogen absorbs gas rapidly at 350° to form a black powder of cerium hydride. If the metal is activated by a preliminary heating, it will absorb hydrogen avidly and exothermically at room temperature. The cerium loses approximately 17.5% of its normal density in the expansion that accompanies hydride formation (3).

The dissociation pressure of cerium hydride is less than 1 mm in the temperature range of 450° to 500°, provided that the composition of the hydride is less than CeH_2. With higher hydrogen/cerium ratios, the dissociation pressure increases and is dependent upon the exact hydrogen content. This has been considered an argument to prove that the normal formula of cerium hydride should be CeH_2 (4). However, a similar effect has been noticed in the ionic hydrides at hydrogen concentrations below those predicted by stoichiometry; thus the argument is not very convincing.

Cerium hydride and lanthanum hydride may be decomposed at elevated temperatures by vacuum outgassing. However, if a hydrogen atmosphere is maintained, these compounds are not completely dissociated at 1100° (1).

Upon exposure to air, cerium hydride ignites and burns to form a mixture of cerium oxide and cerium nitride. Cerium hydride heated to 800° to 900° in nitrogen is converted to cerium nitride (5).

PRASEODYMIUM and NEODYMIUM

PrH_3 (?)—*praseodymium hydride*
Dark powder of indefinite composition
Density: 5.56 g/cc for $PrH_{2.84}$
Heat of formation: 39.52 Kcal/mole H_2 for $PrH_{2.84}$

Praseodymium metal is inert toward hydrogen at room temperature, but at 300° to 400° the metal rapidly absorbs hydrogen. During this process, the normally bright metal turns black and expands into a brittle friable solid (1). The loss in density in the conversion of praseodymium metal to its hydride is ca. 14.6% (3). The behavior of neodymium with hydrogen is similar to that of praseodymium. Both praseodymium hydride and neodymium hydride decompose at elevated temperatures, but their complete decomposition into metal and hydrogen requires temperatures in excess of 1100° if the hydrogen liberated is not pumped away.

Gadolinium and *samarium* also are known to form hydrides. From the little that is known of them, these compounds appear to be similar to the other rare earth metal hydrides. Viallard (6) has studied the reactions of hydrogen and deuterium with gadolinium and cerium. Gadolinium reacts above 150° to form a compound corresponding to a formula of Gd_2H_3. If this compound is cooled in hydrogen it is converted to GdH_2, which, in turn, redissociates to Gd_2H_3 at ca. 250°. The actual formulas of these compounds may not be exact, as written, however.

REFERENCES—RARE EARTH METAL HYDRIDES

1. Smith, *Hydrogen in Metals*, University of Chicago Press, Chicago, Ill., 1948.
2. Rossi, *Nature*, **133**, 174 (1934).
3. Sieverts and Gotta, *Z. Elektrochem.*, **32**, 105 (1926). Sieverts and Gotta, *Z. anorg. Chem.*, **172**, 1 (1928).
4. Zhukov, *J. Russ. Phys. Chem. Soc.*, **45**, 2073 (1913).
5. Dafert and Miklauz, *Monatsh.*, **33**, 911 (1912).
6. Viallard, *Ann. chim.*, **20**, 5, (1935).

THE ACTINIDE ELEMENTS—THORIUM AND URANIUM

It is known now that the elements in the lowest row of the Periodic Table represent the start of a new series of elements analogous to the rare earth elements, or *lanthanides*. Thus, thorium does not belong to the Group IVA elements, nor does uranium belong to the Group VIA elements; rather, both of these elements belong to the group of *actinides*.* They should, therefore, behave rather similarly toward hydrogen. Uranium hydride is the only actinide hydride that has been extensively investigated, although hydrides and hydride compounds of some of the transuranic elements have been prepared. All the known hydrides of this group are exothermic compounds.

* Named from the first element in the series—*actinium*.

THORIUM

ThH₃—*thorium hydride*
Black pyrophoric powder, indefinite composition

Thorium metal in powder form reacts rapidly with hydrogen at temperatures between 300° and 400° to form a black powder of thorium hydride.   The combination of hydrogen with thorium is an exothermic reaction and is accompanied by an expansion of the thorium lattice. Since the highest concentration of hydrogen in thorium achieved in laboratory preparations corresponds to an empirical formula of ThH₃.₂₄ (1), it is uncertain what the normal formula for thorium hydride is.   It is possible that ThH₃ may represent the stoichiometric formula and that ThH₃.₂₄ may have been surcharged with dissolved hydrogen.   Other preparations have yielded material of the composition ThH₃.₀₇ (2).   It is quite certain that thorium hydride is a compound in that it involves chemical bonding between thorium and hydrogen, and it possibly may resemble uranium hydride in the type of internal chemical bonding it exhibits (see below).

The thorium hydride of high hydrogen content, ThH₃.₂₄, is reported to be pyrophoric, that is, igniting upon exposure to air, and to react with water with the evolution of hydrogen gas.   It apparently is a rather strong reducing agent.

Thorium hydride also may be prepared by reducing thorium tetrachloride with lithium hydride at an elevated temperature.

A thorium borohydride is known (see "Complex Hydrides," Chapter 14).

REFERENCES—THORIUM HYDRIDE

1. Sieverts and Gotta, *Z. anorg. Chem.*, **172,** 1 (1928).
2. Sieverts and Roell, *Z. anorg. Chem.*, **153,** 289 (1926).

URANIUM

UH₃—*uranium hydride*
Black or dark gray powder
Specific gravity: ca. 11.4 g/cc
Dissociation pressure: $\log p = \dfrac{-4500}{T} + 9.28$ (1)

Structure.   The structure of uranium hydride has been determined by Rundle (2).   The compound is quite unusual in that it does not appear to be held together by intermetallic bonds, but is bonded primarily by hydrogen "bridge" bonds between the atoms of uranium. The structure is cubic (a = 6.63 A. U.), and the unit cell contains eight uranium atoms. This structure is greatly different from the orthorhombic structure of metallic uranium. According to Rundle there are two types of uranium atoms in the compound; "a" atoms and "c" atoms. Each "a" atom is bonded to twelve "c" atoms by hydrogen "bridges," the U—H—U distance being a total of 3.707 A. U. Each of the "c" atoms is bonded to four "a" atoms through hydrogen and is bonded directly to two other "c" atoms at a U—U spacing of 3.316 A. U. It is pointed out that the properties of the compound, that is, high melting point, hardness, brittleness, etc., are completely inconsistent with a covalent bonding between uranium and hydrogen. The "bridge" type of bonding, in which a hydrogen atom forms "half bonds" with each of two neighboring atoms, would seem to account for the properties of the compound as well as for the frequently occurring 3.707 A. U. separation of uranium atoms.

Preparation. Massive uranium heated in hydrogen to temperatures between 250° and 350° absorbs hydrogen very rapidly, and the metal is converted to a fine black pyrophoric powder. Under high pressures of hydrogen the absorption reaction begins at lower temperatures; for example, at a pressure of 126 atm, absorption begins at 130°. With finely powdered uranium metal, freshly prepared by the thermal dissociation of uranium hydride, the absorption of hydrogen is rapid at room temperature and is fairly rapid even at the temperature of dry ice. The absorption reaction is quite exothermic (1).

Uranium deuteride may be prepared by heating uranium metal with deuterium, although the absorption reaction is much slower than with hydrogen.

Uranium hydride also has been prepared by the action of steam on metallic uranium, although uranium oxide is formed simultaneously.

Uranium has been observed to dehydrogenate certain organic compounds such as decalin and tetralin (hydrogenated naphthalenes), with the formation of uranium hydride.

Properties. Uranium hydride appears to be somewhat metallic in character. It conducts electricity with a conductivity of the same order of magnitude as that of uranium metal. It is, however, considered to be a true chemical compound since the ratio of uranium to hydrogen is very close to the stoichiometric ratio. This conclusion is supported by the structure determination (2). It has been definitely proved that the hydride is not a solid solution of hydrogen in a metal as many of the transitional hydrides seem to be. It can be shown, moreover, by the linearity of the relation between density and composition that, in mixtures of uranium and uranium hydride containing a total of less than three hydrogen atoms per uranium atom, the system comprises only two phases; uranium and its hydride, UH_3. This conclusion is confirmed by X-ray analysis. The extreme state of sub-division produced in the synthesis reaction suggests that the compound is very brittle.

The dissociation pressures of hydrogen over UH_3 at some various temperatures are: 307°, 32.5 mm; 357°, 134 mm; 444°, 1010 mm. The dissociation pressure of uranium deuteride is about 40% greater than the hydride at a given temperature.

Uranium hydride is a pyrophoric compound, that is, it ignites spontaneously upon exposure to air, and it is considered to be a dangerous material to handle. Material transfer and manipulations usually are done in an inert atmosphere of nitrogen or carbon dioxide.

Chemically, uranium hydride is a powerful reducing agent. If sizable amounts of the compound are treated with water, a violently exothermic reaction ensues, with the formation of uranium oxide, UO_2, and hydrogen. If small quantities are completely covered with water, however, the reaction is extremely slow. Reaction also is slow upon similar treatment with non-oxidizing acids such as hydrochloric and dilute sulfuric.

Concentrated sulfuric acid is reduced to sulfur dioxide, free sulfur, and even to hydrogen sulfide. Nitric acid reacts quite vigorously, occasionally with ignition, to form uranyl nitrate. A violent reaction also occurs with 30% hydrogen peroxide in the presence of acids to form uranyl salts. A number of oxidizing anions, including manganate, bromate, chlorate, and dichromate, catalyze the decomposition of uranium hydride in acid. The decomposition and hydrolysis of uranium hydride also are catalyzed by certain heavy metal cations such as silver, mercury, bismuth, and copper (3).

In contrast to this behavior, alkalies have little or no effect on uranium hydride.

Uranium hydride is violently attacked by the gaseous halogens at elevated temperatures to form halides of uranium. These reactions proceed more rapidly than with uranium metal and may be convenient reactions for the preparation of uranium halide compounds. Uranium hydride also reacts vigorously with organic halides, dehalogenating these compounds, with the formation of free carbon.

Uranium hydride decomposes ammonia at 250°, with the formation of uranium nitride.

Derivatives. A volatile borohydride compound of uranium, $U(BH_4)_4$, has been prepared and studied. (See Chapter 14.)

Uses. In addition to its possible application as an intermediate in the preparation of uranium compounds, uranium hydride may be used as a source of very pure hydrogen (or deuterium) for laboratory investigations, since the temperature range over which absorption and release of hydrogen occur is fairly narrow and conveniently located.

REFERENCES—URANIUM HYDRIDE

1. Spedding et al., *Nucleonics*, **4**, 4 (1949).
2. Rundle, *J. Am. Chem. Soc.*, **69**, 1719 (1947).
3. Newton et al., *Nucleonics*, **4**, 17 (1949).

THE GROUP IVA ELEMENTS—TITANIUM, ZIRCONIUM, AND HAFNIUM

The hydrides of the Group IVA elements are exothermic compounds, and the values for their heats of formation are in the same general range as the heats of formation of the ionic hydrides. Although the Group IVA hydrides do not have exact, or stoichiometric, formulas, they undoubtedly involve chemical bonding between the metal atoms and the hydrogen atoms. The hydrogen atoms probably occupy interstitial positions in the metal lattices, but it also is possible that hydrogen atoms may act to form "bridge" bonds between metal atoms as in the structure of uranium hydride.

Inasmuch as hafnium has been separated from zirconium only recently, there is little direct knowledge of a hafnium hydride *per se*. The properties of hafnium hydride would be expected to resemble those of zirconium hydride rather closely; indeed, zirconium compounds normally contain some hafnium as an impurity.

TITANIUM

TiH_2—*titanium hydride*
Brittle gray powder of indefinite composition
Density: 3.912 g/cc for $TiH_{1.62}$
Heat of formation: 31.1 Kcal/mole for $TiH_{1.75}$

Structure. The system titanium-hydrogen possibly may exist in several distinct phases, depending upon the amount of absorbed hydrogen present in the metal. If the amounts of hydrogen are small, the observed effect is a simple expansion of the normal titanium lattice with no change in structural type. When large amounts of hydrogen are present in the metal, new crystal forms may be established to relieve the strains resulting from the lattice expansion; titanium suffers a 15.5% loss in density upon being converted to $TiH_{1.75}$. The hydrogen-rich phase, presumably TiH_2, is reported to have a face-centered cubic structure with $a = 4.46$ A. U.; normal titanium has a hexagonal structure (1). There is, however, no assurance that TiH_2 represents the normal formula for titanium hydride; forms such as $TiH_{1.75}$ may be supercharged with physically adsorbed hydrogen.

Preparation. Titanium hydride is an article of commerce and is manufactured in several different ways. The simplest method of preparation is to heat titanium metal in hydrogen to temperatures over 200° and allow the metal to cool in a hydrogen atmosphere. Many of the same problems are encountered in this synthesis that are observed in the reactions of hydrogen with other transitional metals. That is, the initial diffusion of hydrogen into the metal structure may be slow until the metal structure has been rifted or "opened up" by the process of lattice expansion. Thus a sample of titanium that has been hydrided and then degassed may absorb hydrogen much more rapidly than a fresh sample of titanium metal. Titanium resembles palladium in that the diffusion of hydrogen into the metal occurs through rifts and structure defects; this rapid rift diffusion then is followed by a slower penetration and alloying of the solid metal with hydrogen (2). After alloy formation is complete there is a possibility that considerable amounts of hydrogen may be adsorbed in the rifts; thus the compound may be supercharged with hydrogen.

Since titanium metal may be difficult or uneconomical to prepare as an intermediate, a convenient method for the preparation of titanium hydride is to reduce a titanium compound, such as titanium dioxide, with an active metal or metal hydride, such as calcium hydride, and convert the freshly formed titanium metal to titanium hydride *in situ* (3).

Properties. Titanium hydride loses most of its hydrogen at rather low temperatures. The greater part (ca. 80%) of the hydrogen content is lost at 400°, although the decomposition reaction is not rapid, and the metal is essentially outgassed at equilibrium at 800° to 1000°.

Titanium hydride will burn if it is ignited, but so will titanium metal powder. The hydride powder seems to be quite safe to handle and it is not affected by air or moisture. Like titanium metal, it can be attacked by very strong oxidizing agents, but it is inert to most chemical reagents.

It has been observed that titanium hydride will act as a catalyst for certain organic hydrogenation reactions. At 175°, in the presence of 1500 to 2000 pounds per square inch of hydrogen, titanium hydride will catalyze the hydrogenation of olefins, for example, phenylacetylene to styrene and phenylethane; nitro compounds, for example, nitro-benzene to aniline; and nitriles to amines (4).

Derivatives. A borohydride derivative of titanium has been prepared. (See Chapter 14.)

Uses. Titanium hydride has a number of interesting and industrially important uses.

1. It can be added to metal powder mixtures being used in the fabrication of articles by powder metallurgy techniques. Titanium hydride increases the density of the compacted powder and improves the physical properties of the finished piece by reducing or preventing oxidation of the metal powder during the sintering process. The decomposition of the titanium hydride furnishes a protective atmosphere (5).

2. It is a ready source of pure titanium metal and may be used to form corrosion-resistant coatings of titanium on other metals. It also may be used as a convenient intermediate for adding small amounts of titanium to copper in the preparation of hard copper-titanium alloys.

3. It may be decomposed on a ceramic surface to deposit a layer of titanium metal that then may be used as a base for soldering, such as in the soldering of metal parts to ceramic parts. This technique, developed by R. J. Bondley of the General Electric Research Laboratory, is being used in the fabrication of electronic tubes and other manufactured components.

4. It may be used as a specific catalyst for organic hydrogenation reactions. (See *Properties* above.)

ZIRCONIUM

ZrH_2—*zirconium hydride*
Brittle black powder of indefinite composition
Density: 5.47 g/cc for $ZrH_{1.92}$
Heat of formation: 38.9 Kcal/mole for $ZrH_{1.92}$

Structure. Like the titanium-hydrogen system, the system zirconium-hydrogen can exist in several phases, depending upon the amount of hydrogen present in the metal. As small amounts of hydrogen are occluded, the normal hexagonal lattice merely expands; with larger amounts of hydrogen, the lattice rearranges to relieve strains set up by the lattice expansion. It has been reported that the hydrogen-rich phase, ZrH_2, has a tetragonal structure, but one or more intermediate phases may exist and the system is far from simple. The zirconium metal loses 15.4% of its normal density in the formation of $ZrH_{1.92}$.

Preparation. The methods described for the preparation of titanium hydride are applicable to the preparation of zirconium hydride. The simplest method of synthesis is to heat zirconium to ca. 900° in hydrogen and allow the metal to cool in a hydrogen atmosphere. Like titanium, zirconium resembles palladium in that the rapid diffusion of hydrogen into the metal occurs through rifts, and the formation of the interstitial alloy or compound is a relatively slow process. It also has been observed that the presence of small amounts of oxygen in the metal will inhibit or retard the occlusion of hydrogen (2). This may have an important bearing on the indefiniteness of the formulas of the transitional metal hydrides, since many metals, titanium and zirconium in particular, are very difficult to obtain free of all traces of oxygen.

Properties. Zirconium hydride appears to be a stable powder that is unaffected by air or moisture under normal conditions. It may be handled like any metallic powder provided that precautions are taken against accidental ignition of the material by open flames or sparks. The thermal dissociation of zirconium hydride is similar to that of titanium hydride, and the compound decomposes to hydrogen and metallic zirconium at a red heat. Like titanium hydride, zirconium hydride will catalyze certain organic hydrogenation reactions. It is inert toward most chemical reagents at room temperature.

Derivatives. Zirconium borohydride has been prepared and studied. (See Chapter 14.)

Uses. The decomposition of zirconium hydride on ceramic surfaces forms films of zirconium metal that may be used as bases for soldering. On metals, zirconium films formed by the decomposition of zirconium hydride may serve to protect the base metal from corrosion. Zirconium hydride finds some use in the electronics industry as a "getter" for vacuum tubes. The decomposition of a small amount of zirconium hydride within an electronic tube during the evacuation and just prior to the seal-off flashes a layer of metallic zirconium onto the tube wall, where it remains to adsorb any gases liberated during the operation of the tube. Zirconium hydride also is used as a convenient form of zirconium in the hardening of copper and the preparation of hard copper-zirconium alloys.

REFERENCES—TITANIUM AND ZIRCONIUM HYDRIDES

1. Sieverts and Gotta, *Ann.*, **453**, 289 (1927).
2. Smith, *Hydrogen in Metals*, University of Chicago Press, Chicago, Ill., 1948.
3. Alexander, U.S. Patent 2,427,338; 2,427,339 (1947).
4. Whitman, U.S. Patent 2,418,441 (1947).
5. Strauss, Steel, **118**, (18) 138, 160 (1946).

THE GROUP VA ELEMENTS—VANADIUM, NIOBIUM (COLUMBIUM), TANTALUM

All the elements in Group VA occlude hydrogen exothermically, but the heats of formation of the "hydrides" are relatively small.

Vanadium metal, if fresh, is almost inert to hydrogen, even at elevated temperatures. However, if the vanadium is activated by repeated exposure to hydrogen and outgassing at temperatures between 800° and 1100°, it will readily absorb several hundred times its own volume of hydrogen gas (1). The highest concentration of hydrogen in vanadium as yet reported corresponds to a formula of $VH_{0.71}$. Since the absorption of hydrogen causes an expansion of the crystal structure of the metal, the density of the vanadium hydride is less than that of vanadium metal by about 6 to 10%, depending upon the composition of the hydride (2). Much of the hydrogen in vanadium hydride probably is held in solid solution, although this is not known for certain.

Niobium (*columbium*) can absorb hydrogen gas in large quantities at elevated temperatures to form a brittle gray or black solid, niobium hydride. Normally, fresh niobium metal shows no absorptive capacity for hydrogen at room temperature, but, if the niobium is activated by heating in hydrogen at a high temperature, then on cooling to room temperature in hydrogen the metal will continue to absorb hydrogen slowly until a composition corresponding to $NbH_{0.86}$ is reached (3). The composition NbH is considered to be the limiting formula. The equilibrium amount of hydrogen in niobium hydride depends on the temperature; the H/Nb ratio at 900° is only 0.03, and the hydrogen can be removed entirely by vacuum outgassing at elevated temperatures. It is quite probable that the system niobium-hydrogen is a solid solution alloy of hydrogen in niobium. It appears fairly certain, however, that the diffusion of hydrogen into and through the metal occurs mainly in rifts in the metal structure.

Niobium metal also has been observed to absorb hydrogen and become brittle when it is used as a cathode in the electrolysis of sulfuric acid solutions (1).

Tantalum behaves similarly to niobium with hydrogen. If a tantalum wire or a piece of tantalum metal is heated in hydrogen, the ordinarily shiny and ductile metal assumes a dark gray appearance and is converted to a very hard and brittle solid tantalum hydride. The maximum hydrogen/tantalum ratio obtained experimentally corresponds to a formula of $TaH_{0.76}$. The absorption of hydrogen is accompanied by an expansion in the body-centered crystal lattice of the tantalum and an increase in molecular volume. The density of $TaH_{0.76}$ is 15.1 g per cc as compared to a value of 16.64 g per cc for tantalum metal (4). The electrical resistance of the tantalum metal rises during the process of hydrogen absorption; the resistance to $TaH_{0.76}$ is about double that of Ta.

The hydrogen can be removed from tantalum hydride by vacuum degassing at high temperatures, but the metal does not regain its original properties of sheen, ductility, or electrical resistance, and the original crystal lattice of the metal is not recovered. The process of hydrogen absorption and desorption appears to change the structure of the metal permanently.

Tantalum also becomes hardened by hydrogen absorption if the metal is used as a cathode in aqueous electrolyses. In this and in other respects, the behavior of tantalum toward hydrogen resembles that of palladium. Undoubtedly, the hydride of tantalum comprises a solid solution or interstitial alloy of hydrogen in tantalum metal; the diffusion of hydrogen into tantalum appears to occur largely through intergranular rifts.

The hardening of tantalum that occurs during hydrogen absorption is utilized in the fabrication of acid- and wear-resistant articles, such as spinnerets for rayon manufacture. The desired parts are machined from normal ductile tantalum metal; then these parts are surface-hardened or converted into very hard material by heating them in hydrogen. The volume change that accompanies hydride formation can be calculated and compensated for in the initial design.

Both tantalum hydride and niobium hydride exhibit electrical superconductivity at low temperatures (5).

REFERENCES—GROUP VA METAL HYDRIDES

1. Smith, *Hydrogen in Metals*, University of Chicago Press, Chicago, Ill., 1948.
2. Sieverts and Gotta, *Z. anorg. Chem.*, **172**, 1 (1928).
3. Sieverts and Moritz, *Z. anorg. Chem.*, **247**, 124 (1941).
4. Sieverts and Gotta, *Z. anorg. Chem.*, **187**, 156 (1930).
5. Horn and Ziegler, *J. Am. Chem. Soc.*, **69**, 2762 (1947).

THE GROUP VIA ELEMENTS—CHROMIUM, MOLYBDENUM, AND TUNGSTEN

With the possible exception of chromium, the Group VIA elements occlude hydrogen endothermically.

Although *chromium* does not form any definite hydride compound, it is possible for chromium metal to absorb large volumes of hydrogen under certain circumstances. Electrolytic chromium metal prepared by the electrolysis of chromium salts in aqueous solution may contain as much as 300 volumes of hydrogen per unit volume of metal (1). This hydrogen is held either by occlusion in rifts in the loose brittle structure of the electrodeposited metal, or possibly in solid solution as a hydrogen-chromium alloy. It can be shown that the absorbed hydrogen is not the cause of the hardness of electrolytic chromium.

The hydrogen-containing chromium ordinarily obtained by electrolytic deposition has the same body-centered crystal lattice as normal chromium except that the lattice is somewhat expanded. The density of chromium corresponding to the empirical formula $CrH_{0.26}$ is 6.77 g per cc as compared to the value of 7.03 g per cc for normal chromium. The absorption of hydrogen by chromium appears to be slightly exothermic; the measured heat of absorption at 80° is 3.8 Kcal per mole of H_2 adsorbed (2). Above 300°, however, the absorption process is believed to be endothermic. The hydrogen contained in electrolytic chromium may be quite stable at room temperature, but it can easily be removed by heating the metal to 600° (3).

Snavely (4) has described two new and unusual chromium-hydrogen phases, a hexagonal chromium hydride and a face-centered cubic chromium hydride, prepared by the electrodeposition of chromium at fairly high current densities. Snavely considers that these are hydrogen-chromium solid solution alloys with limiting formulas of CrH and CrH_2. The highest hydrogen/chromium ratio observed in the analysis of these alloys indicated an empirical formula of $CrH_{1.7}$. Snavely's alloys were metallic, but they were very brittle and lost hydrogen rather easily on heating.

Weichselfelder and Thiede (5) have claimed the synthesis of a black solid chromium hydride by the reduction of an ether suspension of chromium trichloride with a phenyl Grignard reagent in the presence of hydrogen gas. It is possible, however, that the material actually obtained by Weichselfelder and Thiede comprised finely divided chromium metal on which considerable amounts of hydrogen may have been occluded or physically adsorbed.

Hydrogen is soluble to a limited extent in *molybdenum* at elevated temperatures, but at ordinary temperatures molybdenum does not occlude hydrogen. Actually, very little is known about the molybdenum-hydrogen system.

Ordinary metallic *tungsten* does not occlude gaseous hydrogen, at least at temperatures up to ca. 1200°. Very stable adsorbed films of hydrogen can form on fresh tungsten surfaces, but such films represent only tiny amounts of hydrogen (3).

Weichselfelder and Thiede (5) claimed to have prepared a tungsten hydride by reducing tungsten trichloride with a Grignard reagent in the presence of hydrogen. This synthesis has not been substantiated, nor has it been disproved. It is possible that considerable amounts of hydrogen might be adsorbed by the finely divided and reactive tungsten metal that is produced by the reduction of tungsten halide with organic reducing agents, or even that unstable hydride compounds might result. However, until a hydride of tungsten is definitely established, we should view the results of Weichselfelder and Thiede with a certain amount of skepticism.

REFERENCES—GROUP VIA METAL HYDRIDES

1. Huttig and Brodkorb, Z. anorg. Chem., 144, 341 (1925).
2. Sieverts and Gotta, Z. anorg. Chem., 172, 1 (1928).
3. Smith, Hydrogen in Metals, University of Chicago Press, Chicago, Ill., 1948.
4. Snavely, Trans. Electrochem. Soc., 92, 552 (1947).
5. Weichselfelder and Thiede, Ann., 447, 64 (1926).

THE GROUP VIIA ELEMENTS—MANGANESE, TECHNETIUM, AND RHENIUM

As yet, no definite hydrides of manganese or of the related elements technetium and rhenium have been prepared. The transient molecule, MnH, has, however, been observed and studied in the spectra of electrical discharges in hydrogen between electrodes of manganese (1). Presumably, similar hydride molecules could be observed for technetium and rhenium.

Hydrogen appears to be quite soluble in, or readily absorbed by, manganese. It has been found that 100 g of freshly prepared electrolytic manganese may contain as much as 250 cc of hydrogen. This hydrogen, however, may be removed by heating the metal to 400° to 500° in air or in a vacuum (2). The careful work of Sieverts and Moritz also indicates that hydrogen is appreciably soluble in manganese. These authors consider that this solubility is much higher than that observed with the related elements, chromium, iron, cobalt, and nickel. This investigation did not disclose the formation of any new solid phases that might be indicative of a manganese hydride within a temperature range of 20° to 1320° and under hydrogen pressure of one atmosphere. The various phase transformations of the manganese structure, however, were observed as discontinuities on the curves of solubility versus temperature since the solubility of hydrogen is different in the different phases (3).

REFERENCES—GROUP VIIA ELEMENTS

1. Pearse and Gaydon, *Nature*, **139**, 590 (1937).
2. Potter, Hayes, and Lukens, *Chem. Abstr.*, **39**, 3735 (1945).
3. Sieverts and Moritz, *A. physik. Chem.*, **A180**, 249 (1937).

THE GROUP VIII ELEMENTS—IRON, COBALT, AND NICKEL

There is a great deal of information to be found in the chemical literature about "hydrides" of iron, cobalt, and nickel. Much of this information is rather confusing, however, and there are serious doubts that hydride compounds of these metals really exist.

It appears to be well established that iron, cobalt, and nickel have only small capacities for occluding hydrogen gas as compared with the occluding capacities of other transitional metals, even when they are considered over a rather wide temperature range. Such occlusion of hydrogen as does occur is an endothermic process, and there is good evidence to show that no chemical bonds are formed between hydrogen atoms and metal atoms within the metal structures. It is possible for some diffusion of hydrogen to occur in rifts in the metal structures, or even for hydrogen to produce such rifts at high temperatures as it is known to do with other transitional metals. However, it is safe to say that iron, cobalt, and nickel do not combine with hydrogen at elevated temperatures (1).

The above argument does not disprove the existence of hydrides of iron, cobalt, or nickel, however, and a number of investigators have reported the preparation of what they considered to be hydrides of these elements by reducing metallic salts with organic reducing agents at relatively low temperatures in the presence of hydrogen. The products of such reactions are dark, finely divided powders that often contain large amounts of hydrogen. The powders so prepared usually are pyrophoric, that is, they ignite and burn upon exposure to air, and they usually are very active as catalysts for organic hydrogenation reactions. It should be realized, however, that the very finely divided metal powders that are prepared by such reduction techniques may have a tremendous amount of active surface area and, consequently, an immense adsorptive power for gases and liquids; the surface undoubtedly is very active chemically. Indeed, the catalytic activity of such metal powders must depend to a considerable extent on these properties. Therefore, many compounds that originally were considered to be true hydrides because they contained large amounts of hydrogen may have been only finely divided reduced metals, with considerable amounts of hydrogen physically adsorbed on the surfaces. Such finely divided metals also would show a somewhat different pattern by X-ray diffraction than would the normal metals.

We may argue in such cases that the adsorbed hydrogen is probably held on the metal surfaces as atomic hydrogen, and that chemical bonds are formed between the hydrogen atoms and the metal atoms. This point can hardly be denied, but it does lead to arguments about the definition of a compound. We shall consider that a compound must be a three-dimensional structure rather than a two-dimensional surface phenomenon.

Banus and Gibb (2) have attempted to repeat the synthesis of iron and nickel hydrides, as reported by Schlenk, Weichselfelder, and Thiede (3). This synthesis entails the reduction of iron or nickel chloride in ether with phenylmagnesiumbromide under an atmosphere of hydrogen. Banus and Gibb concluded that the reactions did not lead to hydrides of iron or nickel.

REFERENCES—HYDRIDES OF Fe, Co, AND Ni

1. Smith, *Hydrogen in Metals*, University of Chicago Press, Chicago, Ill., 1948.
2. Banus and Gibb, Paper presented at the American Chemical Society 119th Meeting, Cleveland, Ohio, April, 1951.
3. Schlenk and Weichselfelder, *Ber.*, **56**, 2230 (1923). Weichselfelder and Thiede, *Ann.*, **447**, 64 (1926).

THE NOBLE METALS

There appears to be very little consistency in the behavior of *ruthenium, osmium, rhodium, iridium*, and *platinum* with hydrogen. Although hydrogen has a very low solubility in these metals, all of them will exhibit some absorption of hydrogen at elevated temperatures, or under the unusual conditions of electrolysis or electrical discharge.

It is considered that hydrogen absorbed by any of the noble metals, except *palladium*, probably is merely occluded in rifts or defects in the metal structures, as well as physically adsorbed to some extent on the surface of the metal. Thus the absorption depends greatly upon the previous history of the particular metal sample investigated; in any case, the amount of hydrogen absorbed is relatively small. There is evidence to suggest that the occluded hydrogen is ionized in the rifts, or activated in some way, since the noble metals, platinum in particular, are good catalysts for many chemical reactions involving hydrogen as a reactant.

The system *palladium-hydrogen* has been the subject of much investigation since metallic palladium readily absorbs and holds large volumes of hydrogen even at room temperature and pressure. A piece of palladium acting as a cathode in an electrolytic dissociation of water will rapidly absorb many times its own volume of hydrogen, and, at the same time, the metal will undergo a noticeable expansion in volume. The absorption of hydrogen by palladium is accompanied by a large change in the crystal structure of the palladium. The face-centered crystal lattice of the metal simply expands from its normal value, $a = 3.883$ A. U., to a slightly larger size, $a = 3.894$ A. U., with the initial adsorption of hydrogen; then it undergoes a rapid expansion to a much larger lattice, $a = 4.08$ A. U., and keeps on growing if still more hydrogen is taken into the structure. At the same time, the electrical resistance of the metal rises slightly. Experimentally, samples of palladium have been made to adsorb over 1000 times their own volume of hydrogen.

It is believed that the initial absorption of hydrogen into the palladium is through rifts in the metal structure since the previous history of the metal sample may have a considerable bearing on the rate at which absorption occurs. For example, a vacuum-annealed sample of palladium will absorb hydrogen only very slowly, but a sample of palladium that previously has absorbed hydrogen and then has had that hydrogen removed by vacuum treatment at a moderate temperature will rapidly reabsorb hydrogen. There also is good evidence to suggest that the mechanism whereby hydrogen will diffuse through a thin sheet of palladium (used in the purification of hydrogen) or into the interior of a solid piece of palladium is via rifts created in the structure by the lattice expansion that accompanies the absorption process.

The diffusion of hydrogen into the rifts is followed by an alloying of the hydrogen with the palladium in the solid metal adjacent to the rifts. This alloying is, in effect, the formation of a solid solution of *metallic hydrogen* in palladium in which the hydrogen probably is present as protons occupying interstices between palladium atoms in the palladium crystal lattice and taking part in the metallic bonding in the crystal. The limiting composition depends on the temperature, but normally it is about $PdH_{0.7}$ to $PdH_{0.8}$. Once formed, this alloy may be stable for long periods at room temperature, even in a vacuum.

At elevated temperatures in vacuum, the hydrogen will slowly diffuse out of solution and the expanded palladium lattice will collapse.

GENERAL REFERENCES—HYDRIDES OF THE NOBLE METALS

Smith, *Hydrogen in Metals*, University of Chicago Press, Chicago, Ill., 1948.
Müller and Schwabe, *Z. physik. Chem.*, **154**, 143 (1931).
Bredig and Allolis, *Z. physik. Chem.*, **126**, 49 (1927).

CHAPTER

16

The Borderline Hydrides

Chapter 6 described how the hydrides of beryllium and magnesium represent a transition in type between the predominantly ionic hydrides of lithium and sodium and the predominantly covalent hydrides of the remaining elements in the upper rows of the Periodic Table.

The borderline hydrides to be described in this chapter are the hydrides of elements in Groups IB, IIB, and IIIB (*copper, silver, gold, zinc, cadmium, mercury, indium,* and *thallium*) that should represent a transition in type between the metallic hydrides of the transitional elements and the covalent hydrides in the lower rows of the Periodic Table. However, a number of these elements do not form stable hydrides and, as a whole, these compounds do not fit so nicely into a general descriptive scheme as do the hydrides of beryllium and magnesium.

The existence of the hydrides of *copper* and *zinc* appears to be fairly well proved and, from the little that is known about these compounds, they do appear to be intermediate in type. Copper, for example, forms both an unstable solid hydride and an unstable volatile gaseous hydride observable only at elevated temperatures. There are indications that zinc may behave somewhat similarly.

If we consider the covalent hydrides as a group, we notice that thermal stability decreases both in descending a given group and in passing from right to left back along any given row in the Periodic Table. Thus the anticipated covalent hydrides of *indium, thallium, cadmium,* and *mercury* all appear to be too unstable to exist at room temperature.

Silver and *gold* should behave more like the transitional metals immediately preceding these elements than like the elements that form covalent hydrides. Experimental observations seem to support this conclusion. Silver and gold resemble the noble metals and are rather inert to hydrogen, but under some conditions they may occlude small amounts of hydrogen. In no case has the existence of a definite gold or silver hydride compound been established, although descriptions of such compounds are to be found in the literature.

COPPER

CuH—*copper hydride*
Solid red-brown powder
CuH?—*transient volatile compound*

Structure. The structure of the solid hydride of copper has not been determined. The existence of this compound as a definite substance is confirmed, however, by X-ray diffraction studies. It has a face-centered cubic lattice and a lattice constant of 4.33 A. U. This may be compared to the value of 3.62 A. U., for copper metal to show that an expansion of the copper lattice does occur upon hydride formation. The density of copper hydride as determined by X-ray analysis is 5.30 g per cc (1).

Preparation. The solid hydride of copper is prepared by reducing a solution of copper sulfate with sodium hypophosphite or hypophosphorous acid at about 70°. The resulting precipitate of reddish-brown copper hydride is washed with water, then with ether, and is dried at room temperature, (2). The material usually contains water of hydration (1).

The existence of a transient volatile hydride of copper can be observed when freshly reduced and finely divided copper, as in the form of copper powder or copper filings, is heated to a temperature of 250° to 400° in a stream of hydrogen. Under these conditions copper is picked up and volatilized by the hydrogen stream, and is redeposited as a copper mirror on the walls of the tube. This effect frequently is observed in small laboratory hydrogen purifiers in which hydrogen to be purified is passed over copper gauze or copper shot heated in a Pyrex tube. Examination of such an apparatus after it has been in use for some time usually reveals that the Pyrex tube has been coated with a mirror of copper metal. The transitory nature of the volatile copper hydride, at the temperature of the reaction at least, is indicated by the relatively short distances over which the transport of copper takes place.

It has been reported that the action of atomic hydrogen on copper metal yields an unstable hydride. This material is described as being unstable in air, oxidizing rapidly to copper oxide (3).

Properties. The solid form of copper hydride, if dry, begins to decompose at about 60°, with the formation of hydrogen and elemental copper. Upon exposure to air it is partially oxidized to copper oxide. It is decomposed by acids, and hydrogen is liberated. Copper hydride is a reducing agent, and it is capable of reducing certain ions in solution, such as chlorate to chloride, ferricyanide to ferrocyanide, etc. (4). The compound is attacked by the halogens. Copper hydride has been tried as a reducing agent for some organic syntheses, but it has been shown to be a relatively poor reducing agent for such applications. It will not, for example, reduce benzoyl chloride to benzoic acid (5). It will, however, reduce diazonium salts to aryl halides, or diazonium sulfate to phenol. In these examples a small amount of benzene is formed also (6).

Uses. Since the solid hydride of copper does decompose at moderate temperatures to form elemental copper, it has been suggested that this compound might be employed to copper-plate various articles. This may be useful particularly in those cases where electroplating is impossible, such as on a ceramic body (7). Copper hydride may be an active intermediate in the formation of compounds containing silicon-bonded hydrogen by the reaction of copper-catalyzed silicon with hydrogen chloride–hydrogen mixtures (8).

REFERENCES—COPPER HYDRIDE

1. Huttig and Brodkorb, *Z. anorg. u. allgem., Chem.*, **153,** 235 (1926).
2. Wurtz, *Ann. chim. phys.* (3), **11,** 250.
3. Pietsch and Josephy, *Naturwissenschaften*, **19,** 737 (1931).
4. Gladstone and Tribe, *J. Chem. Soc.*, **1878,** 33, 306.
5. Nuenhofer and Nerdl, *J. prakt. Chem.*, **144,** 63 (1935).
6. Niogi and Mitra, *J. Chem. Soc.*, **1928,** 1332.
7. Wagner, *Osterr. Chem. Ztg.*, **40,** 425 (1937).
8. Rochow, *Chemistry of the Silicones*, Wiley, New York, 1951.

SILVER

There is some chemical evidence for the existence of a hydride of silver although no definite compounds have been isolated and characterized.

Pietsch and Seuferling (1) have described the preparation of a solid hydride of silver by subjecting a silver plate to a stream of atomic hydrogen. The absorption reaction is exothermic. The white salt-like powder thus formed is dissociated by water to form gaseous hydrogen and silver hydroxide. It is reported to be stable in air or in hydrogen to a temperature of 500°, volatilizing at higher temperatures. In view of the low thermal stability of the solid hydrides of copper and gold, and the chemical reactivity of copper hydride, this seems surprising.

Stareck and Taft (2) observed that, when they electrolyzed a solution of silver nitrate with platinum electrodes at rather high current densities, the silver deposit on the cathode became black in color and increased in volume. Although no quantitative analyses were made, the investigators concluded that the chemically reactive black deposit was a hydride of silver since it appeared to have strong reducing properties. The material liberated hydrogen upon treatment with acids, was soluble in a solution of sodium cyanide or sodium thiosulfate, and reduced sodium sulfite to free sulfur. It is possible, however, that the deposit comprised hydrogen adsorbed on silver in a very finely divided form.

The study of the band spectra of the molecule AgH, occurring in electric discharges between silver electrodes in hydrogen, has been of theoretical interest to a number of investigators.

REFERENCES—SILVER HYDRIDE

1. Pietsch and Seuferling, *Naturwissenschaften*, **19**, 573 (1931).
2. Stareck and Taft, *Trans. Electrochem. Soc.*, **67**, 357 (1935).

GOLD

It has been reported by Pietsch and Josephy (1) that gold foil exposed to atomic hydrogen becomes covered with a layer of a solid gold hydride. This compound is described as a white material which decomposes upon being heated in hydrogen at temperatures above 100°, and which is destroyed upon exposure to air.

There also is evidence for a transient volatile hydride of gold from the observed volatility of gold in a stream of hydrogen at a temperature above 1200°. This phenomenon is similar to that observed with copper except that the temperature required is much higher (2).

REFERENCES—GOLD HYDRIDE

1. Pietsch and Josephy, *Naturwissenschaften*, **19**, 737 (1931).
2. Mostowitsch and Pletneff, *Met. Chem. Eng.*, **16**, 153 (1915).

ZINC

ZnH$_2$—*zinc hydride*
Non-volatile white solid

Prior to 1947, the only hydride of zinc reported in the chemical literature was the transient hydride, ZnH, whose band spectra have been observed in electrical discharges. With the discovery of powerful hydride reducing agents such as lithium aluminum hydride, however, it has become possible to prepare hydride compounds of zinc by metathetical reactions.* The most satisfactory reaction is the interaction of dimethyl zinc with lithium aluminum hydride in an ether solution:

$$Zn(CH_3)_2 + 2LiAlH_4 \rightarrow ZnH_2 + 2LiAlH_3CH_3$$

Zinc hydride is a white, non-volatile solid which does not appear to be soluble in ether. Presumably it is highly polymerized through hydrogen bridge bonds similar to those responsible for the high molecular weight and insolubility of the hydrides of beryllium, magnesium, and aluminum. It decomposes very slowly at room temperature. Surprisingly enough, zinc hydride reacts only slowly with water, and acid is necessary to complete the hydrolysis of this compound. Zinc hydride suspended in ether readily adds diborane to form *zinc borohydride*, $Zn(BH_4)_2$; this compound has not been investigated in detail as yet.

CADMIUM

Attempts to prepare a cadmium hydride by the reaction of a cadmium dialkyl, such as dimethylcadmium, with lithium aluminum hydride at the temperature of Dry Ice have indicated the formation of a white solid hydride.* This compound, presumably CdH_2, appears to be stable at $-78.5°$, but it cannot be warmed to room temperature without complete decomposition into hydrogen and metallic cadmium; the decomposition reaction occurs very rapidly at about $2°$.

The transient molecule CdH has been observed in the spectra of electrical discharges between cadmium electrodes in hydrogen gas, and has been studied by a number of investigators.

MERCURY

A solid hydride of mercury has been reported by Geib and Harteck,† who treated mercury with atomic hydrogen at the temperature of liquid nitrogen. Although not all the mercury was converted to a hydride, the investigators found that concentrations of hydrogen corresponding to 72% of a compound HgH, or 36% HgH_2, were absorbed by the mercury. It was ascertained further that only active hydrogen, that is, atomic hydrogen, was absorbed. The mercury

---

* Barbaras, Dillard, Finholt, Wartik, Wilzbach, and Schlesinger, *J. Am. Chem. Soc.*, **73**, 4585 (1951). These authors also have indicated the formation of intermediate compounds, such as methyl zinc hydride.

† Geib and Harteck, *Ber.*, **B65**, 1550 (1932).

hydride compound was quite unstable; its decomposition began at −125° and was complete at −100°.

Attempts by Barbaras and his coworkers* to prepare mercury hydride by the reaction of a mercury alkyl with lithium aluminum hydride at −80° have not been successful.

A transient hydride of mercury, HgH, is observed in the spectra of electric discharges in mercury vapor tubes containing hydrogen. This molecule has been the subject of a considerable number of theoretical investigations.

INDIUM

No definite hydride compounds of indium have as yet been isolated or characterized. There are, however, indications that such compounds may exist, at least in a transitory form. From a consideration of the known hydrides of the Group III elements, that is, those of boron, aluminum, and gallium, the normal covalent hydride of indium might be expected to be a volatile compound, In_2H_6 (possibly InH_3), which, in any case, would be rather unstable thermally.

In his experimentation with the action of atomic hydrogen on metals, Pietsch (1) observed that indium vapor reacted with atomic hydrogen to form a volatile hydride which could be frozen out of the gas stream with liquid nitrogen. When it was allowed to warm up and volatilize, this compound decomposed to leave a deposit of metallic indium on the surface of the glass container.

Downes and Kahlenberg (2) melted pure indium metal in pure hydrogen and noticed a brown deposit that formed on the surface of the indium as soon as the metal melted (155°). At about 330° this deposit suddenly disappeared, leaving the metal clean and bright. If the temperature was lowered, the deposit reappeared at 330°. Both the reactants were very pure, and it was assumed by the investigators that the deposit was a hydride of indium unstable at temperatures above 330°. Since this behavior is inconsistent with that which might be expected of a covalent hydride of indium, it is surmised that the deposit observed may have been a metallic hydride.

Wiberg and Schmidt (3) have reported the observation of unstable derivatives of indium hydride, such as *indium aluminum hydride*, In (AlH₄)₃, and, possibly, *lithium indium hydride*, LiInH₄. These compounds have not been characterized as yet, and they appear to decompose rapidly at rather low temperatures. They have been

* See footnote on page 197 for reference. In one experiment a transitory white precipitate was observed briefly before decomposition into mercury and hydrogen ensued.

prepared by the reaction of indium trichloride with lithium aluminum hydride or lithium hydride.

REFERENCES—INDIUM HYDRIDE

1. Pietsch, Z. Elektrochem., **39,** 583 (1933).
2. Downes and Kahlenberg, Trans. Electrochem. Soc., **63,** 155 (1933).
3. Wiberg and Schmidt, Z. Naturforschg., **6b,** 172 (1951).

THALLIUM

Although no definite hydrides of thallium have been isolated and characterized, Pietsch* has found chemical evidence for the existence of a volatile thallium hydride formed by the action of atomic hydrogen on elemental thallium. When atomic hydrogen was passed over compacted elemental thallium at a temperature of 136° and at a total pressure of about 1 mm, a mirror of metallic thallium formed on the wall of the reaction tube about 4 cm downstream from the thallium compact. The identity of the mirror as thallium was shown by chemical tests. At the operating temperature of 136° the vapor pressure of thallium is only 10^{-9} mm so that the formation and decomposition of a volatile thallium hydride comprise the only mechanism that can account for the transport of thallium. Undoubtedly, thallium hydride is a very unstable compound.

* Pietsch, Z. Elektrochem., **39,** 577 (1933).

CHAPTER

17

Nomenclature of the Hydrides

In this book the term *hydride* has been used rather loosely as a very general name for a large number of the compounds of hydrogen. This has been done largely for convenience (generic names are useful word-savers), but also because for many of the hydrides not enough is known to permit the assignment of proper names based on chemical and structural considerations. In this book an attempt has been made to use, as far as possible, the most common and generally accepted name for each compound discussed.

The nomenclature of the inorganic compounds of hydrogen is as complex as that in any field of chemistry, not only because hydrogen forms compounds with most of the chemical elements, but also because hydrogen assumes such a wide variety of chemical properties in these compounds. The problem is further complicated in that some of the hydrides have been familiar since ancient times and have common names not readily adaptable to a systematic nomenclature. Examples of this are *water* and *ammonia*. A proper naming of the derivatives of hydrides and the mixed hydride systems not only is difficult, but also in many of these cases a particular problem exists in correlating the inorganic nomenclature with accepted organic nomenclature.

It is the purpose of this chapter to describe the various methods by which hydride compounds are named, and to indicate some instances where a reform in nomenclature might be desirable, rather than to lay down a set of rules for naming hydrides. In considering the examples that follow, it should be borne in mind that certain of the compounds named as convenient examples actually may not be known.

The "ide" System. A system of nomenclature that is used extensively in inorganic chemistry for naming binary compounds is the *"ide"* system. In this system a compound always is considered as a derivative of its more electropositive component element. The negative component is designated by attaching the suffix "ide" to the word stem of the element name. Thus, for example, we have the name *sodium chloride*. The number of component atoms in the molecule may be designated by prefixes: *calcium dichloride*, $CaCl_2$; *dialuminum trioxide*, Al_2O_3, etc. In practice, however, a knowledge of the valence is usually assumed, and the prefixes are not used in naming familiar compounds. Composition may also be indicated by identifying the particular valence state of the positive component if this is known to have more than one valence state: *ferric chloride* or *iron*(III) *chloride*, $FeCl_3$; *cuprous oxide* or *copper*(I) *oxide*, Cu_2O.

The relative positivities and negativities of the elements with respect to each other have been defined for nomenclature purposes in a list adopted by the International Union of Chemistry:

B, Si, C, Sb, As, P, N, H, Te, Se, S, I, Br, Cl, F, O.

It will be observed that there are some irregularities in this listing, although in general it does correspond to the relative electronegativity of the elements.

A strict interpretation of the term *hydride*, taking into consideration the accepted use of the "ide" system, should limit its use to those compounds in which hydrogen obviously is the negative component of the molecule; for example, *sodium hydride* and *calcium hydride*. Consistent with this system of nomenclature, those compounds in which hydrogen is the more positive component (positivity again being defined by the I. U. C. list of elements) should be named as *hydrogen ———ides*. This is, of course, the customary usage in naming the hydrides of Groups VI and VII elements, for example, *hydrogen fluoride* and *hydrogen sulfide*. The problem of denoting valence or the number of component atoms is relatively simple in naming the binary hydrides since multiple valence states are encountered only in a few cases.

The "ide" system becomes unsatisfactory when an attempt is made to apply it to the hydrides of the elements of intermediate electropositivity. These compounds are covalent rather than ionic, and it is difficult in some cases to decide, except arbitrarily, where the dividing line is to be drawn between those elements more positive and those more negative than hydrogen. Use of the "ide" system would, in several cases, result in a reversal of the nomenclature pattern within a group of related elements if a nomenclature based strictly on relative electronegativity was followed. Furthermore, the more familiar compounds have well-established common names which have set a general pattern for naming the hydrides of other elements within the same group in the Periodic System.

A few examples of common hydride compounds and the names that have been or might be assigned to them under the "ide" system are:

Common Name and Formula	General Name	Specific Name
Sodium hydride, NaH	Sodium hydride	Sodium hydride
Calcium hydride, CaH_2	Calcium hydride	Calcium dihydride
Diborane, B_2H_6	Boron hydride	Diboron hexahydride
Methane, CH_4	Carbon hydride	Carbon tetrahydride
Silane, SiH_4	Silicon hydride	Silicon tetrahydride
Ammonia, NH_3	Nitrogen hydride	Nitrogen trihydride
Bismuthine, BiH_3	Bismuth hydride	Bismuth trihydride
Hydrogen sulfide, H_2S	Hydrogen sulfide	Dihydrogen sulfide
Hydrogen telluride, TeH_2	Hydrogen telluride	Dihydrogen telluride
Hydrogen chloride, HCl	Hydrogen chloride	Hydrogen chloride

The specific names are, in most cases, used only rarely if at all. Note that, according to the rule of precedence established by the I. U. C. list, H_2Te is named as a derivative of hydrogen even though tellurium probably is more electropositive than hydrogen. Similarly, ammonia would be named as a derivative of nitrogen, although nitrogen appears to be more electronegative than hydrogen.

It will be appreciated that for the hydrides of the alkali and alkaline earth metals the "ide" system is accepted usage. There is no doubt as to the role of hydrogen as the negative component in these compounds. The "ide" system also is used generally for naming the hydrogen compounds of Group VI and VII elements since in most (but not all) of these compounds the hydrogen, although not ionic, is more positive than its chemical partner. For naming the hydrides of the intermediate elements a different system is employed.

The "ine"-"ane" System. Most of the covalent hydrides have single word names derived from those of the parent elements. These names are formed by adding a suffix *"ine"* or *"ane,"* depending on the valence of the parent element, to the stem of the name of the parent element. Thus, for example:

Borine, BH_3	*Silane,* SiH_4
Phosphine, PH_3	*Germane,* GeH_4
Stibine, SbH_3	*Stannane,* SnH_4
Arsine, AsH_3	*Plumbane,* PbH_4

Members of a homologous series of hydrides are distinguished by the proper prefix denoting the number of atoms of the parent element. Thus:

Diborane, B_2H_6	*Tetrasilane,* Si_4H_{10}
Disilane, Si_2H_6	*Pentaborane,* B_5H_9
Trigermane, Ge_3H_8	*Decaborane,* $B_{10}H_{14}$

The derivatives of covalent hydrides may be named accordingly:

Dimethylsilane, $(CH_3)_2SiH_2$
Chlorostannane, SnH_3Cl
Trimethylarsine, $(CH_3)_3As$
Dichloromethylgermane, $(CH_3)GeHCl_2$
Bromodichlorosilane, $SiHBrCl_2$
Chlorodiborane, B_2H_5Cl
Diphenylstibine, $(C_6H_5)_2SbH$

Note that when more than one substituent is present in the molecule an alphabetical order of listing is followed. Unless substituted, the hydrogen atoms are taken for granted, and only the substituting groups are indicated in the names. Even when all the hydrogens have been substituted by other groups the pattern of nomenclature is maintained.

This general procedure is not followed exactly in naming the more common compounds of carbon with hydrogen since these have characteristic names of long standing. The "ane" ending is used, however, in naming the saturated hydrocarbons, *methane, ethane, etc.* The "ine" ending also is used to denote the apparent valence of three for double-bonded carbon in the unsaturated hydrocarbons, although with the spelling "ene," for example, *ethylene* or *ethene*, *butylene* or *butene*. Hydrocarbons in which carbon is triply bonded to carbon and has an apparent valence of two are named under the Geneva System with the ending "yne": *ethyne,* C_2H_2; *propyne*, $CH_3C\equiv CH$, etc. The aliphatic hydrocarbons of high molecular weight are named systematically according to the number of carbon atoms they contain, with appropriate endings to denote the kind and amount of unsaturation. Derivatives are named according to the system outlined above. Thus it may be seen that there is a reasonable amount of consistency between the nomenclature of the hydrocarbons and that of other covalent hydrides.

Although the hydride of nitrogen, *ammonia*, is not called *nitrine* or even *ammine*, it is of interest to note that ammonia in complex coordination compounds is designated by the term *ammine*, for example, *hexamminechromium(III) chloride,* $Cr(NH_3)_6Cl_3$. Derivatives of ammonia use the "ine" ending as in *methylamine, hydroxylamine,* and *hydrazine.*

The "ine"-"ane" system has much to recommend its use for naming the simple covalent hydrides and their derivatives. It is reasonably consistent, and, with the exception of the well-established common names for the compounds of carbon and nitrogen, the hydride names are derived easily from those of the parent elements. Difficulties are encountered, however, when a very complex system of organic derivatives is to be named. · In this category, for example, are the organic compounds of arsenic, many of which can be considered derivative of *arsine*. The "*ine*"-"*ane*" system has not been applied to the hydrides of the Groups VI and VII elements, although these compounds are predominantly covalent, and characteristic endings corresponding to the low valences of the halogens and chalcogens have not been developed.

Complex Hydrides. The complex hydrides are divided generally into two classes, the mixed, or molecular complex, hydrides formed by substitution reactions or equivalent processes, and the hydrides containing complex hydride anions or cations.

The mixed hydrides are relatively easy to name according to the customary procedure of adding the suffix "yl" to denote the radical form of the substituting group and considering the compound as a derivative of the other hydride involved. Thus:

> *Methylsilane*, CH_3SiH_3
> *Dimethyldiborane*, $(CH_3)_2B_2H_4$
> *Bis-disilylmethane*, $(Si_2H_5)_2CH_2$
> *Methylarsine*, CH_3AsH_2
> *Trimethylborine*, $(CH_3)_3B$
> *Germanylamine*, GeH_3NH_2

Note the use of the prefix "bis," which eliminates confusion by distinguishing between two *silyl* groups and the *disilyl* group, $Si_2H_5^-$. The order in which the groups comprising the complex hydride are named usually is determined by convenience; thus CH_3SiH_3 could be called either *silylmethane* or *methylsilane*. For convenience, the more complex compounds are generally considered to be derivatives of the element bonded to the largest number of groups other than hydrogen; thus $(CH_3)_3SiH$ usually is named *trimethylsilane*.

Certain of the more complex mixed hydrides have structures comprising heterocyclic rings. For example, a complex derivative of diborane and ammonia, $B_3N_3H_6$, has a ring structure of alternate boron and nitrogen atoms, each attached to one hydrogen atom. At present this compound is known as *borazole* or *triborinetriammine*, and its derivatives are named accordingly with appropriate prefixes to indicate the position of the substituting groups. Thus $B_3N_3H_5Cl$ with the halogen attached to a boron atom is called *B-chloroborazole*. Although these names are quite satisfactory to one familiar with the complex chemistry of the boranes, they do not indicate the cyclic nature of the compound, and thus are not as specific as might be desired.

It has been suggested that complex ring compounds might be named as derivatives of closely analogous hydrocarbon structures. This would be advantageous in one sense in that a person having some knowledge of organic chemistry would have no trouble in making the indicated substitutions in the compound name and arriving at the correct structural formula. Thus borazole would be named 1,3,5-*tribora*- 2,4,6-*triazabenzene*. The suffix "a" denotes a substituent in the ring structure. Similarly, the compound *cyclotrisiloxane*, $Si_3H_6O_3$, would be 1,3,5-*trisila*-2,4,6-*trioxacyclohexane*. Although names in this system are easily translatable into structural formulas, the system has not been adopted as yet, and there is a considerable amount of opposition on the part of inorganic chemists to naming purely inorganic compounds in terms of organic ring structures.

In the case of Groups I and VII hydrides no mixed hydrides are possible. The complex hydride derivatives of Group VI hydrides generally have special names. Examples of them are:

> *Methanol*, CH_3OH
> *Methylmercaptan*, CH_3SH
> *Silanol*, SiH_3OH
> *Trimethylsilanol*, $(CH_3)_3SiOH$
> *Disiloxane*, $H_3SiOSiH_3$

It will be seen that most of these can be considered as derivatives of water.

The complex ionic hydrides are divided into two general classes according to the positive or negative character of the complex hydride ion. The class in which complex hydride cations are present includes many familiar compounds such as the ammonium salts, the phosphonium compounds, and the hydronium ions. The name of the parent cation is made in each case by adding the suffix "onium" to the proper stem. Thus:

> *Ammonium* (from *ammine*), NH_4^+
> *Phosphonium*, PH_4^+
> *Arsonium*, AsH_4^+
> *Hydronium*, H_3O^+

Derivatives, if known, are named accordingly:

> *Methylammonium*, $CH_3NH_3^+$
> *Tetramethylammonium*, $(CH_3)_4N^+$
> *Tetraethylstibonium*, $(C_2H_5)_4Sb^+$

Complex hydrides in which there are complex hydride anions are relatively new, and no systematic nomenclature has been adopted as yet for such compounds. The procedure usually has been to describe the compound simply as a double hydride, making no indication of the ionic structure. Thus:

Sodium aluminum hydride, $NaAlH_4$
Lithium gallium hydride, $LiGaH_4$

Or, more precisely,

Sodium aluminum tetrahydride, etc.

In the case of the complex ionic hydrides in which boron is the central atom in the complex hydride anion the term *borohydride* is used, for example, *lithium borohydride*, $LiBH_4$.

It would be consistent with the general terminology for complex inorganic anions to name the complex anionic hydrides as salts of parent complex acids, the names of which would be derived from those of the corresponding oxyacids. Thus:

Lithium tetrahydroborate, $LiBH_4$
Lithium methanotrihydroaluminate, $LiAl(CH_3)H_3$
Sodium methoxytrihydroborate, $NaB(OCH_3)H_3$
Sodium tetramethanoborate, $NaB(CH_3)_4$

This procedure, if followed, would greatly simplify the naming of highly complex derivatives as well as establish a pattern for the naming of new complex hydrides as they are discovered.

Although some objections have been raised to the use of the "ate" ending for compounds containing no oxygen, it may be pointed out that the terms *fluoborate*, *chloroaluminate*, *thioarsenate*, etc., are in general use to designate salts of complex acids. At least with the alkali metal salts of the complex hydride anions of boron, aluminum, and gallium, there is no doubt as to the ionic nature of the compounds nor as to the existence of definite anions, such as BH_4^-. However, the compound known as *aluminum borohydride*, $Al(BH_4)_3$, almost certainly is covalent and would be misnamed as *aluminum tris(tetrahydroborate)*. Similarly, *beryllium borohydride* is only partly ionic in nature. For such cases, the "ide" terminology has been suggested. Thus aluminum borohydride could be called simply *aluminum boranide*, with the "ide" ending added to the hydride word stem rather than to the element name stem to denote the relatively negative component of the molecule. Lithium aluminum hydride similarly might be called *lithium aluanide,* derived from the name *aluane* for the hydride of aluminum.

Metal Derivatives. With the exception of the metal hydroxides and the metal derivatives of the hydrocarbons, that is, the metal alkyls and aryls, there are very few known metallic derivatives of the covalent hydrides. Most of them are named similarly to the metal alkyls by adding the suffix "yl" to the name stem of the hydride and following this with the name of the metal. Thus, for example:

$$Germanylsodium, \text{ GeH}_3\text{Na}$$
$$Trimethylsilylsodium, \text{ Si(CH}_3)_3\text{Na}$$

The metallic derivatives of ammonia are called *amides:* for example, *calcium amide,* $Ca(NH_2)_2$; *lithium amide,* $LiNH_2$. The name of the sodium derivative is usually abbreviated as *sodamide.* The nomenclature of the metal amides is, of course, inconsistent with the general use of the term *amide* in organic nomenclature and with the usual terminology for ammonia derivatives in inorganic nomenclature.

The Transitional Hydrides. The hydrides of the transitional elements have no systematic nomenclature and are named simply as *hydrides* whether or not they are considered definite compounds, for example, *titanium hydride, cerium hydride, palladium hydride.* In view of the general lack of knowledge concerning the structure and composition of the transitional hydrides this is the only approach possible at present.

Progress in Nomenclature. At present the nomenclature committees of the American Chemical Society and the National Research Council are collaborating with the International Union of Chemistry in working toward the establishment of a systematic and consistent set of rules for naming chemical compounds. It is hoped that much of the confusion in the present methods of nomenclature can be clarified and that the various conflicts between organic and inorganic nomenclature can be resolved to the mutual satisfaction of all chemists. This is particularly desirable in the field of hydride chemistry, which not only has grown rapidly in recent years but also considerably overlaps the domains of both inorganic and organic chemistry.

GENERAL REFERENCES

Jorissen et al., *J. Am. Chem. Soc.*, **63**, 889 (1941).
Scott, *Chem. Abst.*, **39**, 5867 (1945).

APPENDIX A

Deuterides

In general, the chemical properties of hydride compounds containing the heavier isotope of hydrogen, or *deuterium*, in place of normal hydrogen, or *protium*, will exhibit only minor differences from those of the normal hydrides. Furthermore, only a few *deuterides* or deuterium containing hydrides have been investigated to such an extent that valid comparisons with the normal hydrides can be made. For these reasons, very little has been said in this book about deuterides and deuterium compounds. Practically nothing is known about the corresponding compounds of the heaviest hydrogen isotope, *tritium*.

Structure. We should not expect the structural pattern of a hydride molecule to be changed appreciably by the substitution of deuterium for protium. Any differences in bond length and bond angle should be relatively minor.

Preparation of Deuterides. All the general methods for the synthesis of hydrides are applicable to the synthesis of deuterides. This assumes that pure deuterium gas or pure deuterium oxide is available as a starting material. For example, the hydrolysis of magnesium nitride in heavy water yields *deutero-ammonia*, or *ammonia-d3*;

$$Mg_3N_2 + 3D_2O \rightarrow 2ND_3 + 3Mg(OD)_2$$

By the direct reaction of deuterium with an alkali metal, an ionic deuteride can be formed:

$$2Li + D_2 \rightarrow 2LiD \; (lithium \; deuteride)$$

This ionic deuteride can then be used as an active reducing agent in the preparation of other deuterides:

$$4LiD + AlCl_3 \rightarrow LiAlD_4 + 3LiCl$$

Lithium aluminum deuteride formed in this fashion can be used as a general reagent to prepare covalent deuterides:

$$LiAlD_4 + SiCl_4 \rightarrow SiD_4 + LiCl + AlCl_3$$

Those compounds, such as ammonia, hydrogen sulfide, and the hydrogen halides, which are involved in proton transfer reactions in their aqueous solutions will undergo exchange reactions in heavy water:

$$NH_3 + D_2O \leftrightharpoons NH_3, NH_2D, NHD_2, ND_3$$

Many examples of such exchange reactions have been investigated.

Exchange reactions proceed only very slowly, if at all, with non-ionizing compounds such as methane and deutero-methane, unless certain catalytic agents are present to activate proton transfer.

Physical Properties. Because deuterium is heavier than protium, we should expect to find some differences between the physical properties of the hydrides and those of the corresponding compounds of deuterium. However, we also should expect to find that such differences are small with compounds of high molecular weight. A few comparisons follow (1):

Compound	Melting Point, °K	Boiling Point, °K	Heat of Vaporization, cal/mole
HCl	162.2	188.1	4,081
DCl	158.2	191.6	4,151
HI	222.3	237.5	4,724
DI	221.5	237.0	4,713
NH$_3$	195.3	239.8	5,797
ND$_3$	199.6	242.1	5,990
H$_2$O	273.2	373.2	10,735
D$_2$O	277.0	374.6	11,109

Chemical Properties. The heats of formation and thermal dissociation equilbria of deuterides as compared to hydrides usually are somewhat different. At 345°, the dissociation pressures of *sodium deuteride* and *potassium deuteride* are twice the dissociation pressures of the corresponding hydrides. The heat of formation of *potassium deuteride* is 14,450 cal per mole as compared to a value of 14,150 cal per mole for *potassium hydride*. The heat of formation of *sodium deuteride* is 15,800 cal per mole as compared to a value of 14,400 for *sodium hydride* (2). The decomposition pressure of *uranium deuteride* is about 1.4 times as great as the decomposition pressure of uranium hydride at temperatures within the range of 300° to 400°. The rate of reaction of deuterium with uranium metal at 357° is only about one-fourth as great as the rate of reaction of hydrogen with uranium metal at the same temperature (3). These differences in the reaction rates and dissociation pressures of deuterides as compared to hydrides have been suggested as a means for separating deuterium from hydrogen. It is expected that the *tritides* will show even larger differences from the hydrides in their dissociation pressures.

Heavy water, or *deuterium oxide*, is less basic than ordinary water, so that the ionization of acids does not proceed to as great an extent in heavy water as in ordinary water. The difference in degree of ionization becomes more pronounced as the strength of the acid decreases. Chemical reactions in heavy water generally are slower than in ordinary water; this difference in reaction rate probably applies generally to the hydrides and deuterides.

REFERENCES

1. Clusius, *Z. Elektrochem.*, **44**, 25 (1938).
2. Sellers and Crenshaw, *J. Am. Chem. Soc.*, **59**, 2015, 2724 (1937).
3. Spedding et al., *Nucleonics*, **4**, (1), 4 (1949).

APPENDIX B

Toxicology of the Hydrides

Although some references have been made in the preceding sections to certain hydrides which are particularly poisonous, it is considered appropriate and desirable to include a general survey of hydride toxicology. Personal safety in laboratory work and in industrial operations cannot be over emphasized; it is a matter of vital concern to everyone involved.

Since the action of poisonous substances is described most concisely in medical terminology, the following list defines some medical terms which are pertinent to hydride toxicology:

Anesthetic. An agent producing sleep or unconsciousness.

Anuria. Suppression of the urine.

Asphyxiant. An agent causing suffocation through deprivation of oxygen.

Dyspnea. Difficult or labored breathing.

Edema. Infiltration of body serum into tissue, fluid congestion.

Hemoglobinemia. The dissolution of hemoglobin from red corpuscles by body fluids.

Hemoglobinuria. Presence of hemoglobin in urine due to decomposition of red corpuscles.

Hemolytic. Causing changes in the blood; rupture of red blood corpuscles.

Hyperemia. Excessive congestion of blood in tissue or body member.

Protoplasmic poison. An agent destroying cell matter in general.

Systemic poison. An agent affecting operation of the organism as a whole.

Terms such as *nausea* and *irritant* are self-explanatory.

The Ionic Hydrides. Since the ionic hydrides are not volatile, they do not present serious internal toxicological problems. They are, however, very strong dehydrating agents, and the alkali residues produced by their reactions with moisture are irritating and corrosive to skin and other body tissues. The dusts of the ionic hydrides can be very irritating to the sensitive tissues of the eyes, nose, throat, and lungs. Simple safety precautions, such as gloves and dust filter masks, allow the safe handling of solid ionic hydrides. Of course,

212

proper precautions must be taken against fire as these materials are highly inflammable and may ignite upon contact with moisture.

The Transitional Metal Hydrides. As far as is known, the transitional metal hydrides present no toxicological problems. These materials are solid, non-volatile, and of a low order of chemical reactivity in general. We should, of course, avoid the inhalation of any metallic dusts, and general precautions, such as the use of dust filter masks, should be taken in handling the transitional metal hydrides in powder form.

The Volatile Covalent Hydrides. Many of the covalent hydrides present serious toxicological problems since vapors of these compounds can be present in relatively large concentrations in air. It is true that most of the covalent hydrides have strong characteristic odors, and many of these compounds can be detected by smell in very low concentrations. Smell is not a reliable indicator, however, as some of the covalent hydrides will rapidly paralyze one's ability to smell to the extent that really dangerous concentrations of poisonous gas are not noticed until serious physiological damage has been done.

The values of maximum allowable concentration (M.A.C.) listed in the discussion that follows have been adopted by the American Association of Governmental and Industrial Hygienists as of April, 1950. The values are in terms of parts per million of air and are for 8-hour exposures. It should be mentioned, however, that the limits are only approximate and that different individuals will vary widely in their susceptibilities to the various gases.

The *hydrogen halides* are very strong irritants since they dissolve in body moisture to form strong acids. If breathed into the lungs, the hydrogen halides may cause serious pulmonary edema. *Hydrogen fluoride* is especially dangerous since the fluoride ion is a direct protoplasmic poison. The M.A.C. of HF is 3 ppm. The M.A.C. of *hydrogen chloride* is 5 ppm. These values may be compared to the value of 10 ppm for the well-known poison hydrogen cyanide. Less is known of the toxic action of *hydrogen bromide* and *hydrogen iodide* although both bromide ion and iodide ion have bad physiological effects if present in the body in more than small concentrations.

With the exception of *water*, all Group VIA hydrides are highly poisonous. *Hydrogen sulfide* is an irritant, affecting the cornea of the eye in moderate concentrations and the respiratory tract in higher concentrations. In large concentrations, hydrogen sulfide can cause pulmonary edema. Although it can be detected by smell in concentrations as low as 0.18 ppm, hydrogen sulfide rapidly paralyzes the sense of smell and the function of the nervous system. Large concentrations of hydrogen sulfide will cause rapid death by a paralysis of the respiratory system. The M.A.C. of hydrogen sulfide is 20 ppm. *Hydrogen selenide* and *hydrogen telluride* are considerably more toxic than hydrogen sulfide. Hydrogen selenide is known to have a hemolytic effect; a short exposure to this gas may cause death several weeks later. Selenium compounds in general seem to be systemic poisons. The M.A.C. of hydrogen selenide is 0.05 ppm; it is believed to be more toxic than hydrogen telluride because of the instability of the latter gas.

Ammonia is very irritating as well as having a strong influence on the nervous system. Death from ammonia poisoning may result from cessation of breathing caused by respiratory paralysis. The gas may be detected by smell at a concentration of 53 ppm; large quantities may cause olfactory paralysis. The M.A.C. of ammonia is 100 ppm.

Phosphine is not as strong an irritant as ammonia but is considerably more toxic; the M.A.C. of phosphine is 0.05 ppm. Like ammonia, phosphine affects the nervous system, causing dyspnea, weakness, and convulsions. In small concentrations, phosphine does not appear to be a hemolytic agent, but it may cause hyperemia, especially in the lungs, kidneys, and brain. Chronic phosphorus poisoning may result from the decomposition of phosphine in the body.

Arsine is not an irritant, and there may be no immediate symptoms during or shortly after exposure to dangerous concentrations of this gas. Arsine, however, is a strong hemolytic agent, and, once the gas is inhaled, changes in the blood and the resulting deterioration of the liver, lungs, and kidneys may cause death within a few days to a week. Pathological symptoms of arsine poisoning include hemoglobinemia, hemoglobinuria, anuria, and anemia. Needless to say, arsine is highly toxic; the M.A.C. of this gas is 0.05 ppm. Some tolerance to arsine may be acquired by long exposure to small concentrations.

Stibine and *bismuthine* appear to be similar to arsine in their physiological action. Stibine is known to be a powerful hemolytic agent, and, in severe cases, it may produce pulmonary edema. Both stibine and bismuthine are probably more poisonous than arsine. The M.A.C. of stibine is 0.1 ppm; it probably should be much lower than this value, however.

Methane and the lower *hydrocarbons* act primarily as asphyxiants and, in some cases, may act as anesthetics. However, certain higher hydrocarbons, such as *benzene,* are known to be quite toxic. The M.A.C. of benzene is 35 ppm, whereas most aliphatic hydrocarbons have M.A.C. values ranging between 500 and 1000 ppm.

Little is known of the toxicity of *silane* except that breathing this gas may cause headache and nausea. The hydrolysis of silane in body tissues would form silicic acid or hydrated silica.

Germane has been shown to be a hemolytic agent, and thus it should be considered a poison. Its toxicity is similar in action to that of arsine, but it is not considered to be dangerous to the same degree.

The *hydrides* of tin and *lead* are considered to be even more toxic than arsine. The inhalation of *stannane* produces hyperemia as well as severe disturbances of the nervous system. Stannane may possibly be a hemolytic agent also.

Although the *hydrides* of *boron* have not been extensively investigated to determine their physiological action, sufficient evidence is at hand to show that these compounds are highly toxic (1). The inhalation of small quantities of *diborane, pentaborane*, etc., can produce headache, nausea, weakness, tremors, and convulsions as well as a general mental lassitude. The boranes may have a specific effect on the nervous system. Although the hydrolysis of these materials in the body produces boric acid or boric acid derivatives, they are much more poisonous than can be accounted for on this basis alone.

In the laboratory, the precautions that we can take against poisoning by the covalent hydrides are simple and obvious. Work should be done in a well-designed hood supplied with a good draft. The major hazard of the volatile hydrides comes in industrial operations where such materials may be produced accidentally. Here, the use of gas masks is indicated, provided that means or devices are available for detecting the poisonous gases. A simple automatic monitoring system has been developed to indicate the presence of boron hydrides in dangerous amounts. It likely will be applicable to the detection of other poisonous volatile hydrides (2).

REFERENCES

1. Rozendaal, A. M. A. *Archives of Industrial Hygiene and Occupational Medicine.* **4**, 257 (1951).
2. Etherington and McCarty, A. M. A. *Archives of Industrial Hygiene and Occupational Medicine*, May (1952).

GENERAL REFERENCES

Webster, *J. Indust. Hyg. & Toxicol.*, **28**, 167 (1946).
Sax, *Handbook of Dangerous Materials*, Reinhold, New York. 1951.

APPENDIX C

The Vacuum Manipulation of Volatile Compounds

For a complete discussion of the techniques of vacuum manipulation of volatile compounds, the reader should consult one or both of the following references:

R. T. Sanderson, *Vacuum Manipulation of Volatile Compounds*, Wiley, New York, 1948.

A. Stock, *The Hydrides of Boron and Silicon*, Cornell University Press, Ithaca, N.Y., 1933.

In brief, the handling, distillation, purification, and storage of volatile compounds, as well as the conducting of chemical reactions and the measuring of physical properties, can be accomplished at sub-atmospheric pressures and relatively low temperatures in closed systems. Such systems are, for laboratory work at least, made entirely of glass. However, all-metal systems, or systems comprising combinations of metal and glass, may be employed for larger-scale work if the particular compounds being handled do not react with the metals of construction. Metal systems are much less fragile than glass systems, but they may be more difficult to make vacuum-tight.

Figure 4 illustrates a very simple type of "vacuum system." (It will be appreciated that very complicated systems may be constructed for special purposes.) If it is desired, for example, to distill and condense a volatile gas, for example, from the storage bulb into bulb A, we merely evacuate the system and the bulb A (the storage bulb is shut off from the system during the evacuation), then cool bulb A in a suitable refrigerant, such as liquid nitrogen or Dry Ice, depending upon the volatility of the volatile compound. Opening the stop-cocks (1) and (2) then allows the gas to flow from the storage bulb and condense in bulb A. Similarly, if bulb B should contain a different gas or volatile liquid which is to be added as a reactant to the material in bulb A, opening stopcock (3) will allow the material in bulb B to distill over into bulb A. If desired, a measurement can be made of the quantity of the reactant added to A by first filling the storage bulb (of known capacity) to the calculated pressure, then transferring the material by condensation into bulb A. As bulb A is allowed to warm up and the reaction proceeds, the progress of the reaction may

216

be observed by pressure measurements with the manometer. For general laboratory use, vacuum systems are assembled with standard taper ground joints, or ground ball and socket joints, with stopcocks both above and below the joints so that bulbs may be removed or connected to the system, or material insertions and removals made, as desired.

The vacuum system may also be used for fractional distillation. If bulb A were to contain a mixture of two materials of different volatil-

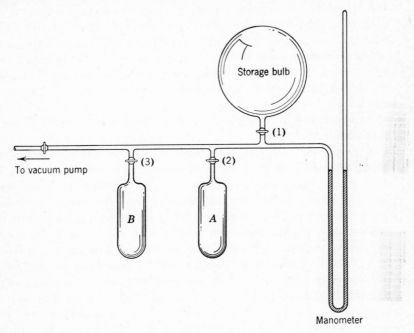

FIGURE 4

ity, then by cooling bulb A to one temperature and bulb B to a lower temperature (temperatures again determined by the volatilities), and connecting the two bulbs through the system, it would be possible to effect a separation of the components in bulb A through their differences in volatility. The most volatile fraction would condense mainly in bulb B, whereas the less volatile fraction would remain primarily in bulb A. The system is, in effect, a one-plate distillation unit, and the degree of separation will depend on the relative volatilities of the components. By using a *series* of bulbs at different temperatures, it is possible to achieve a distillation separation with an efficiency of several theoretical plates, or separate a multicomponent mixture.

Two rather considerable advantages are inherent in the vacuum manipulation technique. Dangerous materials that may be poisonous or spontaneously inflammable in air can be handled with complete safety, barring accidental leaks or breakage of the system. (CAUTION. Liquid *air* should never be used as a refrigerant. Liquid *nitrogen* should always be used for temperatures in the lower ranges.) The use of low temperatures to achieve the pressure differentials necessary for distillation and material transfer makes possible the handling and investigation of many thermally unstable substances that cannot exist at room temperature, or that might decompose at the higher temperatures necessary for distillation at atmospheric pressure.

This discussion was meant to be simple, and it is intended only to serve as a very brief introduction to some of the possibilities of the vacuum manipulation technique. The reader is well advised to consult the references mentioned above if he is interested in learning more about this elegant method of working with volatile chemical substances.

It might be added that a "dry box" is a very useful tool for those who wish to work with solid and liquid substances that are hygroscopic, spontaneously inflammable, or are otherwise decomposed by the normal laboratory atmosphere. A "dry box" in its most simple form is a square box of wood or metal with a window at one side or the top through which the operator can observe what he is working with, a pair of rubber gloves projecting into the box from the front side into which the operator can put his hands to manipulate articles inside the box, an easily opened port at one or both ends of the box through which articles and materials may be passed in and out of the box, a can or tray of desiccant to keep the gas in the box dry, and a set of inlet and outlet pipes on opposite sides of the box by means of which the box may be purged of air and filled with an inert gas such as nitrogen. Such a "dry box" may be made almost any convenient size, depending upon the sort of manipulations that are required. Through the gloves, the operator can open bottles, pour and measure liquids, weigh and transfer solids, etc., without ever exposing the compounds to the air. Of course the box should be tight, and a slight positive pressure of gas usually is maintained inside the box to prevent any leakage of air into it. A fancier design of "dry box" may include a separate chamber outside the entrance port. A small chamber of this sort may be flushed quickly, and it eliminates the necessity of having to reflush the large chamber each time the box is opened. Articles transferred from it to the larger box may be manipulated at once.

APPENDIX D

Sources of Hydrides

Some references have already been made in the descriptive part of this book to places where particular hydride compounds of industrial importance may be obtained. It will probably be convenient, however, to refer to the following list of vendors. There has been no attempt to make this list as complete as possible.

Metal Hydrides, Inc.   Beverly, Mass.
  Hydrides of Lithium
                  Sodium
                  Calcium
                  Titanium
                  Zirconium
  Sodium borohydride (this is a ready source of diborane)
  Lithium Aluminum Hydride
Metalloy Corp.   Minneapolis, Minn.
  Lithium Hydride
DuPont Electrochemicals Dept.   Wilmington, Del.
  Sodium Hydride
Matheson Chemical Co.   East Rutherford, N.J.
  Hydrocarbons, including methane
  Ammonia
  Hydrogen fluoride
  Hydrogen chloride
  Hydrogen sulfide

Metal Hydrides, Inc., the A. D. MacKay Co., New York, N.Y., and the National Registry of Rare Chemicals, Illinois Institute of Technology, Chicago, Ill., should be consulted for the procurement of rare hydride compounds to be used in research quantities.

APPENDIX E

Extended Tables of Physical Properties and Thermodynamic Data for the Boron Hydrides

	BH$_3$	B$_2$H$_6$	B$_5$H$_9$	B$_{10}$H$_{14}$
M.P., °C		−165.5	−46.82	99.5
B.P., °C		−92.53	58.4	213
Density (solid), g/ml		0.577 at −183°		0.94 at 25°
Density (liquid), g/ml		0.447 at −112° (1)	0.63 at 16° (1)	0.78 at 100°
Vapor pressure, mm		6 at −148°	66 at 0°	1.4 at 65°
		(27 atm at 0°)		19 at 100°
Surface tension, dynes/cm^2		16.95 at −112.5° (2)		
Parachor		122.1 at −112.5° (2)		
Viscosity, millipoises		1.77 at −109° (1)		
Critical temperature, °C		16.7 (3)		
Critical pressure		581 psi (3)		
Critical density		0.18 g/ml		
ΔH of fusion, Kcal/mole		1.06 (4)	1.466 (5)	7.8
				19.4 (subl)
ΔS of fusion, E. U.		9.8	6.5	20.9
				52.0 (subl)
ΔH of vaporization, Kcal/mole		3.45	7.7	11.6 at m.p.
ΔS of vaporization, E. U.		19.1	23.3	31.1 at m.p.
ΔH of formation, Kcal/mole*	73.8 (6)	6.73 (7)	7.8 (liq)	
			12.99 (vap) (8)	
ΔF of formation, Kcal/mole*	67.1	19.1	38.8 (liq)	
			39.6 (vap)	
S, E. U.*	39.62	55.44	44.16 (liq)	42.48 (9)
			65.75 (vap)	
C_p, cal/mole/deg.*	6.95	13.45	35.8 (liq)	52.42 (9)
			19(vap)	
Heat of combustion, Kcal/mole		515 (7)	1078(vap) (8)	

Azeotropes of diborane (10)

  70.1 % B$_2$H$_6$–29.9 % HCl, b.p., −94°C
  41.6 % B$_2$H$_6$–58.4 % BF$_3$, b.p., −106°C
  none with BCl$_3$, C$_2$H$_6$, HBr, or HCl—BCl$_3$ (ternary)

* Data at 25°

References
1. Smith and Miller, *J. Am. Chem. Soc.*, **72**, 1452 (1950).
2. Laubengayer, Ferguson, and Newkirk, *J. Am. Chem. Soc.*, **63**, 559 (1941).
3. Newkirk, *J. Am. Chem. Soc.*, **70**, 1978 (1948).
4. Johnston, TR 319-7, 309-4. OSU to ONR, Aug. 1, 1948.
5. Johnston, TR 309-6, OSU to ONR, July 8, 1949.
6. Rossini et al., *Selected Values of Chemical Thermodynamic Properties*, Series I and II, ONR and NBS, Dec. 31, 1947.
7. Prosen, Johnson, and Yenchius, Report from NBS to ONR, Sept. 30, 1948.
8. Prosen, Johnson, and Yenchius, Report from NBS to ONR, May 31, 1949.
9. Kerr, Hallet, and Johnston, TR 309-7, OSU to ONR, July 19, 1950.
10. McCarty, *J. Am. Chem. Soc.*, **71**, 1339 (1949).

Author Index

Subject Index

Subject Index